D1232086

DEAREST FATHER

FRANZ KAFKA

DEAREST FATHER

STORIES AND OTHER WRITINGS

TRANSLATED BY ERNST KAISER AND EITHNE WILKINS

SCHOCKEN BOOKS / NEW YORK

First printing, June, 1954

Copyright 1954 by Schocken Books, Inc.
342 Madison Avenue, New York 17, N. Y.
Printed in the United States of America by
H. Wolff Book Manufacturing Co., New York

CONTENTS

WEDDING PREPARATIONS IN THE COUNTRY

Wedding Preparations
in the Country [1]

1

WHEN Eduard Raban, coming along the passage,
walked into the open doorway, he saw that it was raining. It was not raining much.

On the pavement straight in front of him there were
many people walking in various rhythms. Every now
and again one would step forward and cross the road. A
little girl was holding a tired puppy in her outstretched
hands. Two gentlemen were exchanging information.
The one held his hands palm-upward, raising and lowering them in regular motion, as though he were balancing a load. Then one caught sight of a lady whose hat
was heavily laden with ribbons, buckles and flowers.
And hurrying past was a young man with a thin
walking stick, his left hand, as though paralyzed, flat on
his chest. Now and then there came men who were
smoking, bearing small upright elongated clouds along
ahead of them. Three gentlemen—two holding lightweight
overcoats on their crooked forearms—several times
walked forward from the front of the buildings to the
edge of the pavement, surveyed what was going on
there, and then withdrew again, talking.

Through the gaps between the passers-by one could
see the regularly laid stones of the carriageway. There
carriages on delicate high wheels were drawn along by
horses with arched necks. The people who sat at ease on
the upholstered seats gazed silently at the pedestrians,

the shops, the balconies, and the sky. If it happened that one carriage overtook another, then the horses would press against each other, and the harness straps hung dangling. The animals tugged at the shafts, the carriage bowled along, swaying as it gathered speed, until the swerve round the carriage ahead was completed and the horses moved apart again, only their narrow quiet heads inclined towards each other.

Some people came quickly towards the front entrance, stopped on the dry mosaic paving, and, turning round slowly, stood gazing out into the rain, which, wedged in by this narrow street, fell confusedly.

Raban felt tired. His lips were as pale as the faded red of his thick tie, which had a Moorish pattern. The lady by the doorsteps over there, who had up to now been contemplating her shoes, which were quite visible under her tightly drawn skirt, now looked at him. She did so indifferently, and she was perhaps, in any case, only looking at the falling rain in front of him or at the small nameplates of firms that were fixed to the door over his head. Raban thought she looked amazed. "Well," he thought, "if I could tell her the whole story, she would cease to be astonished. One works so feverishly at the office that afterwards one is too tired even to enjoy one's holidays properly. But even all that work does not give one a claim to be treated lovingly by everyone; on the contrary, one is alone, a total stranger and only an object of curiosity. And so long as you say 'one' instead of 'I,' there's nothing in it and one can easily tell the story; but as soon as you admit to yourself that it is you yourself, you feel as though transfixed and are horrified."

He put down the suitcase with the checkered cloth cover, bending his knees in doing so. The rain water was already running along the edge of the carriageway in streaks that almost extended to the lower lying gutters.

"But if I myself distinguish between 'one' and 'I,' how then dare I complain about the others? Probably they're not unjust, but I'm too tired to take it all in. I'm even too tired to walk all the way to the station without an effort, and it's only a short distance. So why don't I remain in town over these short holidays, in order to recuperate? How unreasonable I'm being!— The journey will make me ill, I know that quite well. My room won't be comfortable enough, it can't be otherwise in the country. And we're hardly in the first half of June, the air in the country is often still very cool. Of course, I've taken precautions in my clothing, but I shall have to join with people who go for walks late in the evening. There are ponds there; one will go for a walk the length of those ponds. That is where I'm sure to catch cold. On the other hand, I shall make but little showing in conversation. I shan't be able to compare the pond with other ponds in some remote country, for I've never traveled, and talking about the moon and feeling bliss and rapturously climbing up on heaps of rubble is, after all, something I'm too old to do without being laughed to scorn."

People were going past with slightly bent heads, above which they carried their dark umbrellas in a loose grip. A dray also went by; on the driver's seat, which was stuffed with straw, sat a man whose legs were stretched out so negligently that one foot was almost touching the ground, while the other rested safely on straw and rags. It looked as though he were sitting in a field in fine weather. Yet he was holding the reins attentively so that the dray, on which iron bars were clanging against one another, made its way safely through the dense traffic. On the wet surface of the road one could see the reflection of the iron meanderingly and slowly gliding from one row of cobbles to the next. The little boy beside the lady opposite was dressed like an old vintner. His pleated dress formed a great circle at the hem and was only held in, almost under the very armpits, by a leather strap. His hemispherical cap came down to his eyebrows, and a tassel hung down from the top as far as his left ear. He was pleased by the rain. He ran out of the doorway and looked up wide-eyed into the sky in order to catch more of the rain. Often he jumped high into the air so that the water splashed a great deal and passers-by admonished him severely. Then the lady called him and henceforth held him by the hand; yet he did not cry.

Raban started. Had it not grown late? Since he wore his topcoat and jacket open, he quickly pulled out his watch. It was not going. Irritably he asked a neighbor, who was standing a little farther back in the entrance, what the time was. This man was in conversation, and while still laughing together with his companion, said: "Certainly. Past four o'clock," and turned away.

Raban quickly put up his umbrella and picked up his suitcase. But when he was about to step into the street, his way was blocked by several women in a hurry and these he therefore let pass first. In doing so he looked down on a little girl's hat, which was made of plaited red straw and had a little green wreath on the wavy brim.

He went on remembering this even when he was in the street, which went slightly uphill in the direction he wished to follow. Then he forgot it, for now he had to exert himself a little; his small suitcase was none too light, and the wind was blowing straight against him, making his coat flutter and bending the front spokes of his umbrella.

He had to breathe more deeply. A clock in a nearby square down below struck a quarter to five; under the umbrella he saw the light short steps of the people coming towards him; carriage wheels squeaked with the brakes on, turning more slowly; the horses stretched their thin forelegs, daring as chamois in the mountains.

Then it seemed to Raban that he would get through the long bad time of the next fortnight, too. For it was only a fortnight, that was to say, a limited period, and even if the annoyances grew ever greater, still, the time during which one had to endure them would be growing shorter and shorter. Thus, undoubtedly courage would increase. "All the people who try to torment me, and who have now occupied the entire space around me, will quite gradually be thrust back by the beneficent passage of these days, without my having to help them even in the very least. And, as it will come about quite naturally, I can be weak and quiet and let everything happen to me, and yet everything must turn out well, through the sheer fact of the passing of the days.

"And besides, can't I do it the way I always used to as a child in matters that were dangerous? I don't even need to go to the country myself, it isn't necessary. I'll send my clothed body. If it staggers out of the door of my room, the staggering will indicate not fear but its nothingness. Nor is it a sign of excitement if it stumbles on the stairs, if it travels into the country, sobbing as it goes, and there eats its supper in tears. For I myself am meanwhile lying in my bed, smoothly covered over with the yellow-brown blanket, exposed to the breeze that is wafted through that seldom aired room. The carriages and people in the street move and walk hesitantly on shining ground, for I am still dreaming. Coachmen and pedestrians are shy, and every step they want to advance they ask as a favor from me, by looking at me. I encourage them and encounter no obstacle.

"As I lie in bed I assume the shape of a big beetle, a stag beetle or a cockchafer, I think."

In front of a shopwindow, in which, behind a wet glass pane, little hats for men were displayed on small pegs, he stopped and looked in, his lips pursed. "Well, my hat will still do for the holidays," he thought and walked on, "and if nobody can stand me because of my hat, then all the better.

"The form of a large beetle, yes. Then I would pretend it was a matter of hibernating, and I would press my little legs to my bulging belly. And I would whisper a few words, instructions to my sad body, which stands close beside me, bent. Soon I shall have done—it bows, it goes swiftly, and it will manage everything efficiently while I rest."

He came to a domed arch at the top of the steep street, leading onto a small square all round which there were many shops, already lit up. In the middle of the square, somewhat obscured by the light round the edge, was a low monument, the seated meditative figure of a man. The people moved across the lights like narrow shutters, and since the puddles spread all the brilliance far and wide, the square seemed ceaselessly changing.

Raban pressed far on into the square, but jerkily, dodging the drifting carriages, jumping from one dry cobble to further dry cobbles, and holding the open umbrella high in his hand in order to see everything all around. Finally, by a lamppost—a place where the electric tram stopped—which was set up on a small square concrete base, he halted.

"But they're expecting me in the country. Won't they be wondering about me by this time? Still, I haven't written to her all the week she's been in the country, until this morning. So they'll end up by imagining that even my appearance is quite different. They may be thinking that I burst forward when I address a person, yet that isn't my way at all, or that I embrace people when I arrive, and that's something I don't do either. I shall make them angry if I try to pacify them. Oh, if I could only make them thoroughly angry in the attempt to pacify them."

At that moment an open carriage drove past, not quickly; behind its two lighted lamps two ladies could be seen sitting on dark leather seats. One was leaning back, her face hidden by a veil and the shadow of her hat. But the other lady was sitting bolt upright; her hat was small, it was edged with thin feathers. Everyone could see her. Her lower lip was drawn slightly into her mouth.

As soon as the carriage had passed Raban, some bar blocked the view of the near horse drawing the carriage; then some coachman—wearing a big top hat—on an unusually high box was moved across in front of the ladies—this was now much farther on—then their carriage drove round the corner of a small house that now became strikingly noticeable, and disappeared from sight.

Raban followed it with his gaze, his head lowered, resting the handle of his umbrella on his shoulder in order to see better. He had put his right thumb into his mouth and was rubbing his teeth on it. His suitcase lay beside him, one of its sides on the ground.

Carriages hastened from street to street across the square, the horses' bodies flew along horizontally as though they were being flung through the air, but the nodding of the head and the neck revealed the rhythm and effort of the movement.

Round about, on the edges of the pavements of all the three streets converging here, there were many idlers standing about, tapping the cobbles with little sticks. Among the groups they formed there were little towers in which girls were pouring out lemonade, then heavy street clocks on thin bars, then men wearing before and behind them big placards announcing entertainments in multicolored letters, then messengers . . . [two pages missing] . . . a little social gathering. Two elegant private carriages, driving diagonally across the square into the street leading downhill, got in the way of some gentlemen from this party, but after the second carriage—even after the first they had timidly tried to do so—these gentlemen formed into a group again with the others, with whom they then stepped onto the pavement in a long cavalcade and pushed their way through the door of a café, overwhelmed by the light of the incandescent lamps hanging over the entrance.

Electric tramcars moved past, huge and very close; others, vaguely visible, stood motionless far away in the streets.

"How bent she is," Raban thought when he looked at the photograph now. "She's never really upright and perhaps her back is round. I shall have to pay much attention to this. And her mouth is so wide, and here, beyond doubt, the lower lip protrudes, yes, now I remember that too. And what a dress! Of course, I don't know anything about clothes, but these very tight-sewn sleeves are ugly, I am sure, they look like bandages. And the hat, the brim at every point turned up from the face in a different curve. But her eyes are beautiful, they're brown, if I'm not mistaken. Everyone says her eyes are beautiful."

Now an electric tramcar stopped in front of Raban and many people round him pushed towards the steps, with slightly open, pointed umbrellas, which they held upright with their hands pressed to their shoulders. Raban, who was holding his suitcase under his arm, was dragged off the pavement and stepped hard into an unseen puddle. Inside the tram a child knelt on a seat, pressing the tips of all its fingers to its lips as though it were saying good-bye to someone going away. Some passengers got out and had to walk a few paces along the tram in order to work their way out of the crowd. Then a lady climbed on to the first step, her long skirt, which she hitched up with both hands, stretched tightly round her legs. A gentleman held on to a brass rod and, with lifted head, recounted something to the lady. All the people who wanted to get in were impatient. The conductor shouted.

Raban, who now stood on the edge of the waiting group, turned round, for someone had called out his name.

"Ah, Lement," he said slowly and held out to a young man coming towards him the little finger of the hand in which he was holding the umbrella.

"So this is the bridegroom on his way to his bride. He looks frightfully in love," Lement said and then smiled with his mouth shut.

"Yes, you must forgive my going today," Raban said. "I wrote to you this afternoon, anyway. I should, of course, have liked very much to travel with you tomorrow; but tomorrow is Saturday, everything'll be so crowded, it's a long journey."

"Oh, that doesn't matter. You did promise, but when one's in love. . . . I shall just have to travel alone." Lement had set one foot on the pavement and the other on the cobbles, supporting his body now on one leg, now on the other. "You were going to get into the tram. There it goes. Come, we'll walk, I'll go with you. There's still plenty of time."

"Isn't it rather late, please tell me?"

"It's no wonder you're nervous, but you really have got plenty of time. I'm not so nervous, and that's why I've missed Gillemann now."

"Gillemann? Won't he be staying out there, too?"

"Yes, with his wife; it's next week they mean to go, and that's just why I promised Gillemann I'd meet him today when he leaves the office. He wanted to give me some instructions regarding the furnishing of their house, that's why I was supposed to meet him. But now somehow I'm late, I had some errands to do. And just as I was wondering whether I shouldn't go to their apartment, I saw you, was at first astonished at the suitcase, and spoke to you. But now the evening's too far gone for paying calls, it's fairly impossible to go to Gillemann now."

"Of course. And so I shall meet people I know there, after all. Not that I have ever seen Frau Gillemann, though."

"And very beautiful she is. She's fair, and pale now after her illness. She has the most beautiful eyes I've ever seen."

"Do please tell me, what do beautiful eyes look like? Is it the glance? I've never found eyes beautiful."

"All right, perhaps I was exaggerating slightly. Still, she's a pretty woman."

Through the windowpane of a ground-floor café, close to the window, gentlemen could be seen sitting, reading and eating, round a three-sided table; one had lowered a newspaper to the table, held a little cup raised, and was looking into the street out of the corners of his eyes. Beyond these window-tables all the furniture and equipment in the large restaurant were hidden by the customers, who sat side by side in little circles. [Two pages missing] . . . "As it happens, however, it's not such an unpleasant business, is it? Many people would take on such a burden, I think."

They came into a fairly dark square, which began on their side of the street, for the opposite side extended farther. On the side of the square along which they were walking, there was an uninterrupted row of houses, from the corners of which two—at first widely distant—rows of houses extended into the indiscernible distance in which they seemed to unite. The pavement was narrow by the houses, which were mostly small; there were no shops to be seen, no carriage passed. An iron post near the end of the street out of which they came had several lamps on it, which were fixed in two rings hanging horizontally, one over the other. The trapeze-shaped flame between conjoined sheets of glass burned in this tower-like wide darkness as in a little room, letting darkness assert itself a few steps farther on.

"But now I am sure it is too late; you have kept it a secret from me, and I shall miss the train. Why?" [Four pages missing.]

. . . "Yes, at most Pirkershofer—well, for what *he's* worth."

"The name's mentioned, I think, in Betty's letters, he's an assistant railway-clerk, isn't he?"

"Yes, an assistant railway-clerk and an unpleasant person. You'll see I'm right as soon as you've got a glimpse of that small thick nose. I tell you, walking through the dreary fields with that fellow. . . . Anyway, he's been transferred now and he goes away from there, as I believe and hope, next week."

"Wait, you said just now you advised me to stay here tonight. I've thought it over; it couldn't very well be managed. I've written to say I'm coming this evening; they'll be expecting me."

"That's quite easy, send a telegram."

"Yes, that could be done—but it wouldn't be very nice if I didn't go—and I'm tired, yes, I'll go all right. If a telegram came, they'd get a fright, into the bargain.—And what for, where would we go, anyway?"

"Then it's really better for you to go. I was only thinking. . . . Anyway I couldn't go with you today, as I'm sleepy, I forgot to tell you that. And now I shall say goodbye, for I don't want to go through the wet park with you, as I should like to drop in at Gillemann's, after all. It's a quarter to six, so not too late, after all, for paying calls on people you know fairly well. Addio. Well, a good journey, and remember me to everyone!"

Lement turned to the right and held out his right hand to say goodbye, so that for a moment Raban was walking against Lement's outstretched arm.

"Adieu." Raban said.

From a little distance Lement then called back: "I say, Eduard, can you hear me? Do shut your umbrella; it stopped raining ages ago. I didn't have a chance to tell you."

Raban did not answer, shut his umbrella, and the sky closed over him in pallid darkness.

"If at least," Raban thought, "I were to get into a wrong train. Then it would at any rate seem to me that the whole enterprise had begun, and if later, after the mistake had been cleared up, I were to arrive in this station again on my way back, then I should certainly feel much better. If the scenery does turn out to be boring, as Lement says, that need not be a disadvantage at all. One will spend more time in the rooms and really never know for certain where all the others are, for if there is a ruin in the district, there will probably be a walk all together to that ruin; it will have been agreed upon some time before. Then, however, one must look forward to it; for that very reason one mustn't miss it. But if there is no such sight to be seen, then there will be no discussion beforehand either, for all will be expected to get together quite easily if suddenly, against all the usual practice, a larger expedition is considered right, for one only has to send the maid into the others' apartments, where they are sitting over a letter or books and are delighted by this news. Well, it is not difficult to protect oneself against such invitations. And yet I don't know whether I shall be able to, for it is not so easy as I imagine it now when I am still alone and can still do everything, can still go back if I want to, for I shall have no one there whom I could pay calls on whenever I like, and no one with whom I could make more strenuous expeditions, no one there who could show me how his crops are doing or show me a quarry he is working there. For one isn't at all sure even of acquaintances of long standing. Wasn't Lement nice to me today?—he explained some things to me, didn't he, and described everything as it will appear to me. He came up and spoke to me and then walked with me, in spite of the fact that there was nothing he wanted to find out from me and that he himself still had something else to do. But now all of a sudden he has gone away, and yet I can't have offended him even with a single word. I did refuse to spend the evening in town, but that was only natural, that can't have offended him, for he is a sensible person."

The station clock struck, it was a quarter to six. Raban stopped because he had palpitations, then he walked quickly along the park pool, went along a narrow, badly lighted path between large shrubs, rushed into an open place with many empty benches leaning against little trees, then went more slowly through an opening in the railings into the street, crossed it, leapt through the station entrance, after a while found the booking office and had to knock for a while on the iron shutter. Then the booking clerk looked out, said it was really high time, took the bank note and slammed down on the counter the ticket he had been asked for and the change. Now Raban tried to count his change quickly, thinking he ought to be getting more, but a porter who was walking nearby hurried him through a glass door onto the platform. There Raban looked round, while calling out "Thank you, thank you!" to the porter, and since he found no guard, he climbed up the steps of the nearest coach by himself, each time putting the suitcase on the step above and

then following himself, supporting himself on his umbrella with one hand, and on the handle of the suitcase
with the other. The coach that he entered was brightly
illuminated by the great amount of light from the main
hall of the station, in which it was standing; in front of
many a windowpane—all were shut right up to the top—a
hissing arc lamp hung at about eye-level, and the many
raindrops on the glass were white, often single ones
would move. Raban could hear the noise from the platform even when he had shut the carriage door and sat
down on the last little free bit of a light-brown wooden
seat. He saw many people's backs, and the backs of their
heads, and between them the upturned faces of people on
the seat opposite. In some places smoke was curling up
from pipes and cigars, in one place drifting limply past
the face of a girl. Often the passengers would change
places, discussing these changes with each other, or they
would transfer their luggage, which lay in a narrow blue
net over a seat, to another one. If a stick or the metal-
covered corner of a suitcase stuck out, then the owner
would have his attention drawn to this. He would go over
and straighten it. Raban also bethought himself and pushed
his suitcase under his seat.

On his left, at the window, two gentlemen were sitting
opposite each other, talking about the price of goods.
"They're commercial travelers," Raban thought and,
breathing regularly, he gazed at them. "The merchant
sends them into the country, they obey, they travel by
train, and in every village they go from shop to shop.
Sometimes they travel by carriage between the villages.
They must not stay long anywhere, for everything must
be done fast, and they must always talk only about their
goods. With what pleasure, then, one can exert oneself in
an occupation that is so agreeable!"

The younger man had jerked a notebook out of the

hip-pocket of his trousers, rapidly flicked the leaves over with a forefinger moistened on his tongue, and then read through a page, drawing the back of his fingernail down it as he went. He looked at Raban as he glanced up and, indeed, when he now began talking about thread prices, did not turn his face away from Raban, as one gazes steadily at a point in order not to forget anything of what one wants to say. At the same time he drew his brows tightly down over his eyes. He held the half-closed note-book in his left hand, with his thumb on the page he had been reading, in order to be able to refer to it easily if he should need to. And the notebook trembled, for he was not supporting his arm on anything, and the coach, which was now in motion, beat on the rails like a hammer.

The other traveler sat leaning back, listening and nod-ding at regular intervals. It was evident that he was far from agreeing with everything and later would give his own opinion.

Raban laid his curved hands palm-down on his knees and, leaning forward, between the travelers' heads he saw the window and through the window lights flitting past and others flitting away into the distance. He did not un-derstand anything of what the traveler was talking about, nor would he understand the other's answer. Much preparation would first be required, for here were people who had been concerned with goods since their youth. But if one has held a spool of thread in one's hand so often and handed it to one's customer so often, then one knows the price and can talk about it, while villages come toward us and flash past, while at the same time they turn away into the depths of the country, where for us they must disappear. And yet these villages are inhabited, and there perhaps travelers go from shop to shop.

In a corner at the far end of the coach a tall man stood up, holding playing cards in his hand, and called out:

"I say, Marie, did you pack the zephyr shirts?"

"Of course I did," said the woman, who was sitting opposite Raban. She had been dozing, and now when the question waked her she answered as though she were talking to herself or to Raban. "You're going to market at Jungbunzlau, eh?" the vivacious traveler asked her. "Jungbunzlau, that's right." "It's a big market this time, isn't it?" "A big market, that's right." She was sleepy, she rested her left elbow on a blue bundle, and her head drooped heavily against her hand, which pressed through the flesh of the cheek to the cheekbone. "How young she is," the traveler said.

Raban took the money that he had received from the cashier out of his waistcoat pocket and counted it over. He held up each coin firmly between thumb and forefinger for a long time and also twisted it this way and that on the inner surface of his thumb with the tip of his forefinger. He looked for a long time at the Emperor's image, then he was struck by the laurel wreath and the way it was fastened with knots and bows of ribbon at the back of the head. At last he found the sum was correct and put the money into a big black purse. But now when he was about to say to the traveler: "They're a married couple, don't you think?" the train stopped. The noise of the journey ceased, guards shouted the name of a place, and Raban said nothing.

The train started again so slowly that one could picture the revolutions of the wheels, but a moment later it was racing down a slope, and all unexpectedly the tall railings of a bridge, outside the windows, were torn apart and pressed together, as it seemed.

Raban was now pleased that the train was going so fast, for he would not have wanted to stay in the last place. "When it is dark there, when one knows no one there, when it is such a long way home. But then it must be terrible there by day. And is it different at the next station or at the previous ones or at the later ones or at the village I am going to?"

The traveler was suddenly talking more loudly. "It's a long way yet," Raban thought. "Sir, you know just as well as I do, these manufacturers send their travlers round the most Godforsaken little villages, they go crawling to the seediest of little shopkeepers, and do you think they offer them prices different from those they offer us big businessmen? Sir, take it from me; exactly the same prices, only yesterday I saw it black on white. I call it villainy. They're squeezing us out of existence; under current conditions it's simply impossible for us to do business."

Again he looked at Raban; he was not ashamed of the tears in his eyes; he pressed the knuckles of his left hand to his mouth because his lips were quivering. Raban leaned back and tugged faintly at his mustache with his left hand.

The shopwoman opposite woke up and smilingly passed her hands over her forehead. The traveler talked more quietly. Once again the woman shifted as though settling down to sleep, half lying on her bundle, and sighed. The skirt was drawn tight over her right hip.

Behind her sat a gentleman with a traveling cap on his head, reading a large newspaper. The girl opposite him, who was probably a relative of his, urged him—at the same time inclining her head towards her right shoulder —to open the window, because it was so very hot. He said, without looking up, he would do it in a moment, only he must first finish reading an article in the newspaper, and he showed her which article he meant.

The shopwoman could not go to sleep again; she sat upright and looked out of the window; then for a long time she looked at the oil lamp and the flame burning yellow near the ceiling of the carriage. Raban shut his eyes for a little while.

When he glanced up, the shopwoman was just biting into a piece of cake that was spread with brown jam. The bundle next her was open. The traveler was smoking a cigar in silence and kept on fidgeting as though he were tapping the ash off the end of it. The other was poking about in the works of a pocket watch with the tip of a knife, so that one could hear it scraping.

With his eyes almost shut Raban still had time to see, in a blurred way, the gentleman in the traveling cap pulling at the window strap. There came a gust of cool air, and a straw hat fell from a hook. Raban thought he was waking up and that was why his cheeks were so refreshed, or someone was opening the door and drawing him into the room, or he was in some way mistaken about things, and, breathing deeply, he quickly fell asleep.

II

THE STEPS of the coach were still shaking a little when Raban climbed down them. Into his face, coming out of the air of the carriage, the rain beat, and he shut his eyes. It was raining noisily on the corrugated iron roof of the station building, but out in the open country the rain fell in such a way that it sounded like the uninterrupted blowing of the wind. A barefoot boy came running up—Raban did not see from where—and breathlessly asked Raban to let him carry the suitcase, for it was raining; but Raban said: Yes, it was raining, and he would therefore go by omnibus. He did not need him, he said. Thereupon the boy pulled a face as though he thought it grander to walk in the rain and have one's suitcase carried than to go by bus, and instantly turned round and ran away. When Raban wanted to call him, it was already too late.

There were two lighted lamps, and a station official came out of a door. Without hesitation he walked through the rain to the engine, stood there motionless with his arms folded, and waited until the engine driver leaned over his rail and talked to him. A porter was called, came, and was sent back again. At many of the windows in the train there were passengers standing, and since what they had to look at was an ordinary railway station their gaze was probably dim, the eyelids close together, as though the train were in motion. A girl came hurrying along from the road to the platform under a parasol with a flowered pattern; she set the open parasol on the ground and sat down, pushing her legs apart so that her skirt should dry better, and ran her fingertips over the tight-stretched skirt. There were only two lamps alight; her face was indistinguishable. The porter came past and complained that puddles were forming under the parasol; he held his arms in a semicircle before him in order to demonstrate the size of these puddles, and then moved his hands through the air, one after the other, like fishes sinking into deeper water, in order to make it clear that traffic was also being impeded by this parasol.

The train started, disappeared like a long sliding door, and behind the poplars on the far side of the railway track there was the landscape, so massive that it took away one's breath. Was it a dark view through a gap or was it woods, was it a pool, or a house in which the people were already asleep, was it a church steeple or a ravine between the hills? Nobody must dare to go there, but who could restrain himself?

And when Raban caught sight of the official—he was

already at the step up to his office—he ran in front of him and stopped him: "Excuse me, please, is it far to the village? That's where I want to go."

"No, a quarter of an hour, but by bus—as it's raining—you'll be there in five minutes."

"It's raining. It's not a very fine spring," Raban said.

The official had put his right hand on his hip, and through the triangle formed by the arm and the body Raban saw the girl, who had now shut the parasol, on the seat where she sat.

"If one is going on one's summer holidays now and is going to stay there, one can't but regret it. Actually I thought I should be met." He glanced round to make it seem plausible.

"You will miss the bus, I'm afraid. It doesn't wait so long. Nothing to thank me for. That's the road, between the hedges."

The road outside the railway station was not lighted; only from three ground-floor windows in the building there came a misty glimmer, but it did not extend far. Raban walked on tiptoe through the mud and shouted "Driver!" and "Hello there!" and "Omnibus!" and "Here I am!" many times. But when he landed among scarcely interrupted puddles on the dark side of the road, he had to tramp onwards with his heels down, until suddenly a horse's moist muzzle touched his forehead.

There was the omnibus; he quickly climbed into the empty compartment, sat down by the windowpane behind the driver's box and hunched his back into the corner, for he had done all that was necessary. For if the driver is asleep, he will wake up towards morning; if he is dead, then a new driver will come, or the innkeeper, and should that not happen either, then passengers will come by the early morning train, people in a hurry, making a noise. In any case one can be quiet, one may even draw the curtains over the windows and wait for the jerk with which the vehicle must start.

"Yes, after all I have already accomplished, it is certain that tomorrow I shall get to Betty and to Mamma; nobody can prevent that. Yet it is true, and was indeed to be foreseen, that my letter will arrive only tomorrow, so that I might very well have remained in town and spent an agreeable night at Elvy's, without having to be afraid of the next day's work, the sort of thing that otherwise ruins every pleasure for me. But look, I've got my feet wet."

He lit a stub of candle that he had taken out of his waistcoat pocket and set it on the seat opposite. It was bright enough, the darkness outside made it appear as though the omnibus had black distempered walls and no glass in the windows. There was no need to think that there were wheels under the floor and in front the horse between the shafts. Raban rubbed his feet thoroughly on the seat, pulled on clean socks and sat up straight. Then he heard someone from the station shouting: "Hi!", if there was anyone in the bus he might say so. "Yes, yes, and he would like to start now, too," Raban answered, leaning out of the door, which he had opened, holding on to the doorpost with his right hand, the left hand held open, close to his mouth.

The rain gushed down the back of his neck, inside his collar.

Wrapped in the canvas of two sacks that had been cut up, the driver came over, the reflection of his stable lantern jumping through the puddles at his feet. Irritably he began an explanation: listen here, he said, he had been playing cards with Lebeda and they had just been getting on fine when the train came. It would really have been impossible for him to take a look outside then, still, he did not mean to abuse anyone who did not understand that. Apart from that, this place here was a filthy dump, and no half measures, and it was hard to see what business a gentleman like this could have here, and he would be getting there soon enough anyway, so that he need not go and complain anywhere. Only just now Herr Pirkershofer—if you please, that's the junior assistant clerk—had come in and had said he thought a small fair man had been wanting to go by the omnibus. Well, so he had at once come and asked, or hadn't he at once come and asked?

The lantern was attached to the end of the shaft; the horse, having been shouted at in a muffled voice, began to pull, and the water on top of the bus, now set stirring, dripped slowly through a crack into the carriage.

The road was perhaps hilly; there was surely mud flying up into the spokes; fans of puddle water formed, with a rushing sound, behind the turning wheels; it was for the most part with loose reins that the driver guided the dripping horse.—Could not all this be used as reproaches against Raban? Many puddles were unexpectedly lit up by the lantern trembling on the shaft, and split up, in ripples, under the wheel. This happened solely because Raban was traveling to his fiancée, to Betty, an oldish pretty girl. And who, if one were going to speak of it at all, would appreciate what merits Raban here had, even if it was only that he bore those reproaches, which admittedly nobody could make openly. Of course he was doing it gladly. Betty was his fiancée, he was fond of her, it would be disgusting if she were to thank him for that as well, but all the same—

Without meaning to, he often bumped his head on the panel against which he was leaning, then for a while he looked up at the ceiling. Once his right hand slipped down from his thigh, where he had been resting it. But his elbow remained in the angle between belly and leg.

The omnibus was now traveling between houses; here and there the inside of the coach had a share of the light from a room; there were some steps—to see the first of them Raban would have had to stand up—built up to a church; outside a park gate there was a lamp with a large flame burning in it, but a statue of a saint stood out in black relief only because of the light from a draper's shop, and Raban saw his candle, which had burnt down, the trickle of wax hanging motionless from the seat.

When the bus stopped outside the inn, and the rain could be heard loudly and—probably there was a window open—so could the voices of the guests, Raban wondered which would be better, to get out at once or to wait until the innkeeper came to the coach. What the custom was in this township he did not know, but it was pretty certain that Betty would have spoken of her fiancé, and according to whether his arrival here was magnificent or feeble, so the esteem in which she was held here would increase or diminish, and with that, again, his own, too. But of course he knew neither what people felt about her nor what she had told them about him, and so everything was all the more disagreeable and difficult. Oh, beautiful city and beautiful the way home! If it rains there, one goes home by tram over wet cobbles; here one goes in a cart through mud to an inn.— "The city is far from here, and if I were now in danger of dying of homesickness, nobody could get me back there today.—Well, anyway, I shouldn't die—but there I get the meal expected for that evening, set on the table, on the right behind my plate the newspaper, on the left the lamp, here I shall be given some dreadfully fat dish—they don't know that I have a weak stomach, and even if they did know—an unfamiliar newspaper—many people, whom I can already hear, will be there, and one lamp will be lit for all. What sort of light can it provide?

Enough to play cards by—but for reading a newspaper?

"The innkeeper isn't coming, he's not interested in guests, he is probably an unfriendly man. Or does he know that I am Betty's fiancé, and does that give him a reason for not coming to fetch me in? It would be in accord with that that the driver kept me waiting so long at the station. Betty has often told me, after all, how much she has been bothered by lecherous men and how she has had to rebuff their insistence; perhaps it is that here too . . . !" [Text breaks off]

[Second Manuscript]

WHEN Eduard Raban, coming along the passage, walked into the open doorway, he could now see how it was raining. It was not raining much.

On the pavement straight in front of him, not higher, not lower, there were, in spite of the rain, many passers-by. Every now and again one would step forward and cross the road.

A little girl was carrying a gray dog on her outstretched arms. Two gentlemen were exchanging information on some subject, at times turning the whole front of their bodies to each other, and then slowly turning aside themselves again; it was like doors ajar in the wind. The one held his hands palm-upward, raising and lowering them in regular motion, as though he were balancing a load, testing the weight of it. Then one caught sight of a slim lady whose face twitched slightly, like the flickering light of the stars, and whose flat hat was loaded high and to the brim with unrecognizable objects; she appeared to be a stranger to all the passers-by, without intending it, as though by some law. And hurrying past

was a young man with a thin walking stick, his left hand,
as though paralyzed, lying flat on his chest. Many were
out on business; in spite of the fact that they walked fast,
one saw them longer than others, now on the pavement,
now below; their coats fitted them badly; they did not
care how they carried themselves; they let themselves be
pushed by the people and they pushed too. Three gentlemen—two holding lightweight overcoats on their
crooked forearms—walked from the front of the building
to the edge of the pavement, in order to see what was
going on in the carriageway and on the farther pavement.

Through the gaps between the passers-by, now fleetingly, then comfortably, one saw the regularly set cobbles in the carriageway, on which carriages, swaying on
their wheels, were swiftly drawn by horses with arched
necks. The people who sat at ease on the upholstered
seats gazed in silence at the pedestrians, the shops, the
balconies, and the sky. If it happened that one carriage
overtook another, then the horses would press against
each other, and the harness straps hung dangling. The
animals tugged at the shafts, the carriage bowled along,
swaying as it gathered speed, until the swerve round the
carriage ahead was completed and the horses moved
apart again, still with their narrow heads inclined towards each other.

An elderly gentleman came quickly towards the front
entrance, stopped on the dry mosaic paving, turned round.
And he then gazed into the rain, which, wedged in by the
narrow street, fell confusedly.

Raban put down the suitcase with the black cloth
cover, bending his right knee a little in doing so. The
rain water was already running along the edge of the
carriageway in streaks that almost extended to the lower
lying gutters.

The elderly gentleman stood upright near Raban, who was supporting himself by leaning slightly against the wooden doorpost; from time to time he glanced toward Raban, even though to do so he had to twist his neck sharply. Yet he did this only out of the natural desire, now that he happened to be unoccupied, to observe everything exactly, at least in his vicinity. The result of this aimless glancing hither and thither was that there was a great deal he did not notice. So, for instance, it escaped him that Raban's lips were very pale, not much less so than the very faded red of his tie, which had a once striking Moorish pattern. Now, had he noticed this, he would certainly have made a fuss about it, at least inwardly, which, again, would not have been the right thing, for Raban was always pale, even if, it was a fact, various things might have been making him especially tired just recently.

"What weather!" the gentleman said in a low voice, shaking his head, consciously, it was true, but still in a slightly senile way.

"Yes, indeed, and when one's supposed to be starting on a journey, too," Raban said, quickly straightening up.

"And it isn't the kind of weather that will improve," the gentleman said and, in order to make sure of it once more for the last time, bent forward to glance in scrutiny up the street, then down, and then at the sky. "It may last for days, even for weeks. So far as I recall, nothing better is forecast for June and the beginning of July, either. Well, it's no pleasure to anyone; I for instance shall have to do without my walks, which are extremely important to my health."

Hereupon he yawned and seemed to become exhausted, since he had now heard Raban's voice and, occupied with this conversation, no longer took any interest in anything, not even in the conversation.

This made quite an impression on Raban, since after all the gentleman had addressed him first, and he therefore tried to show off a little, although it might not even be noticed. "True," he said, "in town one can very easily manage to go without what isn't good for one. If one does not do without it, then one has only oneself to blame for the bad consequences. One will be sorry and in this way come to see for the first time really clearly how to manage the next time. And even if in matters of detail . . . [two pages missing] . . . "I don't mean anything by it. I don't mean anything at all," Raban hastened to say, prepared to excuse the gentleman's absent-mindedness in any way possible, since after all he wanted to show off a little more. "It's all just out of the book previously mentioned, which I, like other people, happen to have been reading in the evening recently. I have been mostly alone. Owing to family circumstances, you see. But apart from anything else, a good book is what I like best after supper. Always has been. Just recently I read in a prospectus a quotation from some writer or other. 'A good book is the best friend there is,' and that's really true, it is so, a good book is the best friend there is."

"Yes, when one is young—" the gentleman said, meaning nothing in particular by this, merely wanting to indicate how it was raining, that the rain was heavier again, and that now it was not going to stop at all; but to Raban it sounded as though at sixty the gentleman still thought of himself as young and energetic and considered Raban's thirty years nothing in comparison, and as though he meant to say besides, in so far as it was permissible, that at the age of thirty he had, of course, been more sensible than Raban. And that he believed even if one had nothing else to do, like himself, for instance, an old man, yet it was really wasting one's time to stand about here in this hall, looking at the rain, but if one spent the time, besides, in chatter, one was wasting it doubly.

Now Raban had believed for some time that nothing other people said about his capabilities or opinions had been able to affect him, on the contrary, that he had positively abandoned the position where he had listened, all submissively, to everything that was said, so that people were now simply wasting their breath whether they happened to be against him or for him. And so he said: "We are talking about different things, since you did not wait to hear what I was going to say."

"Please go on, please go on," the gentleman said.

"Well, it isn't so important," Raban said. "I was only going to say books are useful in every sense and quite especially in respects in which one would not expect it. For when one is about to embark on some enterprise, it is precisely the books whose contents have nothing at all in common with the enterprise that are the most useful. For the reader who does after all intend to embark on that enterprise, that is to say, who has somehow become enthusiastic (and even if, as it were, the effect of the book can penetrate only so far as that enthusiasm), will be stimulated by the book to all kinds of thoughts concerning his enterprise. Now, however, since the contents of the book are precisely something of utter indifference, the reader is not at all impeded in those thoughts, and he passes through the midst of the book with them, as once the Jews passed through the Red Sea, that's how I should like to put it."

For Raban the whole person of the old gentleman now assumed an unpleasant expression. It seemed to him as though he had drawn particularly close to him—but it was merely trifling . . . [two pages missing] . . . "The newspaper, too.—But I was about to say, I am only going into the country, that's all, only for a fortnight; I am taking a holiday for the first time for quite a long period, and it's necessary for other reasons too, and yet for instance a book that I was, as I have mentioned, reading recently taught me more about my little journey than you could imagine."

"I am listening," the gentleman said.

Raban was silent and, standing there so straight, put his hands into his overcoat pockets, which were rather too high. Only after a while did the old gentleman say: "This journey seems to be of some special importance to you."

"Well, you see, you see," Raban said, once more supporting himself against the doorpost. Only now did he see how the passage had filled up with people. They were standing even round the foot of the staircase, and an official, who had rented a room in the apartment of the same woman as Raban had, when he came down the stairs had to ask the people to make way for him. To Raban, who only pointed at the rain, he called out over several heads, which now all turned to Raban, "Have a good journey" and reiterated a promise, obviously given earlier, definitely to visit Raban the next Sunday.

[Two pages missing] . . . has a pleasant job, with which he is indeed satisfied and which has always been kept open for him. He has such powers of endurance and is inwardly so gay that he does not need anyone to keep him entertained, but everyone needs him. He has always been healthy. Oh, don't try to tell me.

"I am not going to argue," the gentleman said.

"You won't argue, but you won't admit your mistake either. Why do you stick to it so? And however sharply you may recollect now, you would, I dare wager, for-

get everything if you were to talk to him. You would reproach me for not having refuted you more effectively
now. If he so much as talks about a book. He's instantly
ecstatic about everything beautiful. . . ."

REFLECTIONS ON SIN, SUFFERING, HOPE,
AND THE TRUE WAY

Reflections on Sin, Suffering, Hope,
and the True Way*

1.   The true way is along a rope that is not spanned high in the air, but only just above the ground. It seems intended more to cause stumbling than to be walked along.

2.   All human errors are impatience, the premature breaking off of what is methodical, an apparent fencing in of the apparent thing.

3.   There are two main human sins from which all the others derive: impatience and indolence. It was because of impatience that they were expelled from Paradise; it is because of indolence that they do not return. Yet perhaps there is only one major sin: impatience. Because of impatience they were expelled, because of impatience they do not return.

4.   Many shades of the departed are occupied solely in licking at the waves of the river of death because it flows from our direction and still has the salty taste of our seas. Then the river rears back in disgust, the current flows the opposite way and brings the dead drifting back into life. But they are happy, sing songs of thanksgiving, and stroke the indignant waters.

* The text followed is the fair copy made by Kafka himself, written—though without a title—in ink on separate slips of paper. The numbering of the aphorisms is also that given by him (see Note 2).

34

5. Beyond a certain point there is no return. This point has to be reached.

6. The decisive moment in human evolution is perpetual. That is why the revolutionary spiritual movements that declare all former things worthless are in the right, for nothing has yet happened.

7. One of the most effective means of seduction that Evil has is the challenge to struggle.

8. It is like the struggle with women, which ends in bed.

9. A is very puffed up, he thinks he is far advanced in goodness since, obviously as an object that is ever seductive, he feels himself exposed to ever more temptations from directons hitherto unknown to him.

10. The proper explanation is however this: that a great devil has taken up residence in him and countless throngs of smaller ones come along to serve the great one.

11-12. Differences in the view one can have of things, for instance of an apple: the view of a little boy who has to crane his neck in order even to glimpse the apple on the table, and the view of the master of the house, who takes the apple and freely hands it to the person sitting at table with him.

13. One of the first signs of the beginnings of understanding is the wish to die. This life appears unbearable, another unattainable. One is no longer ashamed of wanting to die; one asks to be moved from the old cell, which one hates, to a new one, which one will only in time come to hate. In this there is also a residue of belief that during the move the master will chance to come along the corridor, look at the prisoner and say: "This man is not to be locked up again. He is to come to me."

14.* If you were walking across a plain, had an honest intention of walking on, and yet kept regressing, then it would be a desperate matter; but since you are scrambling up a cliff, about as steep as you yourself are if seen from below, the regression can only be caused by the nature of the ground, and you must not despair.

15.   Like a path in autumn: scarcely has it been swept clear when it is once more covered with dry leaves.

16.   A cage went in search of a bird.

17.   This is a place where I never was before: here breathing is different, and more dazzling than the sun is the radiance of a star beside it.

18.   If it had been possible to build the Tower of Babel without climbing up it, it would have been permitted.

19.*   Do not let Evil make you believe you can have secrets from it.

20.   Leopards break into the temple and drink to the dregs what is in the sacrificial pitchers; this is repeated over and over again; finally it can be calculated in advance, and it becomes a part of the ceremony.

21.   As firmly as the hand grips the stone. But it grips it firmly only in order to fling it away all the further. But the way leads into those distances too.

22.   You are the task. No pupil far and wide.

23.   From the true antagonist illimitable courage is transmitted to you.

24.   Grasping the good fortune that the ground on which you are standing cannot be larger than the two feet covering it.

25.   How can one be glad about the world except if one takes one's refuge in it?

26.*   Hiding places there are innumerable, escape is only one, but possibilities of escape, again, are as many as hiding places.

*   There is a goal, but no way; what we call a way is hesitation.

27.   Doing the negative thing is imposed on us, an ad-

dition; the positive thing is given to us from the start.

28.   When one has once accepted and absorbed Evil, it no longer demands to be believed.

29.   The ulterior motives with which you absorb and assimilate Evil are not your own but those of Evil.

*   The animal wrests the whip from its master and whips itself in order to become master, not knowing that this is only a fantasy produced by a new knot in the master's whiplash.

30.   In a certain sense the Good is comfortless.

31.   Self-control is something for which I do not strive. Self-control means wanting to be effective at some random point in the infinite radiations of my spiritual existence. But if I do have to draw such circles round myself, then it will be better for me to do it passively, in mere wonderment and gaping at the tremendous complex, taking home with me only the refreshment that this sight gives *e contrario*.

32.   The crows maintain that a single crow could destroy the heavens. There is no doubt of that, but it proves nothing against the heavens, for heaven simply means: the impossibility of crows.

33.*   Martyrs do not underrate the body, they allow it to be elevated on the cross. In this they are at one with their antagonists.

34.   His exhaustion is that of the gladiator after the fight, his work was the whitewashing of one corner in a clerk's office.

35.   There is no having, only a being, only a state of being that craves the last breath, craves suffocation.

36.   Previously I did not understand why I got no answer to my question; today I do not understand how I could believe I was capable of asking. But I didn't really believe, I only asked.

37.   His answer to the assertion that he did perhaps

possess, but that he *was* not, was only trembling and palpitations.

38. A man was amazed at how easily he went along the road to eternity; the fact was he was rushing along it downhill.

39a. One cannot pay Evil in instalments—and one always keeps on trying to.

It could be imagined that Alexander the Great, in spite of his youthful triumphs in warfare, in spite of the superb army he built up, in spite of the energies he felt in himself that were directed to transforming the world, might have halted at the Hellespont and not have crossed it, and this not from fear, not from irresolution, not from weakness of will, but from the force of gravity.

39b. The way is infinitely long, nothing of it can be subtracted, nothing can be added, and yet everyone applies his own childish yardstick to it. "Certainly, this yard of the way you still have to go, too, and it will be accounted unto you."

40. It is only our conception of time that makes us call the Last Judgment by this name. It is, in fact, a kind of martial law.

41. It is comforting to reflect that the disproportion of things in the world seems to be only arithmetical.

42. Letting the head that is filled with disgust and hate droop on the breast.

43. The hunting dogs are still romping in the yard, but the prey will not escape them, however much it may be stampeding through the woods even now.

44. A ridiculous way you have girded yourself up for this world.

45. The more horses you harness to the job, the faster the thing goes—that is to say, not tearing the block out of its base, which is impossible, but tearing the

straps to shreds, and as a result the weightless merry journey.

46.   In German the word *sein* stands both for the verb *to be* and for the possessive pronoun *his*.

47.   They were given the choice of becoming kings or the kings' messengers. As is the way with children, they all wanted to be messengers. That is why there are only messengers, racing through the world and, since there are no kings, calling out to each other the messages that have now become meaningless. They would gladly put an end to their miserable life, but they do not dare to do so because of their oath of loyalty.

48.   Believing in progress does not mean believing that any progress has yet been made. That is not the sort of belief that indicates real faith.

49.   A is a virtuoso and heaven is his witness.

50.*   Man cannot live without a permanent trust in something indestructible in himself, though both the indestructible element and the trust may remain permanently hidden from him. One of the ways in which this hiddenness can express itself is through faith in a personal god.

51.*   The mediation by the serpent was necessary: Evil can seduce man, but cannot become man.

52.*   In the struggle between yourself and the world second the world.

53.   One must not cheat anyone, not even the world of its victory.

54.   There is nothing besides a spiritual world; what we call the world of the senses is the Evil in the spiritual world, and what we call Evil is only the necessity of a moment in our eternal evolution.

*   One can disintegrate the world by means of very strong light. For weak eyes the world becomes solid,

for still weaker eyes it seems to develop fists, for eyes weaker still it becomes shamefaced and smashes anyone who dares to gaze upon it.

55. Everything is deception: seeking the minimum of illusion, keeping within the ordinary limitations, seeking the maximum. In the first case one cheats the Good, by trying to make it too easy for oneself to get it, and the Evil by imposing all too unfavorable conditions of warfare on it. In the second case one cheats the Good by not striving for it even in earthly terms. In the third case one cheats the Good by keeping as aloof from it as possible, and the Evil by hoping to make it powerless through intensifying it to the utmost. What would therefore seem to be preferable is the second case, for the Good is always cheated, and in this case, or at least to judge by appearances, the Evil is not cheated.

56. There are questions we could not get past if we were not set free from them by our very nature.

57. For everything outside the phenomenal world, language can only be used allusively, but never even approximately in a comparative way, since, corresponding as it does to the phenomenal world, it is concerned only with property and its relations.

58.* One tells as few lies as possible only by telling as few lies as possible, and not by having the least possible opportunity to do so.

59.* A stair not worn hollow by footsteps is, regarded from its own point of view, only a boring something made of wood.

60. Anyone who renounces the world must love all men, for he renounces their world too. He thus begins to have some inkling of the true nature of man, which cannot but be loved, always assuming that one is its peer.

61.* Anyone who loves his neighbor within the limits of the world is doing no more and no less injustice than someone who loves himself within the limits of the world. There remains only the question whether the former is possible.

62. The fact that there is nothing but a spiritual world deprives us of hope and gives us certainty.

63. Our art is a way of being dazzled by truth: the light on the grotesquely grimacing retreating face is true, and nothing else.

64-65. Expulsion from Paradise is in its main aspect eternal: that is to say, although expulsion from Paradise is final, and life in the world unavoidable, the eternity of the process (or, expressed in temporal terms, the eternal repetition of the process) nevertheless makes it possible not only that we might remain in Paradise permanently, but that we may in fact be there permanently, no matter whether we know it here or not.

66. He is a free and secure citizen of this earth, for he is attached to a chain that is long enough to make all areas of the earth accessible to him, and yet only so long that nothing can pull him over the edges of the earth. At the same time, however, he is also a free and secure citizen of heaven, for he is also attached to a similarly calculated heavenly chain. Thus, if he wants to get down to earth, he is choked by the heavenly collar and chain; if he wants to get into heaven, he is choked by the earthly one. And in spite of this he has all the possibilities, and feels that it is so; indeed, he even refuses to attribute the whole thing to a mistake in the original chaining.

67. He runs after facts like a beginner learning to skate, who, furthermore, practices somewhere where it is forbidden.

68. What is gayer than believing in a household god?

69. Theoretically there is a perfect possibility of happiness: believing in the indestructible element in oneself and not striving towards it.

70-71.   The indestructible is one: it is each individual human being and, at the same time, it is common to all, hence the incomparably indivisible union that exists between human beings.

72.*   In one and the same human being there are cognitions that, however utterly dissimilar they are, yet have one and the same object, so that one can only conclude that there are different subjects in one and the same human being.

73.   He gobbles up the leavings and crumbs that fall from his own table; in this way he is, of course, for a little while more thoroughly sated than all the rest, but he forgets how to eat from the table itself. In this way, however, there cease to be any crumbs and leavings.

74.   If what is supposed to have been destroyed in Paradise was destructible, then it was not decisive; but if it was indestructible, then we are living in a false belief.

75.*   Test yourself on mankind. It is something that makes the doubter doubt, the believer believe.

76.   This feeling: "Here I shall not anchor"—and instantly to feel the billowing, supporting swell around one!

*   A veering round. Peering, timid, hopeful, the answer prowls round the question, desperately looking into its impenetrable face, following it along the most senseless paths, that is, along the paths leading as far as possible away from the answer.

77.   Association with human beings lures one into self-observation.

78.   The spirit becomes free only when it ceases to be a support.

79.   Sensual love deceives one as to the nature of heavenly love; it could not do so alone, but since it unconsciously has the element of heavenly love within it, it can do so.

80.   Truth is indivisible, hence it cannot recognize itself; anyone who wants to recognize it has to be a lie.

81.   Nobody can desire what is ultimately damaging to him. If in individual cases it does appear to be so after all—and perhaps it always does so appear—this is explained by the fact that someone in the person demands something that is, admittedly, of use to someone, but which to a second someone, who is brought in half in order to judge the case, is gravely damaging. If the person had from the very beginning, and not only when it came to judging the case, taken his stand at the side of the second someone, the first someone would have faded out, and with him the desire.

82.   Why do we complain about the Fall? It is not on its account that we were expelled from Paradise, but on account of the Tree of Life, lest we might eat of it.

83.   We are sinful not only because we have eaten of the Tree of Knowledge, but also because we have not yet eaten of the Tree of Life. The state in which we are is sinful, irrespective of guilt.

84.   We were created in order to live in Paradise, and Paradise was ordained to serve us. What was ordained for us has been changed; it is not said that this has also happened with what was ordained for Paradise.

85.   Evil is a radiation of the human consciousness in certain transitional positions. It is not actually the sensual world that is a mere appearance; what is so is the evil of it, which, admittedly, is what constitutes the sensual world in our eyes.

86.   Since the Fall we have been essentially equal in our capacity to know Good and Evil; nevertheless it is precisely here we look for our special merits. But only on the far side of this knowledge do the real differences begin. The contrary appearance is caused by the following fact: nobody can be content with knowledge alone, but must

strive to act in accordance with it. But he is not endowed with the strength for this, hence he must destroy himself, even at the risk of in that way not acquiring the necessary strength, but there is nothing else he can do except make this last attempt. (This is also the meaning of the threat of death associated with the ban on eating from the Tree of Knowledge; perhaps this is also the original meaning of natural death.) Now this is an attempt he is afraid to make; he prefers to undo the knowledge of Good and Evil (the term 'the Fall' has its origin in this fear); but what has once happened cannot be undone, it can only be made turbid. It is for this purpose that motivations arise. The whole world is full of them: indeed the whole visible world is perhaps nothing other than a motivation of man's wish to rest for a moment—an attempt to falsify the fact of knowledge, to try to turn the knowledge into the goal.

87.   A belief like a guillotine—as heavy, as light.

88.   Death is in front of us, rather as on the schoolroom wall there is a reproduction of Alexander's Battle. The thing is to darken, or even indeed to blot out, the picture in this one life of ours through our actions.

89.   A man has free will, and this of three kinds: first of all he was free when he wanted this life; now, of course, he cannot go back on it, for he is no longer the person who wanted it then, except perhaps in so far as he carries out what he then wanted, in that he lives.

Secondly, he is free in that he can choose the pace and the road of this life.

Thirdly, he is free in that, as the person who will sometime exist again, he has the will to make himself go through life under every condition and in this way come to himself, and this, what is more, on a road that, though it is a matter of choice, is still so very labyrinthine that there is no smallest area of this life that it leaves untouched.

This is the trichotomy of free will, but since it is simultaneous it is also a unity, an integer, and fundamentally is so completely integral that it has no room for any will, free or unfree.

90.*   Two possibilities: making oneself infinitely small or being so. The second is perfection, that is to say, inactivity, the first is beginning, that is to say, action.

91.*   Towards the avoidance of a piece of verbal confusion: What is intended to be actively destroyed must first of all have been firmly grasped; what crumbles away crumbles away, but cannot be destroyed.

92.   The first worship of idols was certainly fear of the things in the world, but, connected with this, fear of the necessity of the things, and, connected with this, fear of responsibility for the things. So tremendous did this responsibility appear that people did not even dare to impose it upon one single extra-human entity, for even the mediation of one being would not have sufficiently lightened human responsibility, intercourse with only one being would still have been all too deeply tainted with responsibility, and that is why each thing was given the responsibility for itself, more indeed, these things were also given a degree of responsibility for man.

93.*   Never again psychology!

94.   Two tasks at the beginning of your life: to narrow your orbit more and more, and ever and again to check whether you are not in hiding somewhere outside your orbit.

95.*   Evil is sometimes in one's hand like a tool; recognized or unrecognized it can, if one has the will to do so, be laid aside without contradiction.

96.   The joys of this life are not life's, but our fear of

ascending into a higher life; the torments of this life are not life's, but our self-torment on account of that fear.

97.   Only here is suffering suffering. Not in such a way as if those who suffer here were because of this suffering to be elevated elsewhere, but in such a way that what in this world is called suffering in another world, unchanged and only liberated from its opposite, is bliss.

98.*   The notion of the infinite expanse and copiousness of the cosmos is the result of the mixture, carried to the extreme limit, of laborious creation and free self-determination.

99.   How much more oppressive than the most inexorable conviction of our present sinful state is even the weakest conviction of the coming eternal justification of our temporality. Only strength in the endurance of this second conviction, which in its purity entirely comprehends the first, is the measure of faith.

*   Many people assume that besides the great primal deception there is also in every individual case a little special deception provided for their benefit, in other words that when a drama of love is performed on the stage, the actress has, apart from the hypocritical smile for her lover, also an especially insidious smile for the quite particular spectator in the top balcony. This is going too far.

100.   There can be knowledge of the diabolical, but no belief in it, for more of the diabolical than there is does not exist.

101.   Sin always comes openly and can at once be grasped by means of the senses. It walks on its roots and does not have to be torn out.

102.   We too must suffer all the suffering around us. We all have not *one* body, but we have *one* way of growing, and this leads us through all anguish, whether in this or in that form. Just as the child develops through all the

stages of life right into old age and to death (and fundamentally to the earlier stage the later one seems out of
reach, in relation both to desire and to fear), so also do
we develop (no less deeply bound up with mankind than
with ourselves) through all the sufferings of this world.
There is no room for justice in this context, but neither
is there any room either for fear of suffering or for the
interpretation of suffering as a merit.

103.   You can hold yourself back from the sufferings of
the world: this is something you are free to do and is in
accord with your nature, but perhaps precisely this holding back is the only suffering that you might be able to
avoid.

105.   This world's method of seduction and the token
of the guarantee that this world is only a transition are
one and the same. Rightly so, for only in this way can
this world seduce us, and it is in keeping with the truth.
The worst thing, however, is that after the seduction
has been successful we forget the guarantee and thus actually the Good has lured us into Evil, the woman's
glance into her bed.

106.   Humility provides everyone, even him who de-
spairs in solitude, with the strongest relationship to his
fellow man, and this immediately, though, of course,
only in the case of complete and permanent humility. It
can do this because it is the true language of prayer, at
once adoration and the firmest of unions. The relationship to one's fellow man is the relationship of prayer, the
relationship to oneself is the relationship of striving; it is
from prayer that one draws the strength for one's striving.

*   *Can* you know anything other than deception? If
ever the deception is annihilated, you must not look in
that direction or you will turn into a pillar of salt.

107.   Everyone is very kind to A., more or less as one

tries to guard an excellent billiard table even from good players, until the time when the great player comes, who will carefully examine the table, will not put up with any damage done to it previously, but then, when he himself begins to play, lets himself go wildly, in the most inconsiderate manner.

108.   "But then he returned to his work just as though nothing had happened." This is a remark that we are familiar with from a vague abundance of old stories, although perhaps it does not occur in any of them.

109.   "It cannot be said that we are lacking in faith. Even the simple fact of our life is of a faith-value that can never be exhausted." "You suggest there is some faith-value in this? One *cannot* not-live, after all." "It is precisely in this 'Cannot, after all' that the mad strength of faith lies; it is in this negation that it takes on form."

*   There is no need for you to leave the house. Stay at your table and listen. Don't even listen, just wait. Don't even wait, be completely quiet and alone. The world will offer itself to you to be unmasked; it can't do otherwise; in raptures it will writhe before you.

THE EIGHT OCTAVO NOTEBOOKS

The Eight Octavo Notebooks[3]

The First Octavo Notebook[4]

EVERYONE CARRIES a room about inside him. This fact can even be proved by means of the sense of hearing. If someone walks fast and one pricks up one's ears and listens, say in the night, when everything round about is quiet, one hears, for instance, the rattling of a mirror not quite firmly fastened to the wall.

He stands with chest sunken, shoulders forward, arms dangling, feet that can scarcely be picked up, his gaze fixed in a stare on one spot. A stoker. He shovels up coal and flings it into the furnace, the opening full of flames. A child has come stealing through the twenty court-yards of the factory and tugs at his apron. "Father," it says, "I've brought you your soup."

[5] Is it warmer here than down on the wintry earth? How white it towers all around, my coal bucket the only thing that's dark. If I was high up before, now I am far down, and gazing up at the hills almost dislocates my neck. White, frozen plains of ice, streaked into slices here and there by the tracks of skaters since disappeared. On the high snow, which doesn't give more than an inch, I follow the tracks of the small arctic dogs. My riding has lost all meaning, I have dismounted and am carrying the coal scuttle on my shoulder.

V.W.[6]

My heartfelt thanks for the Beethoven book. I am beginning the Schopenhauer today. What an achievement this book is. It is devoutly to be hoped that with your so utterly delicate hand, with your so utterly intense vision of true reality, with the disciplined and mighty underground fire of your poetic nature, with your fantastically extensive knowledge, you will raise yet more such monuments—to my unspeakable joy.

Old, in the fullness of the flesh, suffering slight palpitations, I was lying on the sofa after lunch, one foot on the floor, and reading a historical work. The maid came and, with two fingers laid on her pursed lips, announced a visitor.

"Who is it?" I asked, irritated at having to entertain a visitor at a time when I was expecting my afternoon coffee.

"A Chinaman," the maid said and, turning convulsively, suppressed a laugh that the visitor outside the door was not supposed to hear.

"A Chinese? To see me? Is he in Chinese dress?"

The maid nodded, still struggling with the desire to laugh.

"Tell him my name, ask if I am really the person he wants to see, unknown as I am even to the people next door, and how very unknown then in China."

The maid tiptoed over to me and whispered: "He has only a visiting card, it says on it that he asks to be admitted. He can't talk German at all, he talks some incomprehensible language. I was frightened to take the card away from him."

"Let him come!" I exclaimed, in the agitation that my heart trouble often brings on, flinging the book to the floor, and cursing the maid for her awkwardness.

Standing up and stretching my gigantic form, which could not fail to be a shock to any visitor in this low-ceilinged room, I went to the door. And in fact, the Chinese had no sooner set eyes on me than he flitted straight out again. I merely reached out into the passage and carefully pulled the man back inside by his silken belt. He was obviously a scholar, small, weakly, wearing horn-rimmed spectacles, and with a thin, grizzled, stiff goatee. An amiable mannikin, his head inclined to one side, smiling, with half-closed eyes.

The advocate Dr. Bucephalus sent for his housekeeper one morning when he was still in bed and said to her: "To-day the great hearing begins in the case of my brother Bucephalus against the firm of Trollhätta. I am appearing for the plaintiff, and since the trial will last for several days at least, and, what's more, without any real break, I shall not be coming home at all for the next few days. As soon as the case is finished, or there is a prospect of its being finished, I shall telephone you. More I can't say at the moment, nor can I answer the slightest question, since of course I must concentrate on preserving the full strength of my voice. For this reason will you bring me two raw eggs and tea with honey for my breakfast?" And, slowly sinking back on his pillows, his hand over his eyes, he fell silent.

The chatterbox of a housekeeper, who was at any moment prepared to die of fright in her master's presence, was greatly taken aback. So suddenly had such extraordinary instructions come. Only the evening before, the master had been talking to her, but without giving any hint of what was to come. Surely the time of the trial could not have been fixed during the night? And were there cases that went on for days without a break? And why did the master mention the names of the parties in the case, which he never told her at any other time? And what sort of tremendous case could the master's brother have, that small greengrocer Adolf Bucephalus, with whom, incidentally, the master had not been on good terms for quite a long time? And was it in keeping with the incredible exertions confronting the master that he should now be lying in bed so wearily and keeping his hand over his face, which, if the early morning light was not deceptive, was somehow haggard? And he wanted only tea and eggs brought him, and not also, as at other times, a little wine, and ham, in order to restore his vital energies completely? With such thoughts the housekeeper withdrew to the kitchen, sat down just for a little while in her favorite place at the window, near the flowers and the canary, glanced over at the far side of the court, where two children were romping and wrestling together, half naked, behind a barred window, then turned away, sighing, poured out the tea, fetched two eggs out of the larder, arranged everything on a tray, could not bring herself not to take the bottle of wine too, as a beneficent temptation, and took it all along to the bedroom.

The room was empty. What, surely the master had not gone? He could surely not have dressed inside one minute? But his underclothes and his suit were nowhere to be seen. What on earth is the matter with the master? Quick, into the hall! Coat, hat, and stick have gone, too. To the window! In heaven's name, there is the master walking out of the front door, his hat on the back of his head, his coat open, clutching his briefcase, his stick hanging by the crook from a pocket of his coat.

You know the Trocadéro in Paris? In that building, the extent of which you cannot possibly imagine from photographs of it, the main hearing in a great lawsuit is going on at this very moment. You may wonder how it is possible to heat such a building adequately in this frightful winter. It is not heated. To start by thinking of heating in such a case is something people can do only in the pretty little country town where you spend your life. The Trocadéro is not being heated, but this does not interfere with the progress of the case; on the contrary, in the midst of this cold, which radiates up and down from all sides, litigation is going on at exactly the same pace, this way and that, lengthwise and across.

Yesterday I was visited by a swoon. She lives in the house next door; I have quite often seen her disappearing through the low gateway, bent down, in the evenings. A tall lady in a long flowing dress and a broad-brimmed hat with feathers on it. Very hastily with rustling skirts, she came in through my door, like a doctor who's afraid he has come too late to a patient whose life is flickering out.

"Anton," she exclaimed in a hollow voice that yet rang with self-pride, "I come, I am here!"

She dropped into the chair at which I pointed.

"How high up you live, how high up you live," she said, moaning.

Huddled in my armchair, I nodded. Innumerable, the stairs leading up to my rooms hopped before my eyes, one after the other, tireless little waves.

"Why so cold?" she asked, pulling off her long, old fencing gloves, throwing them on the table, and, her head inclined, blinked at me.

I felt as if I were a sparrow, practicing my jumps on the step, and she were ruffling my soft, fluffy gray feathers.

"I'm sorry from the bottom of my heart that you have been pining for me. I have often looked with genuine sadness at your careworn face, when you were standing in the courtyard, gazing up at my window. Well, I am not unfavorably inclined to you, and though you may not yet have won my heart, you have a good chance of doing so."

To what indifference people may come, to what profound conviction of having lost the right track for ever.

A mistake. It was not my door, up there in the long corridor, that I opened. "A mistake," I said and was on the point of going out again. Then I saw the occupant, a gaunt, beardless man with compressed lips, sitting at a little table on which there was only an oil lamp.

In our house, this immense building in an outer suburb, a tenement house the fabric of which is interspersed with indestructible medieval ruins, the following manifesto was distributed today, on this foggy, icy winter morning. To all my fellow lodgers:

I am in possession of five toy rifles. They are hanging in my wardrobe, one on each hook. The first belongs to me, and the others can be claimed by anyone who wishes to send in his name. If more than four people send in their names, the supernumerary claimants must bring their own rifles with them and deposit them in my wardrobe. For uniformity must be maintained; without uniformity we shall get nowhere. Incidentally, I have only rifles that are quite useless for any other purpose, the mechanism is broken, the corks have got torn off, only the cocks still click. So it will not be difficult, should it prove necessary, to provide more such rifles. But fundamentally I am prepared, for a start, to accept even people without rifles. At the decisive moment we who have rifles will group ourselves round those who are unarmed. Why should not tactics that proved successful when used by the first American farmers against the Red Indians not also prove successful here, since after all the conditions are similar? And so it is even possible to do without rifles permanently, and even the five rifles are not absolutely necessary, and it is only because they are, after all, there, that they ought also to be used. But if the four others do not want to carry them, they need not do so. So then only I, as the leader, shall carry one. But we ought not to have any leader, and so I, too, shall then break my rifle or put it away.

That was the first manifesto. Nobody in our house has either time or inclination to read manifestoes, far less to think about them. Before long the little sheets of paper were floating in the stream of dirty water that, beginning in the attics and fed by all the corridors, pours down the staircase and there collides with the other stream mounting up from below. But after a week there came a second manifesto.

Fellow inmates:

Up to now nobody has sent in his name to me. Apart from the hours during which I have to earn my living, I have been at home all the time, and in the periods of my absence, when the door of my room has always been left open, there has been a piece of paper on my table, for everyone who wished to do so to put down his name. Nobody has done so.

Sometimes I think I can expiate all my past and future sins through the aching of my bones when I come home from the engineering works at night or, for that matter, in the morning, after a night-shift. I am not strong enough for this work, I have known that for a long time and yet I do nothing to change anything.

In our house, this immense building in an outer suburb, a tenement house the fabric of which is interspersed with medieval ruins, there is a government clerk lodging with a worker's family, on the same floor as myself. Although they call him an official, he can't be more than a little clerk who spends his nights on a paillasse on the floor, right in the middle of a den of strangers, the married couple and their six children. And so if he is a little clerk, what concern is he of mine? Even in this building, in which there is a concentration of the misery brewed by the city, there are certainly more than a hundred people. . . .

On the same floor as myself a small tailor lodges, who does mainly repair jobs. In spite of all the care I take, I wear my clothes out too quickly, and recently I again had to take a coat to the tailor. It was a fine warm summer evening. The tailor has only one room, which is also the kitchen, for himself, his wife, and six children. Apart from this, he also has a lodger, a clerk from the tax department. Such overcrowding is really a little beyond what is usual even in our building, where it is certainly bad enough. All the same, everyone is left to do as he likes; the tailor doubtless has irrefutably good reasons for his thriftiness, and no outsider would dream of inquiring into those reasons.

February 19, 1917.

Today read *Hermann und Dorothea*, passages from Richter's *Memoirs*,[7] looked at pictures by him, and finally read a scene from Hauptmann's *Griselda*. For the brief span of the next hour am a different person. True, all prospects as misty as ever, but pictures in the mist now different. The man in the heavy boots I have put on today for the first time (they were originally intended for military service) is a different person.

I lodge with Herr Krummholz, I share the room with a clerk from the tax department. Apart from this, there are in the room two daughters of Krummholz's sleeping in the one bed, one six-year-old and one seven-year-old girl. Since the first day when the clerk moved in—I myself have lodged with Krummholz for years—I have been suspicious of him, at first in a quite undefined way. A man of less than middle height, weakly, lungs probably not too good, with gray clothes that hang loose on him, furrowed face of no particular age, grayish fair hair, rather long and combed over his ears, spectacles slipping down his nose, and a little goatee beard, also turning gray.

It was not a very cheerful life I led at that time, working on the building of the railway in the interior of the Congo.

I used to sit on the roofed veranda of my wooden shack. Stretched across the front, in place of a wall, there was an extraordinarily fine-meshed mosquito net, which I had bought from one of the foremen, the chieftain of a tribe through whose territory our railway was to go. A hempen net, at once stronger and more delicate than can be manufactured anywhere in Europe. It was my pride and I was generally much envied for it. Without this net it would simply not have been possible to sit peacefully on the veranda in the evening and turn on the light, as I now did, taking an old European newspaper, to study it, and puff away mightily at my pipe.[8]

I have—who else can speak so freely of his abilities?—the wrist of a lucky, untiring, old angler. For instance, I sit at home before I go out fishing, and, watching closely, turn my right hand first this way and then that. This is enough to reveal to me, by the look and the feeling of it, the result of the fishing expedition on which I am about to set out, and often down to the very details. A prophetic intuition of this pliant joint, which, when I am resting, I enclose in a gold bracelet in order to let it gather strength. I see the water of the place where I shall fish and the particular current at the particular hour; a cross section of the river appears to me; distinct in number and species, at up to ten, twenty, or even a hundred different places, fish thrust towards the edge of this cross section; now I know how to cast the line; some thrust their heads through the edge without coming to harm, then I let the hook dangle before them, and at once there they are hanging on it; the brevity of this moment of destiny delights me even at the table at home; other fish thrust forward up to the belly, now it is high time, some I still manage to overtake, others again slip through the dangerous edge right up to their tails and for the time being are lost to me, only for this time though, from a real angler no fish escapes.

The Second Octavo Notebook [9]

[Note appended to *A Sport**]
A LITTLE BOY had a cat that was all he had inherited from his father and through it became Lord Mayor of London. What shall I become through my animal, my inheritance? Where does the huge city lie?

The history of the world, as it is written and handed down by word of mouth, often fails us completely; but man's intuitive capacity, though it often misleads, does lead, does not ever abandon one. And so, for instance, the tradition of the seven wonders of the world has always had associated with it the rumor that there was

* This piece appears in *The Great Wall of China*.

another, an eighth wonder of the world, and concerning this eighth wonder there were various, perhaps contradictory, statements made, the vagueness of which was explained by the obscurity of ancient times.

You will admit, ladies and gentlemen—more or less thus did the Arab in European clothes address the party of tourists, who were not really listening, but, positively bowed down with awe, were contemplating the incredible edifice that rose out of the bare stony ground in front of them—you will surely admit that my firm by far outdoes all other travel agencies, even those that have rightly been famous for many years. While our rivals, in the old approved fashion, take their clients only to the seven wonders of the world mentioned in the history books, our firm shows you the eighth wonder.

No, no.

Some say he is a hypocrite, others, again, that he only seems to be one. My parents know his father. When the latter came to see us last Sunday, I asked him outright about his son. Now the old gentleman is very sly, it is difficult to tackle him properly, and I lack any sort of skill in making such attacks. The conversation was lively, but scarcely had I interjected my question when silence fell. My father began nervously toying with his beard, my mother got up to see about the tea, the old gentleman however glanced at me out of his blue eyes, smiling, and inclined his furrowed pallid face with the thick white hair to one side. "Ah yes, the boy," he said and turned his gaze to the table lamp, which was already lit on this early winter's evening. "Have you ever talked to him?" he then asked. "No," I said, "but I have heard a lot about him and I should very much like to talk to him sometime, if he would receive me."

"What is it? What is it?" I exclaimed, still held down in bed by sleep, and stretched my arms upwards. Then I got up, still far from being conscious of the present, and with the feeling that I must thrust aside various people who were in my way, made the necessary gestures, and so at last reached the open window.

Helpless, a barn in the spring, a consumptive in the spring.

Sometimes it happens, the reasons being often scarcely imaginable, that the greatest bullfighter chooses as the place where he will fight some decayed arena in a remote little town whose name the Madrid public has scarcely heard of. An arena that has been neglected for centuries, here overgrown with grass, a place where children play, there hot with bare stones, a place where snakes and lizards bask. The tops of the walls long ago carried away, a quarry for all the houses round about. Now only a little cauldron that will seat scarcely five hundred people. No annex building, above all no stables, but the worst thing of all is that the railway line has not yet been extended so far and there are three hours to travel by cart, seven hours to cover on foot, from the nearest station.

My two hands began a fight. They slammed the book I had been reading and thrust it aside so that it should not be in the way. Me they saluted, and appointed me referee. And an instant later they had locked fingers with each other and were already rushing away over the edge of the table, now to the right, now to the left, according to which of them was bringing most pressure to bear on the other. I never turned my gaze from them. If they are my hands, I must referee fairly, otherwise I shall bring down on myself the agonies of a wrong decision. But my function is not easy, in the darkness between the palms of the hands various holds are brought into play that I must not let pass unnoticed, and so I press my chin on the table and now nothing escapes me. All my life long I have made a favorite of the right, without meaning the left any harm. If the left had ever said anything, indulgent and just as I am, I should at once have put a stop to the abuse. But it never grumbled, it hung down from me, and while, say, the right was raising my hat in the street, the left was timidly fumbling down my thigh. That was a bad way of preparing for the struggle that is now going on. How in the long run, left wrist, will you resist the pressure of this powerful right hand? How maintain your girlish finger's stand in the grip of the five others? This seems to me to be no longer a fight, but the natural end of the left hand. Even now it has been pushed to the extreme left rim of the table, and the right is pounding regularly up and down on it like the piston of an engine. If, confronted with this misery, I had not got the saving idea that these are my own hands and that with a slight jerk I can pull them away from each other and so put an end to the fight and the misery—if I had not got this idea, the left hand would have been broken out of the wrist, would have been flung from the table, and then the right, in the wild recklessness of knowing itself the victor, might have leapt, like five-headed Cerberus, straight into my attentive face. Instead, the two now lie one on top of the other, the right stroking the back of the left, and I, dishonest referee, nod in approval.

At last our troops succeeded in breaking into the city through the southern gate. My contingent encamped in a suburban garden, among half-burnt cherry trees, waiting for orders. But when we heard the high clangor of the trumpets from the southern gate, nothing could hold us any longer. With whatever weapons each of us had snatched up, in disorder, each with an arm round his comrade, yelling our battle cry of "Kahira Kahira," we trotted in long columns through the marshes towards the city. At the southern gate all we found now were corpses and yellow smoke, billowing over the ground and hiding everything from sight. But we did not want merely to be the rear guard and at once turned into narrow side streets that had hitherto remained unscathed by the battle. The door of the first house splintered under my ax, and so wildly did we push into the hall that at first we were churning around each other in confusion. An old man came towards us out of a long empty passage. A strange old man—he had wings. Wide, outspread wings, the tips taller than himself. "He has wings," I called out to my brothers-in-arms, and those of us in front fell back somewhat, as far as we could for those behind, who were pushing on. "You are amazed," the old man said. "We all have wings, but they have not been of any avail to us and if we could tear them off, we would do so." "Why did you not fly away?" I asked. "Fly away out of our city? Leave home? Leave the dead and the gods?"

The Third Octavo Notebook [10]

OCTOBER 18, 1917. Dread of night. Dread of not-night.

October 19. Senselessness (too strong a word) of the separation of what is one's own and what is extraneous in the spiritual battle.

All science is methodology with regard to the Absolute. Therefore, there need be no fear of the unequivocally methodological. It is a husk, but not more than everything except the One.

We are all fighting a battle. (If, attacked by the ultimate question, I reach out behind me for weapons, I cannot choose which of those weapons I will have, and even if I could choose, I should be bound to choose some that don't belong to me, for we all have only one store of weapons.) I cannot fight a battle all of my own; if for once I believe I am independent, if for once I see nobody around me, it soon turns out that as a consequence of the general constellation, which is not immediately or even not at all intelligible to me, I have had to take this post over. This, of course, does not exclude the fact that there is a cavalry spearhead, stragglers, snipers, and all the usual and abnormal items of warfare, but there is no one who fights an independent battle. [Humiliation] of vanity? Yes, but also a necessary encouragement, and one in accordance with the truth.

I digress. [Here follows Aphorism 1 from: *Reflections on Sin, Suffering, Hope, and the True Way*.]*

Always first draw fresh breath after outbursts of vanity and complacency. The orgy while reading the story in *Der Jude*.[11] Like a squirrel in its cage. Bliss of movement. Desperation about constriction, craziness of endurance, feeling of misery confronted with the repose of what is external. All this both simultaneously and alternatingly, still in the filth of the end.

A sunray of bliss.

* *Publisher's Note.* The reader is asked to refer back to the previous section, where the Aphorisms are printed consecutively, both here and in all subsequent cases where the omission of one or more in the body of the text is indicated by a bracket.

Weakness of memory for details and the course of one's own comprehension of the world—a very bad sign. Only fragments of a totality. How are you going even to touch the greatest task, how are you going even to sense its nearness, even dream its existence, even plead for its dream, dare to learn the letters of the plea, if you cannot collect yourself in such a way that, when the decisive moment comes, you hold the totality of yourself collected in your hand like a stone to be thrown, a knife for the kill? However: there is no need to spit on one's hands before clasping them.

Is it possible to think something unconsoling? Or, rather, something unconsoling without the breath of consolation? A way out would seem to lie in the fact that recognition as such is consolation. And so one might well think: You must put yourself aside, and yet one might maintain oneself, without falsifying this recognition, by the consciousness of having recognized it. That, then, really means having pulled oneself out of the swamp by one's own pigtail. What is ridiculous in the physical world is possible in the spiritual world. *There* there is no law of gravity (the angels do not fly, they have not overcome any force of gravity, it is only we observers in the terrestrial world who cannot imagine it in any better way than that), which is, of course, beyond our power of conception, or at any rate conceivable only on a very high level. How pathetically scanty my self-knowledge is compared with, say, my knowledge of my room. (Evening.) Why? There is no such thing as observation of the inner world, as there is of the outer world. At least descriptive psychology is probably, taken as a whole, a form of anthropomorphism, a nibbling at our own limits. The inner world can only be experienced, not described.—Psychology is the description of the reflection of the terrestrial world in the heavenly plane, or, more correctly, the description of a reflection such as we, soaked as we are in our terrestrial nature, imagine it, for no reflection actually occurs, only we see earth wherever we turn.

Psychology is impatience. [Aphorism 2.]

Don Quixote's misfortune is not his imagination, but Sancho Panza.

October 20. In bed. [Aphorism 3.]

Seen with the terrestrially sullied eye, we are in the situation of travelers in a train that has met with an accident in a tunnel, and this at a place where the light of the beginning can no longer be seen, and the light of the end is so very small a glimmer that the gaze must continually search for it and is always losing it again, and, furthermore, both the beginning and the end are not even certainties. Round about us, however, in the confusion of our senses, or in the supersensitiveness of our senses, we have nothing but monstrosities and a kaleidoscopic play of things that is either delightful or exhausting according to the mood and injury of each individual. What shall I do? or: Why should I do it? are not questions to be asked in such places.

[Aphorisms 4, 5, and 6.]

The history of mankind is the instant between two strides taken by a traveler.

Evening walk to Oberklee.

From outside one will always triumphantly impress theories upon the world and then fall straight into the ditch one has dug, but only from inside will one keep oneself and the world quiet and true.

[Aphorisms 7 and 8.] A married man's true deviations from the path of virtue are, rightly understood, never gay.

October 21. In the sunshine.

The voices of the world becoming quieter and fewer.

An Everyday Confusion*

AN EVERYDAY OCCURRENCE: the way he endures an everyday confusion. A has an important business deal to conclude with B, who lives in H. He goes to H to confer about it, gets there and back in ten minutes each way, and at home boasts of this particular quickness. The next day he goes to H again, this time for the final settlement of the deal. Since this is likely to take several hours, A leaves very early in the morning. But although all the attendant circumstances, at least in A's opinion, are exactly the same as on the previous day, this time it takes him ten hours to get to H. When he arrives there at evening, very tired, he is told that B, annoyed at A's failure to arrive, left half an hour ago for A's village and that they really ought to have met on the way. A is advised to wait. But A, anxious about the deal, at once takes his departure and hurries home.

This time, without paying any particular attention to the fact, he covers the distance in no more than an instant. At home he discovers that B had already come

* Under the title "A Common Confusion" this piece appears in *The Great Wall of China*.

in the morning, straight after A had left, indeed, he is told that B met him on the doorstep and reminded him about the deal, but that he, A, said he had no time, was in a hurry, must go.

In spite of A's incomprehensible behavior, however, B (A is told) stayed there, waiting for A. True, he had often asked whether A was not yet back, but he was still upstairs in A's room. Happy at still being able to see B and explain everything to him, A runs upstairs. He is almost at the top when he stumbles, strains a tendon, and, almost fainting with pain, incapable even of screaming, only whimpering there in the dark, he hears B—he is not sure whether at a great distance or somewhere quite close to him—stamp downstairs in a fury and disappear once and for all.

The Diabolical sometimes assumes the aspect of the Good, or even embodies itself completely in its form. If this remains concealed from me, I am of course defeated, for this Good is more tempting than the genuine Good. But what if it does not remain concealed from me? What if a horde of devils, like beaters on a battue, drive me straight into the Good? What if I, an object of disgust, am rolled, stung, thrust into the Good by pin points pricking me all over? What if the visible claws of the Good reach out for me? I fall back a step and retreat, softly and sadly, into Evil, which has been behind me all the time waiting for my decision.

[*A Life.*] A stinking bitch, mother of countless whelps, in places already rotting, but everything to me in my childhood, a faithful creature that follows me unfailingly, which I cannot bring myself to beat, from which I retreat step by step and which nevertheless, if I do not decide otherwise, will push me into the corner between the walls, the corner that I already see, there to decompose completely, upon me and with me, right to the end—is it an honor for me?—the purulent and wormy flesh of her tongue upon my hand.

Evil has ways of surprising one. Suddenly it turns round and says: "You have misunderstood me," and perhaps it really is so. Evil transforms itself into your own lips, lets itself be gnawed at by your teeth, and with these new lips—no former ones fitted more smoothly to your gums —to your own amazement you utter the words of goodness.

The Truth About Sancho Panza*

SANCHO PANZA, who, incidentally, never boasted of it, in the course of the years, by means of providing a large number of romances of chivalry and banditry to while away the evening and night hours, succeeded in diverting the attentions of his devil, to whom he later gave the name Don Quixote, from himself to such an extent that this devil then in unbridled fashion performed the craziest deeds, which however, for lack of a predetermined object, which should, of course, have been Sancho Panza, did nobody any harm. Sancho Panza, a free man, tranquilly, and perhaps out of a certain sense of responsibility, followed Don Quixote on his travels and had much and profitable entertainment from this to the end of his days.

October 22. Five o'clock in the morning.

One of the most important quixotic acts, more obtrusive than fighting the windmill, is: suicide. The dead

* Cf. *The Great Wall of China.*

Don Quixote wants to kill the dead Don Quixote; in order to kill, however, he needs a place that is alive, and this he searches for with his sword, both ceaselessly and in vain. Engaged in this occupation the two dead men, inextricably interlocked and positively bouncing with life, go somersaulting away down the ages.

Morning in bed.

[Aphorisms 9 and 10.]

In the evening went to the forest, moon waxing; confused day behind me. (Max's card.) Sick stomach.

[Aphorisms 11 and 12.]

October 23. Early morning in bed.

The Silence of the Sirens*

EVIDENCE that even inadequate, indeed childish means may serve to save one.

In order to be safe from the Sirens, Odysseus stopped his ears with wax and had himself chained to the mast. All travelers, from the very beginning, could of course have done something of the kind, except those whom the Sirens entranced even from a long way off, but it was common knowledge throughout the world that this was simply of no avail. The Sirens' song penetrated through everything, and the passion of those who heard its magic would have snapped more than chains and a mast. But Odysseus did not think of that, even though he may have heard tell of it. He relied solely on the handful of

* Cf. *The Great Wall of China.*

wax and the network chains, and in innocent delight over his little stratagem he voyaged on towards the Sirens.

Now the Sirens have a weapon even more terrible than their song, namely, their silence. True, such a thing has not happened, yet perhaps it is thinkable that someone might have escaped from their singing; but from their silence certainly never. Nothing earthly can withstand the sense of having overcome them with one's own resources, and the overwhelming arrogance resulting from it.

And in fact, when Odysseus came, the mighty singers did not sing, either because they believed the only way of tackling this opponent was with silence, or because the sight of the utter bliss on Odysseus's face, as he thought of nothing but wax and chains, caused them quite to forget their singing.

But Odysseus—let us put it like this—did not hear their silence, he thought they were singing and that only he was safe from hearing it. Fleetingly he saw first the poise of their necks, their deep breathing, their eyes brimming with tears, their half-open mouths, but he believed this went with the arias that were resounding, unheard, around him. Soon, however, everything slid away from his gaze, which was fixed on the far distance, the Sirens simply vanished in the face of his resolution, and in the very moment when he was nearest to them he had already forgotten them.

But they—more beautiful than ever—stretched and turned, letting their dread hair float free upon the wind and tightening their claws upon the rocks. They no longer wanted to entice anyone; all they wanted was to catch a glimpse for as long as possible of the reflected glory in the great eyes of Odysseus.

If the Sirens had possessed consciousness, they would

have been annihilated at that time. As it was, they remained; only Odysseus escaped them.

For the rest, tradition has a note to add to this. Odysseus, it is said, was a man of so many wiles, was such a cunning fox, that even the goddess of destiny could not penetrate into his inmost being. Perhaps, although this is beyond comprehension by the mind of man, he really noticed that the Sirens were silent, and confronted them and the gods with the pretended trick described above only, so to speak, as with a sort of shield.

Afternoon before the funeral of an epileptic drowned in the well.

"Know thyself" [*Erkenne dich selbst*] does not mean "Observe thyself." "Observe theyself" is what the Serpent says. It means: "Make yourself master of your actions." But you are so already, you are the master of your actions. So that saying means: "Misjudge yourself! [*Verkenne dich*] Destroy yourself!" which is something evil—and only if one bends down very far indeed does one also hear the good in it, which is: "In order to make of yourself what you are."

October 25. Sad, jumpy, physically unwell, dread of Prague, in bed.

There was once a community of scoundrels, that is to say, they were not scoundrels, but ordinary people. They always stood by each other. If, for instance, one of them had made a stranger, someone outside their community, unhappy in some rather scoundrelly way—that is to say, again, nothing scoundrelly, but just what is usual, just the normal sort of thing—and he then confessed to the whole community, they investigated the case, judged it, imposed penances, pardoned, and the like. It was not badly meant, the interests of the individual members and of the community as a whole were strictly safe-guarded, and he who confessed was supplied with the complementary color to the color he had shown:

"What? You mean you are upset about *that*? But what you did was a matter of course, you acted as you were bound to. Anything else would be incomprehensible. You are in a nervous condition, that's all. Pull yourself together and be sensible." So they always stood by each other, and even after death they did not desert the com-munity, but rose to heaven dancing in a ring. All in all it was a vision of the purest childlike innocence to see them fly. But since everything, when confronted with heaven, is broken up into its elements, they crashed, true slabs of rock.

[Aphorism 13.]

November 3. To Oberklee. Evening in room. Ottla and T. write.

[Aphorism 14.]

November 6. [Aphorism 15.]

[Aphorism 16.]

November 7. (Early morning in bed, after an evening spent gossiping.)

The main thing, when a sword cuts into one's soul, is to keep a calm gaze, lose no blood, accept the coldness of the sword with the coldness of a stone. By means of the stab, after the stab, become invulnerable.

[Aphorism 17.]

November 9. To Oberklee.

[Aphorism 18.]

If it had been possible to build the Tower of Babel without climbing it, it would have been permitted.

November 10. Bed.

[Aphorisms 19 and 20.]

A good deal of agitation. (Blüher, Tagger.) [12]

November 12. Long time in bed, resistance.

[Aphorisms 21, 22, 23, 24, and 25.]

November 18. [Aphorisms 26 and 27.]

A cart with three men in it was slowly going uphill in the dark. A stranger came towards them and called out to them. After some brief exchange of words it turned out that the stranger was asking to be given a lift. A place was made for him to sit in and he was helped up. Only when they were driving on did they ask him: "You were coming from the other direction and now you're going back?"—"Yes," the stranger said. "First I was going in your direction, but then I turned back because darkness had fallen earlier than I expected."

You complain about the stillness, about the hopelessness of the stillness, the wall of the Good.

The thornbush is the old obstacle in the road. It must catch fire if you want to go further.

November 21. The unfitness of the object may cause one to overlook the unfitness of the means.

[Aphorisms 28 and 29.]

Evil is whatever distracts.

Evil knows of the Good, but Good does not know of Evil.

Knowledge of oneself is something only Evil has.

One means that Evil has is the dialogue.

The founder brought the laws from the lawgiver; the faithful are meant to announce the laws to the lawgiver.

Is the existence of religions evidence of the impossibility of the individual's being permanently good? The founder tears himself free from the Good, becomes incarnate. Does he do it for the others' sake or because he believes that only with the others can he remain what he was, because he must destroy the world in order not to be compelled to love it?

[Aphorism 30.]

Anyone who believes cannot experience miracles. By day one does not see any stars.

Anyone who does miracles says: I cannot let go of the earth.

Distributing belief rightly between one's own words and one's own convictions. Not letting a conviction escape like steam in the very moment when one becomes aware of it. Not shifting on to the words the responsibility imposed by the conviction. Not letting convictions be stolen by words, harmony between the words and convictions is still not decisive, nor is good faith. Such words can always ram such convictions in, or dig them up, according to the circumstances.

Utterance does not in principle mean a weakening of conviction—that would not be anything to be deplored—but a weakness of conviction.

[Aphorisms 31, 32, 33, and 34.]

November 24. Human judgment of human actions is true and void, that is to say, first true and then void.

Through the door on the right one's fellow men push into a room in which a family council is being held, hear the last word uttered by the last speaker, take it up, with it pour out into the world through the door on the left, and shout out their judgment. The judgment of the word is true, the judgment in itself is void. If they had wanted to judge with final truth, they would have had to stay in the room forever, would have become part of the family council and thus, of course, again incapable of judging.

Only he who is a party can really judge, but as a party he cannot judge. Hence it follows that there is no possibility of judgment in the world, only a glimmer of it.

[Aphorisms 35, 36, and 37.]

Celibacy and suicide are on similar levels of under-standing, suicide and a martyr's death not so by any means, perhaps marriage and a martyr's death.

[Aphorism 38.]

The good walk in step. Without knowing anything of them, the others dance around them, dancing the dances of the age.

[Aphorism 39a.]

The man in ecstasy and the man drowning—both throw up their arms. The first does it to signify harmony, the second to signify strife with the elements.

> I do not know the contents,
> I have not the key,
> I do not believe rumors,
> all as a matter of course,
> for it is myself.

[Aphorisms 39b and 40.]

November 26. Vanity makes ugly, ought therefore really to kill, instead however it merely injures itself, be-coming "injured vanity."

[Aphorism 41.]

Afternoon. Letting the head full of disgust and hatred sink, the chin upon the chest. Certainly, but what if someone is throttling you?

November 27. Reading newspapers.

November 30. The Messiah will come as soon as the most unbridled individualism is possible in faith—as soon as nobody destroys this possibility and nobody tolerates that destruction, that is, when the graves open. And this is perhaps the Christian doctrine, both in the actual demonstration of the example for emulation, an individualistic example, and also in the symbolic demonstration of the resurrection of the Mediator in the individual human being.

Believing means liberating the indestructible element in oneself, or, more accurately, liberating oneself, or, more accurately, being indestructible, or, more accurately, being.

Idleness is the beginning of all vice, the crown of all virtues.

[Aphorisms 43, 44 and 45.]

The various forms of despair at the various stations on the road.

[Aphorism 46.]

December 2.

[Aphorism 47.]

December 4. Stormy night, in the morning telegram from Max, truce with Russia.

The Messiah will come only when he is no longer necessary, he will come only one day after his arrival, he will not come on the last day, but on the last day of all.

[Aphorisms 48 and 49.]

December 6. Pigsticking.

Three different things:
Looking on oneself as something alien, forgetting the sight, remembering the gaze.
Or only two different things, for the third includes the second.
Evil is the starry sky of the Good.

[Aphorism 50.]

Heaven is dumb, echoing only to the dumb.

[Aphorism 51.]

December 8. Bed, constipation, pain in back, irritable evening, cat in the room, dissension.

[Aphorisms 52, 53, 54, 55, 56, 57 and 58.]

If I say to the child: "Wipe your mouth, then you shall have the cake," that does not mean that the cake is earned by means of wiping the mouth, for wiping one's mouth and the value of the cake are not comparable, nor does it make wiping the mouth a precondition for eating of the cake, for apart from the triviality of such a condition the child would get the cake in any case, since it is a necessary part of his lunch—hence the remark does not signify that the transition is made more difficult, but that it is made easier, wiping one's mouth is a tiny benefit that precedes the great benefit of eating cake.

December 9. Annual fair yesterday.

[Aphorism 59.]

The observer of the soul cannot penetrate into the soul, but there doubtless is a margin where he comes into contact with it. Recognition of this contact is the fact that even the soul does not know of itself. Hence it must remain unknown. That would be sad only if there were anything apart from the soul, but there is nothing else.

[Aphorisms 60, 61 and 62.]

December 11. Yesterday Senior Inspector. Today *Der Jude*. Stein: The Bible is a sanctum; the world, sputum.

[Aphorism 63.]

Not everyone can see the truth, but he can be it.

[Aphorisms 64 and 65.]

To every instant there is a correspondence in something outside time. This world here and now cannot be followed by a Beyond, for the Beyond is eternal, hence it cannot be in temporal contact with this world here and now.

December 13. Began Herzen,[13] distracted by *Schöne Rarität* and newspapers.

He who seeks does not find, but he who does not seek will be found.

14. Yesterday, today, worst days. What have contributed: Herzen, a letter to Dr. Weiss,[14] other things not

capable of interpretation. Nauseating meal: yesterday pig's trotters, today tail. Walk to Michelob through the park.

[Aphorism 66.]

December 15. Letter from Dr. Körner.[15] Václac Mehl, from Mother.

Here nothing is decided, but only here can the power of decision be tested.

December 17. Empty days. Letters to Körner, Pfohl, Přibram, Kaiser, parents.

The Negro who, having gone mad from homesickness, was taken home from the World Exhibition and, in his village, surrounded by the lamentations of the tribe, with the most solemn face, by way of tradition and duty, demonstrated the pranks that delighted the European public, who believed they were the rites and customs of Africa.

Self-forgetfulness and self-canceling-out of art: what is an escape is pretended to be a stroll or even an attack.

Gogh letters.

[Aphorism 67.]

December 19. Yesterday announcement of F.'s[16] visit, to-day alone in my room, over there the stove is smoking, walked to Zarch with Nathan Stein, his telling the peasant woman that the world is a theater.

[Aphorism 68.]

There is a down-and-outness under true knowledge and a childlike happy arising from it!

[Aphorism 69.]

December 21. Telegram to F.

Adam's first domestic pet after the expulsion from Paradise was the serpent.

December 22. Lumbago, mental arithmetic in the night.

December 23. Fortunate and to some extent languid journey. Heard a lot.

Slept badly, strenuous day.

[Aphorisms 70 and 71.]

In Paradise, as always: that which causes the sin and that which recognizes it for what it is are one. The clear conscience is Evil, which is so entirely victorious that it does not any longer even consider that leap from left to right necessary.

The worries that are the burden of which the privileged person makes an excuse in dealing with the oppressed person are in fact the worries about preserving his privileged condition.

[Aphorism 72.]

December 25, 26, 27. F. leaves. Weeping. Everything difficult, wrong, and yet right after all.

[Aphorism 73.]

December 30. Not essentially disappointed.

[Aphorism 74.]

January 2. True undoubting is the teacher's part, continual undoubting the part of the pupil.

[Aphorism 75.]

Tomorrow Baum[17] goes away.

[Aphorisms 76, 77 and 78.]

On the pretext of going hunting he leaves the house, on the pretext of wanting to keep an eye on the house he climbs the most unscalable heights, if we did not know that he was going hunting we should hold him back.

January 13. Oskar left with Ottla, walk to Eischwitz.

[Aphorism 79.]

January 14. Dim, weak, impatient.

There are only two things: Truth and lies.

[Aphorism 80.]

January 15. Impatient. Improvement. Walk at night to Oberklee.

[Aphorism 81.]

January 19. Of his own volition, like a fist he turned and shunned the world.

No drop overflows and there is no room for a single drop more.

The fact that our task is exactly commensurate with our life gives it the appearance of being infinite.

[Aphorism 82.]

January 17.

*Prometheus**

THERE ARE four legends about Prometheus. According to the first, because he had betrayed the gods to men he was chained to a rock in the Caucasus and the gods sent eagles that devoured his perpetually renewed liver.

According to the second, Prometheus in his agony, as the beaks hacked into him, pressed deeper and deeper into the rock until he became one with it.

According to the third, in the course of thousands of years his treachery was forgotten, the gods forgot, the eagles forgot, he himself forgot.

According to the fourth, everyone grew weary of what had become meaningless. The gods grew weary, the eagles grew weary, the wound closed wearily.

What remained was the inexplicable range of mountains. Legend tries to explain the inexplicable. Since it arises out of a foundation of truth, it must end in the realm of the inexplicable.

The law of the quadrille is clear, all dancers know it, it is valid for all times. But one or other of the hazards of

* Cf. *The Great Wall of China.*

life, which ought never to occur but ever and again do occur, brings you alone among the ranks of dancers. Perhaps this causes confusion in the ranks, but you know nothing of that, all you know of is your own misfortune.

January 17. Walk to Oberklee. Limitation.

Respecting the devil even in the devil.

January 18. The complaint: If I shall exist eternally, how shall I exist tomorrow?

We are separated from God on two sides: the Fall separates us from Him, the Tree of Life separates Him from us.

[Aphorism 83.]

Tree of Life—Lord of Life.

We were expelled from Paradise, but it was not destroyed. The expulsion from Paradise was in one sense a piece of good fortune, for if we had not been expelled, Paradise would have had to be destroyed.

[Aphorism 84.]

Almost right to the end of the account of the Fall it remains possible that the Garden of Eden will be cursed together with mankind. Only mankind is accursed, the Garden of Eden is not.

On the day he ate of the Tree of Knowledge, God said that Adam would have to die. According to God the instant consequence of eating from the Tree of Knowledge was to be death, according to the serpent (at least it could be understood in this sense) it was to mean becoming like God. Both were wrong in similar ways. Men did not die, but became mortal, they did not become like God, but received an indispensable capacity to become so. Both were also in similar ways correct. It was not man that died, but paradisical man, he did not become God, but knowledge of the Divine.

The Evil One's desolate field of vision: in the very fact of recognizing Good and Evil he believes he sees equality with God. The curse does not seem to make anything in his nature worse: he will measure out the length of the road on his belly.

[Aphorism 85.]

January 22. Attempt to walk to Michelob. Mud.

[Aphorism 86.]

But under all the smoke there is the fire and he whose feet are burning will not be saved by the fact that everywhere he sees nothing but dark smoke.

[In the manuscript of Aphorism 86 the following is added after the words, "has its origins in this fear":]

In giving its advice the serpent did only half its work, now it must also try to falsify what it has brought about, that is to say, in the fullest sense of the words it must bite its own tail.

In amazement we beheld the great horse. It broke through the roof of our room. The cloudy sky was drifting faintly along its mighty outline, and its mane flew, rustling, in the wind.

The point of view of art and that of life are different even in the artist himself.

Art flies around truth, but with the definite intention of not getting burnt. Its capacity lies in finding in the dark void a place where the beam of light can be intensely caught, without this having been perceptible before.

[Aphorisms 87 and 88.]

Dawn, January 25.

The suicide is the prisoner who sees a gallows being erected in the prison yard, mistakenly thinks it is the one intended for him, breaks out of his cell in the night, and goes down and hangs himself.

Knowledge* we *have*. Anyone who strives for it with particular intensity is suspect of striving against it.

Before setting foot in the Holy of Holies you must take off your shoes, yet not only your shoes, but everything; you must take off your traveling garment and lay down your luggage; and under that you must shed your nakedness and everything that is under the nakedness and everything that hides beneath that, and then the core and the core of the core, then the remainder and then the residue and then even the glimmer of the undying fire. Only the fire itself is absorbed by the Holy of Holies and lets itself be absorbed by it; neither can resist the other.

Not shaking off the self, but consuming the self.

There were three possible ways of punishing man for the Fall: the mildest was the way actually used, expul-

---

* *Erkenntis*, here presumably in the sense of Knowledge of Good and Evil. (Translators' note.)

sion from Paradise; the second was destruction of Paradise; the third—and this would have been the most terrible punishment of all—was the cutting off of life everlasting and leaving everything else as it was.

January 28. Vanity, self-forgetfulness for some days.

[Aphorisms 90 and 91.]

A. could neither live congenially with G. nor get [a divorce], hence he shot himself, believing in this way he could reconcile what was irreconcilable, in other words 'go into the arbor' with himself.

"If ———, thou shalt die" * means: knowledge of Good and Evil is both a step leading up to eternal life and an obstacle in the way. If you want to attain eternal life after having gained knowledge—and you will not be able to do otherwise than want it, for knowledge of Good and Evil *is* this will—you will have to destroy yourself, the obstacle, in order to build the step, which is the destruction. Expulsion from Paradise was thus not an act but a happening.

The Fourth Octavo Notebook

BY IMPOSING too great a responsibility, or rather, all responsibility, on yourself, you crush yourself. [Aphorism 92, continuing:]

Man could not do enough for his own satisfaction in the creation of counterweights; this naïve world was the

---

* This refers to Genesis 2:17: "But of the tree of the knowledge of good and evil thou shalt not eat, for in the day that thou eatest of it thou shalt die." (Translator's note.)

most complicated one that ever existed; its naïvety worked out, in life, exclusively in the brutal logical consequence.

If all responsibility is imposed on you, then you may want to exploit the moment and want to be overwhelmed by the responsibility; yet if you try, you will notice that nothing was imposed on you, but that you are yourself this responsibility.

Atlas was permitted the opinion that he was at liberty, if he wished, to drop the Earth and creep away; but this opinion was all that he was permitted.

The apparent silence in which the days, seasons, generations, and centuries, follow upon each other is a harkening; so do horses trot before the cart.

January 31.[18] Gardening, hopelessness of the future.

A fight in which there is no way, at any stage, of getting any protection for one's back. And in spite of knowing this, one keeps on forgetting it. And even when one does not forget it, one seeks such protection all the same, solely in order to rest while seeking it, and in spite of the fact that one knows one will pay for doing so.

February 1. Lenz's letters.

[Aphorisms 93 and 94.]

February 2. Letter from Wolff.[19]

[Aphorisms 95 and 96.]

Evil is sometimes like an instrument in the hand; recognized or unrecognized, it lets itself be laid aside without protest if one so wills.

The delights of this life are not its own, but our fear of the ascent into a higher life; the torments of this life are not its own, but our self-torment because of that fear.

February 4. Lying for a long time, sleeplessness, becoming conscious of the struggle.

In a world of lies the lie is not removed from the world by means of its opposite, but only by means of a world of truth.

Suffering is the positive element in this world, indeed it is the only link between this world and the positive.

[Aphorism 97.]

February 5. A good morning, impossible to remember everything.

Destroying this world would be the task to set oneself only, first, if the world were evil, that is, contradictory to our meaning, and secondly, if we were capable of destroying it. The first seems so to us; of the second we are not capable. We cannot destroy this world, for we have not constructed it as something independent; what we have done is to stray into it; indeed, this world is our going astray, but as such it is itself something indestructible, or, rather, something that can be destroyed only by means of being carried to its logical conclusion, and not by renunciation; and this means, of course, that carrying it to its logical conclusion can only be a series of acts of destruction, but within the framework of this world.

For us there exist two kinds of truth, as they are represented by the Tree of Knowledge and the Tree of Life. The truth of the active principle and the truth of the static principle. In the first, Good separates itself off from Evil; the second is nothing but Good itself, knowing neither of Good nor of Evil. The first truth is given to us really, the second only intuitively. That is what it is so sad to see. The cheerful thing is that the first truth pertains to the fleeting moment, the second to eternity; and that, too, is why the first truth fades out in the light of the second.

February 6. Was in Flöhau.

[Aphorism 98.]

February 7. Soldier with stones, Island of Rügen.

Weariness does not necessarily signify weakness of faith —or does it? In any case weariness signifies insufficiency. I feel too tightly constricted in everything that signifies Myself: even the eternity that I am is too tight for me. But if, for instance, I read a good book, say an account of travels, it rouses me, satisfies me, suffices me. Proofs that previously I did not include this book in my eternity, or had not pushed on far enough ahead to have an intuitive glimpse of the eternity that necessarily includes this book as well.—From a certain stage of knowledge [Erkenntnis] on, weariness, insufficiency, constriction, self-contempt, must all vanish: namely at the point where I have the strength to recognize as my own nature what previously was something alien to myself that refreshed me, satisfied, liberated, and exalted me.

But what if it has this effect only so long as it is supposedly something alien to yourself and with your new knowledge you not only gain nothing in this respect but lose the old consolation as well? True, it had that effect only in that it was something alien, but it did not only have that effect: its influence extended further, raising me then to this higher level. It did not cease to be alien, but merely began *also* to be Myself.—But the alien world that you are is no longer alien to you. With this you deny the Creation of the World and refute yourself.

I should welcome eternity, and when I do find it I am sad. I should feel myself perfect by virtue of eternity—and feel myself depressed?

You say: I should—feel. In saying this do you express a commandment that is within yourself?

That is what I mean.

Now, it is impossible that only a commandment is implanted in you, in such a way that you only hear that commandment and that nothing more happens. Is it a continual or only an occasional commandment?

As to that, I cannot be sure. I believe, however, it is a continual commandment, but that I hear it only occasionally.

From what do you draw that conclusion?

From the fact that I hear it, as it were, even when I do not hear it, in such a way that, although it is not audible itself, it muffles or embitters the voice bidding me do the other thing: that is to say, the voice that makes me ill at ease with eternity.

And do you hear the other voice in a similar way when the commandment of eternity is speaking?

Yes, then too, indeed sometimes I believe I hear nothing but the other voice and everything else seems to be only a dream and it is as though I were just letting the dream go on talking at random.

Why do you compare the inner commandment to a

dream? Does it seem senseless as a dream, incoherent, inevitable, unique, making you happy or frightening you equally without cause, not wholly communicable, but demanding to be communicated?

All that—senseless; for only if I do not obey it can I maintain myself here; incoherent, for I don't know whose command it is and what he is aiming at; inevitable, for it finds me unprepared, descending upon me as surprisingly as dreams descend upon the sleeper, who, after all, since he lay down to sleep, must have been prepared for dreams. It is unique, or at least seems to be so, for I cannot obey it, it does not mingle with reality, and so it keeps its immaculate uniqueness; it makes me happy or frightens me, both without cause, though admittedly it does the first much more rarely than the second; it is not communicable, because it is not intelligible, and for the same reason it demands to be communicated.

Christ, moment.[20]

February 8. Got up early, chance to work.

February 9. The windless calm on some days, the noise made by those arriving, the way our people come running out of the houses to welcome, flags are put out here and there, people hurry down to the cellar to fetch wine, from a window a rose falls on to the cobbles, nobody has any patience, the boats, instantly gripped by a hundred arms, scrape on the beach, the foreign men gaze around them and climb up into the broad daylight of the square.

Why is what is easy so difficult? Of seductions I have had—.

Let there be no enumeration. What is easy is difficult. It is so easy and so difficult. Like a game of tag where the only 'home' is a tree on the far side of the ocean. But why did they ever set forth from that place?—It is on the coast that the billows crash most fiercely, so narrow a room do they have there, and so unconquerable.

Not asking would have brought you back, asking drives you on over yet a further ocean.—It is not they who set forth, but you yourself.

Ever and again the straits will oppress me.

But eternity is not temporality at a standstill. What is oppressive about the concept of the eternal is the justification, incomprehensible to us, that time must undergo in eternity and the logical conclusion of that, the justification of ourselves as we are.

[Aphorism 99.]

February 10. Sunday. Noise. Peace Ukraine.

Now vanish the mists of the generals and artists, of the lovers and the rich, of the politicians and gymnasts, of the seafaring men and . . .

Freedom and bondage are in their essential meaning one. In what essential meaning? Not in the sense that the slave does not lose his freedom, hence in a certain respect is more free than the free man.

The chain of the generations is not the chain of your nature and yet there are certain connections.—Which?—The generations die as do the moments of your life.—In what does the difference lie?

It's the old joke: We hold the world fast and complain that it is holding us.

In a certain sense you deny the existence of this world. You explain life as a state of rest, a state of rest in motion.

February 11. Peace Russia.

In the general conflagration his house escapes, not because he is a devout man but because it is his aim to see that his house escapes.

He who looks on is in a certain sense he who lives with the world, he attaches himself to whatever is alive, he tries to keep pace with the wind. That is something I do not want to be.

Living means being in the midst of life, seeing life with the gaze in which I have created it.

The world can be regarded as good only from the place from which it was created, for only there was it said: And behold, it was good —and only from there can it be condemned and destroyed.

Ever ready, his house is portable, he lives always in his native country.

The decisively characteristic thing about this world is its transience. In this sense centuries have no advantage over the present moment. Thus the continuity of transience cannot give any consolation; the fact that new life blossoms among the ruins proves not so much the tenacity of life as that of death. If I wish to fight against this world, I must fight against its decisively characteristic element, that is, against its transience. Can I do that in this life, and, what is more, really and not only by means of hope and faith?

And so you want to fight against the world and, what is more, with weapons that are more real than hope and faith. There probably are such weapons, but they can be recognized and used only by those who have certain definite qualifications; I want to see first whether you have these qualifications.

Look into it. But if I have not got them, perhaps I can get them.

Certainly, but that is a matter in which I could not help you.

And so you can only help me if I already have the qualifications.

Yes. To put it more precisely, I cannot help you at all, for if you had these qualifications, you would have everything.

If that is how things stand, why then did you want to test me at first?

In order to show you not what you lack, but that you lack something. I might perhaps have been of a certain amount of use to you in this way, for although you know there is something you lack, you do not believe it.

And so, in answer to my original question, all you offer me is the proof that I had to ask the question.

I do offer something more, something that you, in accordance with your present condition, are now quite incapable of defining more precisely. I am offering the proof of the fact that you really ought to have asked the original question in different terms.

And so that means: you either will not or cannot answer me.

"Not answer you"—that is so.

And this faith—this you can give.

February 19. Back from Prague. Ottla in Zarch.

The moonlight dazzled us. Birds shrieked from tree to tree. There was a buzzing and whizzing in the fields.
We crawled through the dust, a pair of snakes.

Intuition and experience.
If "experience" is rest in the Absolute, "intuition" [21] can only be the long way round, through the world, to the Absolute. After all, everything wants to get to the goal, and there is only one goal. Of course, the compromise might be possible in that the splitting up is only in time, that is to say, a splitting up such that, although it exists in every moment, it actually does not occur at all.

[Aphorisms 100 and 101.]

Anyone who takes care only for the future is less careful than someone who takes care only for the moment, for he does not even take care for the moment, but only for its duration.

[Aphorism 102, after the first sentence the following interpolation:]
Christ suffered for mankind, but mankind must suffer for Christ.

February 22.

Contemplation and activity have their apparent truth; but only the activity radiated by contemplation, or rather, that which returns to it again, is truth.

[Aphorism 103.]

Your will is free means: it was free when it wanted the desert, it is free since it can choose the path that leads to crossing the desert, it is free since it can choose the pace, but it is also unfree since you must go through the desert, unfree since every path in labyrinthine manner touches every foot of the desert's surface.

[Aphorism 89.]

February 23. Unwritten letter.

Woman, or more precisely put, perhaps, marriage, is the representative of life with which you are meant to come to terms.

[Aphorism 105.]

February 24. [Aphorism 106.]

Inventions hasten on ahead of us as the coast always hastens on ahead of the steamer, which is ceaselessly shaken by its engine. Inventions achieve all that can be achieved. It is unfair to say, for instance: The airplane does not fly like the bird, or: We shall never be capable of creating a living bird. Of course not, but the error lies in the objection, just as if the steamer were expected ever and again to arrive at its port of departure in spite of keeping on a straight course.—A bird cannot be created by means of an original act, for it is already created, is continually coming into existence as a result of the first act of Creation, and it is impossible to break into this series, created on the ground of an original, unceasing will, a living series continually showering forth; it is just as is recounted in a legend: although the first woman was created out of the man's rib, this was never repeated, but from then on men always took to wife the daughters of others.—The method and tendency of the creation of the bird—this is the point—and of the airplane need not, however, be different; and the savage's way of interpreting things, confusing a shot from a gun with a roll of thunder, may have a limited truth.

Evidence of a real pre-existence: I have seen you before, the marvels of primeval times and at the end of time.

February 25. Morning clearness.

It is not inertia, ill will, awkwardness—even if there is something of all this in it, because "vermin is born of the void"—that cause me to fail, or not even to get near failings: family life, friendship, marriage, profession, literature. It is not that, but the lack of ground underfoot, of air, of the commandment. It is my task to create these, not in order that I may then, as it were, catch up with what I have missed, but in order that I shall have missed nothing, for the task is as good as any other. It is indeed the most primal task of all, or at least the reflection of that task, just as one may, on climbing to heights where the air is thin, suddenly step into the light of the far-distant sun. And this is no exceptional task, either; it is sure to have been set often before. True, I don't know whether it has ever been set to such a degree. I have brought nothing with me of what life requires, so far as I know, but only the universal human weakness. With this—in this respect it is gigantic strength—I have vigorously absorbed the negative element of the age in which I live, an age that is, of course, very close to me, which I have no right ever to fight against, but as it were a right to represent. The slight amount of the positive, and also of the extreme negative, which capsizes into the positive, are something in which I have had no hereditary share. I have not been guided into life by the hand of

Christianity—admittedly now slack and failing—as Kierkegaard was, and have not caught the hem of the Jewish prayer shawl—now flying away from us—as the Zionists have. I am an end or a beginning.

He felt it at his temple, as the wall feels the point of the nail that is about to be driven into it. Hence he did not feel it.

No one creates more here than his spiritual basis of life; the fact that it seems as though he were working for his food, clothing, and so on, is beside the point, for together with each visible morsel he receives also an invisible one, with each visible garment also an invisible garment, and so on. That is every human being's justification. It seems as though he were underpinning his existence with retrospective justifications, but that is only psychological mirror-writing; in actual fact he is erecting his life on his justifications. Admittedly, every human being must be able to justify his life (or his death, which amounts to the same); he cannot escape this task.

We see every human being living his life (or dying his death). This achievement would not be possible without an inner justification; no human being can live an unjustified life. Underestimating human beings: one could conclude from this that everyone underpins his life with justifications.

Psychology is the reading of a mirror-writing, which means that it is laborious, and as regards the always correct result, it is richly informative; but nothing has really happened.

After a person's death, for a short span of time, even on earth, a special beneficial silence sets in with regard to the dead person; a terrestrial fever has ceased, a dying is no longer seen to be continuing, an error seems to have been remedied; even for the living there is an opportunity to breathe freely, for which reason, too, the windows are opened in the room where the death took place—until then everything turns out to have been, after all, only a semblance, and the sorrow and the lamentations begin.

The cruelty of death lies in the fact that it brings the real sorrow of the end, but not the end.

The greatest cruelty of death: an apparent end causes a real sorrow.

The lamentation around the deathbed is actually the lamentation over the fact that here no dying in the true sense has taken place. We must still content ourselves with this sort of dying, we are still playing the game.

February 26. Sunny morning.

The evolution of mankind—a growth of death-force.

Our salvation is death, but not this one.

[Aphorisms 107 and 108.]

Every human being is here asked two questions of creed: first as to the credibility of this life, secondly as to the credibility of his goal. Both questions are answered by everyone, through the very fact of his life, with such a firm and direct "yes" that it might become uncertain whether the questions have been understood rightly. In any case, it is now that one must begin to work one's way through to this, one's own basic Yes, for even far below their surface the answers are confused and elusive under the assault of the questions.

[Aphorism 109.]

[22] The incommunicability of the paradox does perhaps exist, yet it does not manifest itself as such, for Abraham himself does not understand it. Now, he does not need to understand it, or is not supposed to understand it, and hence also he is not supposed to interpret it for himself; but undoubtedly he may try to interpret it for others. In this sense even the General is not unequivocal, which manifests itself in the case of Iphigenia in the fact that the oracle is never unequivocal.

Rest in the General? Equivocation of the General. The General once interpreted as rest, but otherwise as the "universal" oscillation between Particular and General. Only rest is the truly General, but also the final goal.

It is as though the oscillation between the General and the Particular were taking place on the real stage, and as if, on the other hand, life in general were only sketched in on the background scenery.

There is no such thing as this evolution, which would tire me in its senselessness, for which I am only very indirectly to blame. The transient world is not adequate to Abraham's carefulness for the future, hence he decides to emigrate with it into eternity. But whether it is the gate on the way out or the gate on the way in that is too narrow, he cannot get the furniture wagon through. He puts the blame on the weakness of his voice uttering the commands. It is the agony of his life.

[23] Abraham's spiritual poverty and the comparative immotility of this poverty is an advantage, making concen-

tration easier for him; or rather, it is in itself concentration, as a result of which, of course, he loses the advantage that lies in the application of the power to concentrate.

Abraham is laboring under the following delusion: he cannot endure the monotony of this world. Now the fact is that this world is notoriously and uncommonly manifold, which can be put to the test at any moment if one just takes up a handful of World and looks at it a little more closely. Naturally, Abraham knows this too. And so his complaint about the monotony of the world is actually a complaint about an insufficiently profound mingling with the manifold nature of the world. And so it is actually a springboard into the world.

There is an enchantment accompanying his argument of the case. One can escape from an argument into the world of magic, from an enchantment into logic, but both simultaneously are crushing, all the more since they constitute a third entity, a living magic or a destruction of the world that is not destructive but constructive.

He has too much mind, and by means of that mind he travels across the earth as upon a magic chariot, going even where there are no roads. And he cannot find out from himself that there are no roads there. In this way his humble plea to be followed turns into tyranny, and his honest belief that he is "on the road" into arrogance.

The Brotherhood of Poor Workers

OBLIGATIONS: to possess no money, no valuables, and not to accept any. Only the following possessions are permitted: the most simple dress (to be defined in detail), whatever is necessary for work, books, food for one's own consumption. Everything else belongs to the poor.

To get one's living only by working for it. Not to shrink from any work that one's strength suffices to perform without damaging one's health. Either to choose the work oneself or, in the event of this not being possible, to fall in with the arrangements made by the Labor Council, which is responsible to the Government.

To work for no wages other than what is necessary to support life (to be defined in detail according to the various districts) for two days.

Life to be of the utmost moderation. To eat only what is absolutely necessary, for instance as a minimum wage, which is in a certain sense also a maximum wage: bread, water, dates. Food as eaten by the poorest of the poor, shelter like that of the poorest of the poor.

The relationship to the employer to be treated as a relation of mutual trust. The intervention of the courts never to be invoked. Each job taken on to be completed, in all circumstances, except for grave reasons of health.

RIGHTS: maximum working time six hours, for manual work four to five hours.

In sickness and in the incapacity of old age reception into institutions for the aged and into hospitals, these run by the State.

Working life as a matter of conscience and a matter of faith in one's fellow men.

Inherited possessions to be presented to the State for the erection of hospitals and homes.

Provisionally, at least, exclusion of independent persons, married persons, and women.

Council (grave duty) negotiates with the Government.

Also in capitalist enterprises [two words illegible].

In places where one can help, in abandoned districts, almshouses, [as] teacher.

Five hundred men upper limit.

One trial year.

Everything fell in with his intention and contributed to the building. Foreign workers brought the blocks of marble, already hewn and ready to be fitted together. In accordance with the indications given by his moving fingers, the blocks rose up and shifted into place. No building ever rose into being as easily as this temple did, or rather, this temple came into being in the true manner of temples. Only on every block—from what quarry did they come?—there were clumsy scribblings by senseless childish hands, or rather, entries made by barbaric mountain-dwellers in order to annoy or to deface or to destroy completely, scratched into the stone with instruments that were obviously magnificently sharp, intended to endure for an eternity that would outlast the temple.

Upstream towards the wandering water. Clumps of birches. The teacher's voice suddenly raised. Murmuring of the children. Sun fading red, abandoning itself, overawed. Stove door slamming. Coffee is being made. We sit leaning on the table, waiting. Thin little saplings on one side of the road. Month of March. What more do you want? We arise out of the graves and want to go roaming through this world too, we have no definite plan.

So you want to go away from me? Well, it's a decision as good as any other. But where do you mean to go? Where is this away-from-me? On the moon? It is not even there, and anyway you will never get so far. And so why then all this? Wouldn't you rather sit down in the corner and be quiet? Wouldn't that, for instance, be better? There in the corner, warm and dark? You aren't listening? Groping for the door. Yes, but where is there a door? So far as I recall there is none in this room. Who at that time, when this place here was being built, thought of such world-shaking plans as yours are? Well, nothing is lost, such an idea does not get lost, we shall discuss it at the round table, and may the laughter be your reward.

The pale moon rose, we rode through the forest.

Poseidon grew tired of his seas. The trident fell from his grasp. Silent, there he sat on a rocky coast, and a gull, stupefied by his presence, flashed in wavering circles round his head.

The wildly bowling carriage.

> Ah what is set before us here!
> Bed and couch under trees,
> green darkness, dry leafage,
> little sun, damp scent of flowers.
> Ah what is set before us here!
>
> Whither does desire drive us?
> To gain this? to lose this?
> Senselessly we drink the ash
> and suffocate our father.
> Whither does desire drive us?
>
> Whither does desire drive us?
> Driving us out of the house, away

The flute was enticing, the fresh brook was enticing

What to you seemed patient
rustled through the treetop
and the master of the garden spoke.

If in his runes I seek to fathom
the spectacle of change,
words and sores. . . .

The Count was sitting at luncheon; it was noon on a quiet summer's day. The door opened, this time, however, not for the servant but for Brother Philotas. "Brother," the Count said, rising, "again I see you, whom for so long I have seen no more in dreams." A pane in the glass door leading on to the terrace broke into smithereens, and a bird, reddish-brown like a partridge, but larger and with a long bill, flew into the room. "Wait, I'll have it in a moment," the brother said, catching up his cowl in one hand and with the other clutching at the bird. At that very moment the servant came in with a dish of beautiful fruit, into which the bird now began pecking vigorously, flying round the dish in small circles. Transfixed, the servant stood holding the dish and gazing, though not really in astonishment, at the fruit, the bird, and the brother who was still chasing after it. The other door opened and people from the village walked in with a petition, asking for the right of way on a road through the forest, which they needed in order to be able to cultivate their fields better. But they came at the wrong time, for the Count was still a little schoolchild, sitting on a stool and doing his lessons. True, the old Count was now dead, and so the young one ought to have been ruling, but it was not like that, there was a pause in history, and thus the deputation wandered into the void. Where will they end up? Will they ever come back? Will they recognize in time how matters stand? The teacher, who was also a member of it, now stepped out of the group and took over the instruction of the little Count. With a stick he pushed off the table everything that was on it, hoisted it up, top forward, to use it as a blackboard, and with a piece of chalk wrote on it the figure 1.

We were drinking, the sofa was becoming too small for us, the hands of the clock on the wall never ceased to whirl round and round. The servant looked in, we beckoned to him with raised hands. But he was held spellbound by an apparation on the sofa at the window. There an old man in a thin, black, silky, shining robe was slowly rising to his feet, his fingers still toying with the arms of the sofa. "Father," the son exclaimed, and "Emil," the old man exclaimed.

The distance to my fellow man is for me a very long one.

Prague. Religions get lost as people do.

> Little soul,
> you leap in the dance,
> lay your head in warm air,
> lift your feet out of twinkling grass,
> which the wind urges into gentle motion.[24]

The Fifth Octavo Notebook

I MIGHT be very contented. I am a clerk at the town hall. What a fine thing it is to be clerk at the town hall! Little work, adequate salary, plenty of leisure, excessive respect everywhere in the town. If I imagine the situation of a municipal clerk with intensity, I cannot but envy him. And now I am one myself, I am a clerk at the town hall—and if I only could, I should like to give this entire dignity to the office cat to eat, the cat that wanders from room to room every morning to get the remains of midmorning snacks.

For the eventuality that in the near future I may die or become wholly unfit to live—the probability of it is great, since in the last two nights I have coughed a good deal of blood—let me say that I myself have torn myself to shreds. If my father in earlier days was in the habit of uttering wild but empty threats, saying: I'll tear you apart like a fish—in fact, he did not so much as lay a finger on me—now the threat is being fulfilled independently of him. The world—F is its representative—and my ego are tearing my body apart in a conflict that there is no resolving.

I was to pursue my studies in the great city. My aunt met me at the railway station. I had seen her once when I was on a visit to the city with my father. I scarcely recognized her.

You raven, I said, you old bird of ill omen, what are you always doing on my path? Wherever I go, you perch there, ruffling your scanty plumage. Nuisance!

Yes, it said, and paced up and down before me with its head lowered, like a schoolmaster talking to the class, that is true; it is becoming almost distressing even to me.

At last he had reached the city where he was to study. A room was found, his trunk unpacked, a fellow countryman who had been living there for some time conducted him through the streets. Quite by chance there towered up, somewhere at the end of a street opening off that in which he was walking, famous sights of which there were pictures in all schoolbooks. He gasped when he beheld this, but his fellow countryman only waved his arm towards it.

You old rascal, how about our really tidying things up for once here?

No, no, I should be very much against that.

I don't doubt it. Nevertheless you will have to be got rid of.

I shall fetch my relatives.

That, too, is just what I expected. They, too, will have to go to the wall.

Whatever it may be that is pulling me out from between the two millstones that would otherwise pulverize me, I feel it as beneficial, always assuming that it is not accompanied by excessive physical pain.

The little veranda lying flat under the sun, the weir peacefully roaring away forever.

> Nothing holds me.
> Doors and windows open
> terraces broad and empty.

K was a great conjurer. His repertoire was a little monotonous, but, because of the indubitability of the achievement, ever and again an attraction. The performance at which I saw him for the first time is something I naturally remember quite clearly, although it is now twenty years since it happened and I was a very small boy at the time. He came to our little township without previous announcement and gave the perform-

ance on the evening of the very day he arrived. In the
large dining-room of our hotel, round a table in the center, there was a little space left—that was the entire setting of the theatrical scene. As I remember it, the large
room was thronged—well, to a child every room seems
thronged where there are some lights burning and there
is a confused din of grown-ups' voices, a waiter dashing
here and there, and the like—nor did I know why so
many people should have come to this obviously too-
hastily got-up performance, in any case this supposed
overcrowding of the room certainly plays a decisive part
in my memory, in my whole impression of that performance.

Whatever I touch crumbles to pieces.

The year of mourning was over,
the birds' wings were limp.
The moon bared herself in cool nights.
Almond and olive had long been ripe.

The benefaction of the years.

He sat over his accounts. Great columns. Sometimes
he would turn away from them and rest his face on his
hand. What appeared from the accounts? A dreary, dreary
account.

Yesterday I was in the directors' offices for the first
time. Our night shift elected me their spokesman, and
since the construction and mode of filling is defective,
I was to go up and insist on the abolition of this griev-
ance. The appropriate office was pointed out to me; I
knocked and went in. A delicate young man, very pale,
smiled at me from behind his large desk. He nodded his

head a great deal, a great deal too much. I did not know whether I was supposed to sit down; although there was a chair there, I thought on my first visit I had perhaps better not sit down, and so I told the story standing. But obviously I caused the young man some trouble by this very modesty of mine, for he had to turn his face sideways and upwards to me, if he did not want to turn his chair round, and he did not want to do that. On the other hand, in spite of all his willingness, he could not twist his neck quite far enough and hence all during my story he kept it half turned, gazing obliquely up at the ceiling, and I could not help doing the same. When I had finished, he got up slowly, patted me on the back, said: Well, well—well, well, and pushed me into the adjoining room, where a gentleman with a great untrimmed beard had obviously been waiting for us, for there was no trace of any sort of work on his desk, on the contrary; an open glass door led out into a little garden full of flowers and bushes. A little report, consisting of only a few words, whispered to him by the young man, sufficed to enable the gentleman to grasp our many and various complaints. He immediately stood up and said: Well then, my dear—He paused, I thought he wanted to know my name and I was, therefore, just opening my mouth to introduce myself again when he caught me up short: Yes, yes, all right, all right, I know all about you —well then, your request, or that of your workmates and yourself, is certainly justifiable, I myself and the other gentlemen on the board of directors are certainly the last not to see that. The welfare of our men is something we have more at heart, believe me, than the welfare of the firm. And why not? The firm can always be built up all over again, it only costs money, the devil take the money, but if a human being perishes, there it is, a human being perishes, there is then the widow, the children. Ah dear me, yes! And for that reason, then, every suggestion for the introduction of new safeguards, new alleviations, new comforts and luxuries, is extremely welcome to us. Anyone who comes along with such a suggestion is the man for us. And so now you will leave your proposal here with us, we shall investigate it in detail, and if it should turn out that any further brilliant little innovation can be appended to it, we shall certainly not suppress it, and as soon as everything is finished, you men will get the new lamps. But here is something for you to tell your workmates downstairs: we here shall not rest until we have made a drawing-room of your shaft, and if you do not all finally go to your doom in patent-leather shoes, then you shall not go at all. And with this I wish you a very good day!

Trot, little horse,
you are carrying me into the desert,
all cities sink away, the villages and lovely rivers.
Venerable the schools, frivolous the taverns,
girls' faces sink away,
dragged away by the storm from the East.

It was a very large party and I knew nobody there. I therefore resolved to remain quite quiet at first, slowly to find out which people I could best approach, and then with their aid to fit myself in with the rest of the company. The room, with its one window, was fairly small, but there were about twenty people present. I stood at the open window, followed the example of the others, who went on taking cigarettes from a little side table, and smoked in peace and quiet. Unfortunately, in spite of all the attention I paid, I could not understand what was being talked about. Once, it seemed to me, there was talk about a man and a woman, then again about a woman and two men, but since it was always the same three people who were being talked about, only my own slowness of understanding could be to blame for my not being able to work out who the people were that were being discussed, and so much the less, of course, their story. The question, as it seemed to me beyond all doubt, was mooted whether the behavior of these three people, or at least of one of these three people, could be morally approved of or not. The story itself, which was known to all, was not coherently discussed any further.

Evening by the river. A boat in the water. Sun setting among clouds.

He fell down before me. I tell you, he fell down as close to me as this table I am pressing up against is close to me. "Are you mad?" I shouted. It was long after midnight, I had come from a party, felt like walking by myself for a while longer, and now this man had collapsed in front of me. I could not lift the giant, nor did I want to leave him lying there in that lonely district where there was nobody to be seen far and wide.

Dreams flooded over me, I lay weary and hopeless in my bed.

I lay sick. Because it was a severe illness, the paillasses belonging to the other occupants of the room had been taken out and I was alone for days and nights.

So long as I was well, nobody had bothered about me. In general that suited me quite well; I am not going to begin to complain about that now, retrospectively; I only want to stress the difference: as soon as I became ill the visits to the sick began, they are going on almost uninterruptedly, and have not ceased down to this day.

Hopeless was voyaging round the Cape of Good Hope in a little boat. It was early in the morning, a strong wind was blowing. Hopeless hoisted a little sail and leaned back tranquilly. What should he fear in the little boat, which with its tiny draft glided over all the reefs in those dangerous waters with the nimbleness of a living being?

I have three dogs: Hold-him, Seize-him and Nevermore. Hold-him and Seize-him are ordinary little pugs and nobody would notice them if they were alone. But there is Nevermore, too. Nevermore is a mongrel Great Dane and has an appearance that centuries of the most careful breeding could never have produced. Nevermore is a gypsy.

All my free hours—and they are in themselves very many, but I have to sleep through far too many of them, against my will, in order to banish hunger—I spend with Nevermore. On a *chaise longue à la Madame Recamier.* —How this piece of furniture found its way up into my garret I don't know, perhaps it wanted to get into a junk room and, too weak to get there, it remained in my room.

Nevermore is of the opinion that it cannot go on like this and that some way out must be found. At bottom I, too, am of this opinion, but in his presence I pretend the opposite. He runs up and down the room, sometimes jumps on the chair, tugs with his teeth at the piece of sausage I have put down for him, finally flips it over to me with his paw and begins running around again.

A.   What you have resolved on, from whatever side one may regard it, is a very difficult and dangerous undertaking. Admittedly one should not overestimate it either, for there are some that are still more difficult and dangerous. And perhaps precisely at the point where one does not expect it and where for that reason one sets to work in an utterly innocent manner and all unequipped. That is, in fact, my opinion, but, of course, by saying so I don't mean either to stop you from carrying out your plans or to depreciate those plans. By no means. Your cause undoubtedly demands a great deal of strength and is, indeed, worth the expenditure of strength. Yes, but do you actually feel this strength in you?

B. No. I can't say that. I feel emptiness in myself, but no strength.

I rode in through the South gate. Built directly on to the gate is a large hostelry; there I meant to spend the night. I led my mule into the stables, which were already almost overcrowded with mounts, but still, I did find a safe corner. Then I went upstairs into one of the loggias, spread out my blanket and lay down to sleep.

Sweet serpent, why do you stay so far away, come nearer, nearer still, enough, no further, stay there. For you, too, there are no frontiers. How am I to attain mastery over you if you recognize no frontiers? It will be hard work. I begin by asking you to curl yourself up. Curl yourself up, I said, and you stretch yourself. Don't you understand me? You don't understand me. But I speak very clearly: Curl up! No, you don't grasp it. So then I show you, here, with the staff. First of all you must describe a large circle, then inside, adjoining it, a second, and so forth. If then finally you are still holding your little head high, lower it slowly to the tune on the flute that I shall later play, and when I cease, you shall have become quiet too, with your head in the inmost circle.

I was led to my horse, but I was still very weak. I saw the slender animal, quivering with the fever of life.

"That is not my horse," I said when the hostler at the inn led a horse up to me in the morning.

"Your horse was the only one in our stables last night," the hostler said and looked at me, smiling, or, if I may say so, defiantly smiling.

"No," I said, "that is not my horse." The saddlebag slid from my hands, I turned and went upstairs into the room I had just left.[25]

The Sixth Octavo Notebook

I SUPPOSE I really ought to have looked into the matter before, I mean about how it was with this staircase, what implications there were here, what was to be expected here, and how it was to be met. You never heard of this staircase before, I said to myself by way of excuse, and yet the newspapers, and books, are always caviling at everything that exists at all. But there was nothing in them about this staircase. That may be, I answered myself, the fact probably is you read carelessly. You were often absent-minded, left paragraphs out, even contented yourself with the headlines; perhaps the staircase was mentioned there and that was how you missed it. And now you are in need of the very thing you missed then. And I stopped for a moment and reflected on this afterthought. Then I thought I could remember once possibly having read something about a similar staircase in a children's book. It had not been much, probably only the mere mention of its existence; that could not be of any use to me.

When the little mouse, which was loved as none other was in the mouse-world, got into a trap one night and with a shrill scream forfeited its life for the sight of the bacon, all the mice in the district, in their holes, were overcome by trembling and shaking; with eyes blinking uncontrollably they gazed at each other one by one, while their tails scraped the ground busily and senselessly. Then they came out, hesitantly, pushing one another, all drawn towards the scene of death. There it lay, the dear little mouse, its neck caught in the deadly iron, the little pink legs drawn up, and now stiff the feeble body that would so well have deserved a scrap of bacon. The parents stood beside it and eyed their child's remains.

Once, on a winter afternoon, after various annoyances of a business nature, my business seemed to me—every businessman knows such times—so repellent that I decided to shut up shop for the day at once, in spite of the fact that there was still bright wintry light and it was early in the day. Such decisions made of one's own free will always lead to good results.

Shortly after beginning his reign, and even before he had announced the usual amnesty, the young prince visited a prison. Among other things he asked, as had been expected, who had been longest in this prison. It was a man who had murdered his wife, had been sentenced to life imprisonment, and had just completed the twenty-third year of his sentence. The prince wished to see him; he was conducted to the cell; as a precaution the prisoner had been put in chains for the day.

When I came home in the evening, in the middle of the room I found a large, an overlarge, egg. It was almost as high as the table and correspondingly bulging. It rocked slightly to and fro. I was very curious, took the egg between my legs and carefully cut it in two with my pocketknife. It was already hatched out. Crackling, the shell fell apart and out jumped a stork-like, still featherless bird, beating the air with wings that were too short. "What do you want in our world?" I felt like asking, squatted down before the bird and gazed into its timidly blinking eyes. But it left me and hopped along the walls, half fluttering, as though its feet were sore. "One helps the other," I thought, unpacked my supper on the table and beckoned to the bird, which was just pushing its beak in among my few books, on the other side of the room. At once it came over to me, sat down on a chair, obviously a little used to things by now, and, with whistling breath, began to sniff at the slice of sausage that I had set before it, but merely speared it and threw it down again. "A mistake," I thought, "of course, one does not jump out of the egg and then at once begin eating sausage. Here a woman's experience would be useful." And I looked at it sharply to see whether perhaps its appearance would be any guide to its nutritional demands. "If he comes," it occurred to me then, "from the stork family, then I am sure he will like fish. Well, I am prepared even to procure fish for him. Of course, not free of charge. My means do not permit me to keep a pet bird. So if I do make such sacrifices, I want to get an equivalent life-maintaining service from him in my own life. He is a stork, well then, when he is fully grown and fattened up on my fish, let him carry me with him to the countries in the South. For a long time now I have been longing to go there, and I have not done so hitherto only for lack of a pair of stork's wings." I instantly fetched paper and ink, dipped the bird's beak in and, without the bird's offering any resistance, wrote the following: "I, a stork-like bird, pledge myself, in the event that you feed me on fishes, frogs, and worms (these two latter victuals I added for the sake of cheapness) until I am fully fledged, to carry you on my back to the countries in the South." Then I wiped his beak clean and once more held the paper up to the bird's eyes before folding it up and putting it into my wallet. But then I hurried straight out to buy fish; this time I had to pay for them, yet the fishmonger promised me that he would in future always have rotten fish and plenty of worms for me, at a low price. Perhaps the journey to the South would not turn out all too expensive. And I was glad to see how the bird enjoyed what I had brought back for it. It swallowed the fish with a gurgle, and they filled its pinkish little paunch. Day by day, not to be compared with human children, the bird made progress in its development. True, the unbearable stench of the rotten fish always hung about my room and it was not easy always to find the bird's droppings and to remove them, and the cold winter weather and the rising price of coal prohibited the extraordinarily necessary airing of the room—but what did it matter, when spring came I would be floating along on gentle currents of air towards the glorious South. The wings were growing, were becoming covered with feathers, the muscles were growing stronger, it was time to begin flying-practice. Unfortunately there was no stork-mother there, and if the bird had not been so willing, I dare say my instruction would not have sufficed. But it obviously realized that it must compensate for the deficiencies of my capacities to teach by painstaking attentiveness and the greatest of exertions. We began with gliding. I climbed up, it followed, I jumped down with outspread arms, it fluttered after me. Later we passed on to the table and finally to the wardrobe, but all the flying exercises were always systematically repeated many times.

The Tormenting Demon

THE TORMENTING DEMON dwells in the forest. In a long-abandoned cabin dating back to old charcoal-burning times. Going in, one notices only an inexpungable smell of things moldering, and nothing else. Smaller than the smallest mouse, invisible even to an eye that comes very close, the tormenting demon cowers in a corner. Nothing, nothing at all can be noticed; quietly the forest murmurs are heard through the empty window. How lonely it is here, and how well it suits you. Here in the corner you will sleep. Why not in the forest, where the air moves freely? Because now you happen to be here, safe in a cabin, in spite of the fact that the door dropped off its hinges long ago and has been carried away. But still, you grope in the air as though you were trying to pull the door to, then you lie down.

At last I jumped up from the table and smashed the lamp with one blow of my fist. A servant immediately came in with a lantern, bowed, and held the door open for me. I hurried out of my room and down the stairs, the servant behind me. Downstairs a second servant helped me into a fur coat; since I let this be done, as though I had no strength, he did still more, turning up the fur collar and buttoning it up at the neck in front. It was necessary, the cold was killing. I stepped into the spacious sledge that was waiting, became warm tucked up in many rugs, and with a clear tinkling of bells the journey began. "Friedrich," I heard someone whisper from the corner. "You're here, Alma," I said, stretching out my thickly gloved right hand to her. Some more words of satisfaction at our encounter, then we fell silent, for the speed at which we were rushing along robbed us of breath. Dozing off, I had already forgotten my companion when we stopped outside an inn. At the door of the sledge stood the innkeeper, at his side my servant, all craning their necks in preparedness to receive orders from me, whatever they might be. But I leaned forward and only exclaimed: "Why are you standing here? Go on, go on, no stopping!" And I prodded the driver with a stick I found beside me.[26]

The Seventh Octavo Notebook

AN INVIOLABLE DREAM. She was running along the high-road, I did not see her, I only noticed how she swung along as she ran, how her veil flew, how her feet lifted; I was sitting at the edge of the field, gazing into the water of the little stream. She ran through the villages; children standing in the doorways watched her coming and watched her going.

A DISJOINTED DREAM. It was the whim of an earlier prince to ordain that the mausoleum must have a watch-man directly by the sarcophagi. Sensible men had expressed their disapproval; finally the prince, who was otherwise in many ways tied down, was allowed to have his way in this trifling matter. A wounded veteran of a war in the previous century, a widower and the father of three sons who had fallen in the last war, applied for this job. He was taken on, and an aged court official accompanied him to the mausoleum. A washerwoman followed them, laden with various things intended for the watchman. As far as the avenue, which then led straight ahead to the mausoleum, the old soldier kept in step with the court official, in spite of his wooden leg. But now he faltered a little, coughed slightly, and began rubbing his left leg. "Well, Friedrich," said the court official, who had walked on some distance with the washer-woman and now turned round. "I've twinges in my leg," the veteran said, pulling a face, "just a moment, it usually passes off quite quickly."

The Grandfather's Story

IN THE TIMES of the late Prince Leo V, I was the watchman at the mausoleum in Friedrichspark. Naturally I did
not begin by being a mausoleum watchman. I still remember quite clearly how, as an errand boy at the
princely dairies, I was told to take the milk to the mausoleum in the evening for the first time. "Oh," I thought,
"to the mausoleum guard." Does anyone really know exactly what "mausoleum" means? I was a mausoleum
watchman and so I should know, but actually I don't
know. And you people who are listening to my story
will realize at the end that you yourselves, even if you
thought you knew what "mausoleum" means, must confess you no longer know. But at that time I did not yet
bother much about that, I was merely proud, in a quite
general way, of having been sent to the mausoleum
guard. And so I went galloping off with my milk pail
through the mists along the meadow paths leading to the
Friedrichspark. Before the golden trellis-gate I dusted my
jacket, cleaned my boots, wiped the damp off the pail,
then rang and waited, my forehead pressed against the
trellis-work, to see what would happen. The watchman's
cottage seemed to stand among bushes, on a little hill;
light issued from a little door opening, and a very old
woman opened the gate after I had said who I was and
shown the pail as evidence of the truth of what I had
said. Then I had to walk ahead of her, but exactly as
slowly as the woman; it was very uncomfortable, for she
kept a hold on me from behind and twice stopped to
draw breath on the short distance we had to cover. Up
above, on a stone seat above the door, a gigantic man
was sitting, his legs crossed, his hands crossed on his
breast, his head thrown back, his gaze fixed on the

bushes close in front of him, which barred every view
from him. I could not help looking questioningly at the
woman. "That is the mameluke," she said, "don't you
know that?" I shook my head, stared at the man again in
astonishment, especially at his high cap made of Crimean lambskin, but then the old woman pulled me into
the cottage. In a small room, sitting by a table very
neatly covered with books, there was a bearded old gentleman in a dressing gown, looking across at me from
underneath the shade of the table lamp. Naturally I
thought I had not come to the right place and turned
round, about to leave the room again, but the old woman
blocked my way and said to the gentleman: "The new
milk-boy." "Come here, you little brat," the old gentleman said, laughing. Then I sat on a little bench beside
his table and he brought his face quite near to mine. Unfortunately, the kindly treatment I received had made me
somewhat pert.

In the Attic

THE CHILDREN had a secret. In the attic, in a far corner, among all the rubbish accumulated during a whole
century, where no adult could grope his way in any
more, Hans, the advocate's son, had discovered a strange
man. He was sitting on a chest, which was propped up
against the wall, lying on its side. When he caught sight
of Hans, his face showed neither fright nor astonishment,
only apathy; he met Hans's gaze with clear eyes. A big
round cap made of Crimean lambskin was pulled far
down on his head. He had a thick mustache, which stood
out stiffly. He was wearing a loose brown cloak held together by a tremendous system of straps, reminiscent of

a horse's harness. On his lap there lay a short scimitar in
a dimly shining sheath. His feet were shod in spurred
high boots, one foot was placed on a wine bottle, which
had rolled over, the other, on the floor, was slightly
tilted, heel and spur rammed into the wood. "Go away!"
Hans screamed, as the man stretched out his hand slowly
to take hold of him; he ran far away into the newer
parts of the attic and stopped only when the wet washing, hung up there to dry, slapped into his face. But then,
after all, he turned straight back again. The stranger sat
there, his lower lip pouting somewhat contemptuously,
and did not stir. Cautiously creeping nearer, Hans
wanted to make sure whether this immobility was not
merely a trick. But the stranger really seemed to mean
no harm, he sat there quite slackly, indeed so slackly
that his head wagged almost imperceptibly. So Hans
risked pushing aside an old fire screen, riddled with holes,
that was still separating him from the stranger, and went
quite close up to him and finally indeed touched him.
"How dusty you are!" he said wonderingly, withdrawing
his blackened hand. "Yes, dusty," the stranger said, and
nothing else. His accent was so unusual that Hans only
understood the words retrospectively. "I'm Hans," he said,
"the advocate's son. And who are you?" "I see," the stranger said, "I am a Hans too, my name's Hans Schlag, I'm a
huntsman from Baden and come from Kossgarten on the
Neckar. Old stories." "You're a huntsman? You go hunting?" Hans asked. "Oh, you're only a little boy," the
stranger said, "and why do you open your mouth so wide
when you speak?" This was a defect for which the advocate also used to be criticized, but this rebuke was not
very appropriate, coming from the huntsman, whose
speech was scarcely intelligible and who would have
been well advised to open his mouth much wider.

The discord that there had always been between Hans
and his father had erupted so violently after the mother's
death that Hans left his father's business, went abroad,
immediately and as it were absent-mindedly took a little job that happened to be offered to him there, and
avoided all contact with his father, whether through letters or through acquaintances, so successfully that he
only learnt of his father's death from heart failure, which
occurred some two years after his departure, through the
letter from the advocate who had appointed him his
executor. Hans was just standing behind the window of
the draper's shop where he was working as a shop assistant, and gazing through the rain on to the main square
of the little country town, when the postman came
across from the direction of the church. He handed the
letter to the draper's wife, that ponderous, lethargic, everlastingly discontented woman, who was sitting at the
back of the shop on a high upholstered chair, and departed. Hans's attention was somehow caught by the
weak, fading tinkle of the little doorbell, he looked towards it and then he also saw the draper's wife bringing
her bearded face, tied up in black kerchiefs, very close
to the envelope. On such occasions it always seemed to
Hans that her tongue must all at once come rolling out
and that then, instead of reading, she would begin licking like a dog. The little doorbell was still echoing faintly,
and the draper's wife said: "Here's a letter that's come for
you." "No," Hans said and did not stir from the window.
"You are a queer person, Hans," the woman said, "look,
your name's on it, quite distinctly." The letter said that
although Hans had been made the sole heir, the inheritance was so encumbered with debts and legacies that
there would scarcely be anything more left for him, as
he realized from even a superficial estimate, than his parents' house. That was not much: a plain, old, one-story

building. But Hans was very attached to the house, and besides, after his father's death, there was nothing to keep him here abroad any longer; on the contrary, the settling of the bequests made his presence urgently necessary, and so he immediately freed himself from his obligations, which was not difficult, and traveled home.

It was late on a December evening, everything lay deep in snow, when Hans drove up to the house that was his home. The caretaker, who had been expecting him, came out of the door, supported by his daughter; he was a frail old man, who had already served Hans's grandfather. They exchanged greetings, though not very cordially, for Hans had always regarded the caretaker as nothing more than a simple-minded tyrant of his childhood years, and the humility with which he now approached him was embarrassing to him. In spite of this, he told the daughter, who came up the steep, narrow staircase after him, carrying the luggage, that not the slightest change would be made where her father's wages were concerned, and this without consideration of the legacy he had received. The daughter thanked him in tears and confessed that this removed her father's chief worry, which had scarcely let him sleep since the late master's death. Only these thanks made Hans quite conscious of the trouble that this inheritance had caused him and might continue to cause him. He looked forward all the more to being alone in his old room, and with a foretaste of that he gently stroked the tomcat, which, his first unalloyed memory of bygone days, flitted past him, large as life. Now, however, Hans was not taken to his room, which should have been got ready for him in accordance with his written instructions, but into what had been his father's bedroom. He asked why this had happened. The girl, still breathing heavily from carrying her load, stood opposite him; she had grown tall and strong in the two years, and her gaze was strikingly clear. She apologized. The fact was that his Uncle Theodor was settled in Hans's room, and they had not wanted to disturb the old gentleman, particularly as this room was larger and also more comfortable. The information that Uncle Theodor was living here in the house was something new to Hans.[27]

The Eighth Octavo Notebook

I AM in the habit of relying on my coachman in everything. When we came past a high white wall, slowly bulging at the sides and at the top, and ceased to drive ahead, driving along the wall, touching it, the coachman finally said: "It is a forehead."

We had set up a small fishery and built a wooden cabin by the sea.

Strangers recognize me. On a little journey recently I could scarcely push my way through the corridor of an overcrowded coach with my handbag. Then someone who was obviously an utter stranger to me called to me out of the half-darkness of a compartment and offered me his seat.

Work as joy, inaccessible to the psychologists.

Nausea after too much psychology. If someone has good legs and is admitted to psychology, he can, in a short time and in any zigzag he likes, cover distances such as he cannot cover in any other field. One's eyes overbrim at the sight.

I am standing on a piece of waste land. Why I have
not been set down in a better country I do not know.
Am I not worth it? One must not say that. Nowhere can
a bush spread more richly than I.[28]

Concerning the Jewish Theater

IN THE FOLLOWING I shall not bother about figures and
statistics; that I leave to the historians of the Jewish theater. My purpose is quite simple: to present a few pages
of memories of the Jewish theater, with its dramas, its
actors, and its public, as I have seen, learnt and experienced this in the course of more than ten years, or, to
put it differently, to raise the curtain and show the
wound. Only after the disease has been diagnosed, can
a cure be found and, possibly, the true Jewish theater
created.

1

FOR MY DEVOUT Chasidic parents in Warsaw the theater
was naturally *trefe*,[29] nothing less than *chazer*. Only at
Purim was there a theater, for then Cousin Chaskel stuck
a big black beard on top of his little blond goatee, put
his caftan on back to front and played the part of a
jolly Jewish peddlar—I could not turn my little childish
eyes away from him. He was my favorite among all my
cousins, his example left me no peace, and when I was
scarcely eight years old I was already acting in the *cheder* like Cousin Chaskel. Once the Rebbe had gone, there
was always a theatrical performance in the *cheder*, I was
producer, stage manager, in short everything, and the
beatings I afterwards got from the Rebbe were also the

hardest anyone got. But that did not bother us; the Rebbe beat us, but we went on thinking out other plays every day. And the whole year was all a hoping and praying: that Purim might come and that I might again see Cousin Chaskel dressed up. One thing I was resolved on—that as soon as I was grown up I would dress up and sing and dance every Purim too, like Cousin Chaskel.

But that people also dress up at other times than Purim and that there are many other artists like Cousin Chaskel was, of course, something of which I had no inkling. That is, until one day I heard from Israel Feldscher's boy that there was really such a thing as a theater where people acted and sang and dressed up, and every night, not only at Purim, and that there were such theaters even in Warsaw, and that his father had several times taken him to the theater. This news—I was about ten years old at the time—positively electrified me. I was seized with a secret, undreamt-of longing. I counted the days that must yet pass before I was grown up and would at last be allowed to see the theater for myself. At that time I did not even know that the theater was a forbidden and sinful thing.

Soon I discovered that the Grand Theater was opposite the Town Hall, the best, the finest theater in all Warsaw, indeed in the whole wide world. From that time on, even the sight of the building from the outside, when I went past it, positively dazzled me. But once when I asked at home when we were ever going to the Grand Theater, I was shouted at: a Jewish child was not supposed to know anything about the theater, it was not allowed, the theater was there only for the Goyim and sinners. This answer was enough for me, I asked no more, but I had no more rest, and I was very much afraid that I was bound to commit this sin some time and, when I was older, would simply have to go to the theater.

Once when I was going past the Grand Theater in the evening after Yom Kippur, with two cousins, when there were a lot of people in the street where the theater was and I could not turn my eyes away from the "impure" theater, Cousin Mayer asked me: "Would you like to be up there, too?" I said nothing. Probably he did not like my silence, and he himself added: "Now, child, there is no single Jew there—Heaven forbid! On the evening directly after Yom Kippur even the wickedest Jew does not go to the theater." But all I gathered from this was that although no Jew went to the theater at the end of the sacred festival of Yom Kippur, on ordinary evenings all through the year plenty of Jews did go.

In my fourteenth year I went to the Grand Theater for the first time. Little though I had learnt of the language of the country, still, by now I could read the posters, and there I read one day that *The Huguenots* was being performed. There had been talk of *The Huguenots* before this in the "Klaus," and besides, the play was by a Jew, "Meier Beer"—and so I gave myself permission, bought a ticket, and that evening went to the theater for the first time in my life.

What I saw and felt on that occasion is not relevant here, but for one thing: I came to the conclusion that the people there sang better than Cousin Chaskel and also dressed up much better than he did. And there was yet another surprise I got: I found I had long known the ballet music from *The Huguenots*, the tunes were sung in the "Klaus" on Friday evening to the Lecho Lodi. And at that time I could not make out how it was possible that people should be playing in the Grand Theater what had for so long been sung in the "Klaus."

From that time on, I went to the opera frequently. Only I had to see that I did not forget to buy a collar and a pair of cuffs for every performance and to throw them into the Vistula on my way home. My parents must not see such things. While I was soaking myself in *Wilhelm Tell* and *Aida*, my parents were lulled in the belief that I was sitting in the "Klaus" over the folios of the Talmud and studying the Holy Scriptures.

II

SOME TIME LATER I discovered that there was also a Jewish theater. But however much I should have liked to go there too, I did not dare to, for it could have got round to my parents all too easily. However, I frequently went to the opera at the Brand Theater, and later also to the Polish playhouse. In the latter I saw *The Robbers* for the first time. It very much amazed me that there could be such beautiful play acting even without singing and music—I should never have thought it—and oddly enough I was not angry with Franz; perhaps it was he who made the greatest impression on me, and that was the part I should have liked to act, not that of Karl.

Of the boys in the "Klaus," I was the only one who dared to go to the theater. For the rest, however, we boys in the "Klaus" had by that time fed thoroughly on "enlightened books"; at that period I was for the first time reading Shakespeare, Schiller, and Lord Byron. Of Yiddish literature, however, all that found its way into my hands was the great detective stories that America supplied us with in a language that was half German and half Yiddish.

A short time passed, it gave me no rest: there was a Jewish theater in Warsaw, and I was not to see it? And so I risked it, staked everything on the throw, and went to the Jewish theater.

That completely transformed me. Even before the play

began, I felt quite different from the way I felt among "them." Above all, there were no gentlemen in evening dress, no ladies in low-cut gowns, no Polish, no Russian, only Jews of every kind, in caftans, in suits, women and girls dressed in the Western way. And everyone talked loudly and carelessly in our mother tongue, nobody particularly noticed me in my long caftan, and I did not need to be ashamed at all.

The play was a comedy with singing and dancing, in six acts and ten scenes: *Baal-Teshuvah* by Schumor. They did not begin punctually at eight o'clock the way they did at the Polish theater, but only about ten o'clock, and it did not end until long after midnight. The lover and the intrigant spoke High German and I was amazed that all at once—without having any notion of the German language—I could understand such excellent German so well. Only the funny man and the soubrette spoke Yiddish.

On the whole I liked it better than the opera, the dramatic theater, and the operetta, all rolled into one. For first it was, after all, Yiddish; true, it was German-Yiddish, but still Yiddish, a better and more beautiful Yiddish; and secondly here was everything all at once: drama, tragedy, singing, comedy, dancing, all of them together—life! All that night I could not sleep for excitement, my heart telling me that I too must some day serve in the temple of Jewish art, that I must become a Jewish actor.

But on the afternoon of the next day Father sent the children into the next room, telling only Mother and me to remain. Instinctively I felt that here was a *kashe* cooking up for me. Father did not sit down again; he kept on walking up and down the room; with his hand on his little black beard he talked, not to me, but only to Mother. "You must be told: he becomes worse every day. Yesterday he was seen in the Jewish theater."

Mother clasped her hands in horror. Father, quite pale, continued to pace up and down the room. My heart tightened, I sat there like a condemned prisoner, I could not bear to see the sorrow felt by my loyal, devout parents. Today I can no longer remember what I said then, I only know one thing, that after some minutes of oppressive silence Father turned his large black eyes on me and said: "My child, think of this, it will lead you far, very far"—and he was right.

Finally, there was only one person besides myself still in the inn. The innkeeper wanted to shut up for the night and asked me to pay. "There's another man sitting there," I said sullenly, because I saw it was really time to go but I did not feel like going away or going anywhere at all. "That is the difficulty," the innkeeper said, "I can't make the man understand me. Will you help me?" "Hi there," I shouted through my hollowed hands, but the man did not stir, he only went on quietly gazing sideways into his beer glass.

It was already late in the night when I rang the bell at the gate. It was a long time before the gatekeeper came out, evidently from the depths of the courtyard, and opened the gate.

"Master bids you come in," the servant said, bowing, and with a soundless jerk he opened the high glass door. With an almost flying stride the Count hastened towards me from his writing desk, which stood by the open window. We looked into each other's eyes; I was taken aback by the Count's rigid gaze.

I lay on the ground by a wall, writhing in pain, trying to burrow into the damp earth. The huntsman stood beside me and lightly pressed one foot into the small of my back. "A splendid beast," he said to the beater, who was cutting open my collar and coat in order to feel my flesh. Already tired of me and eager for fresh action, the hounds were running senselessly against the wall. The coach came, and, bound hand and foot, I was flung in beside the gentleman, over the back seat, so that my head and arms hung down outside the carriage. The journey passed swiftly and smoothly; perishing of thirst, with open mouth, I breathed in the high-whirling dust, and now and then felt the gentleman's delighted touch on my calves.

What do I carry on my shoulders? What specters cling to me?

It was a stormy evening, I saw the little ghost creeping out of the bushes.
The gate slammed, I stood eye to eye with him.

The lamp splintered into pieces, a strange man with a fresh light came into the room, I rose, my family with me, we greeted him, no notice was taken.

The robbers had bound me and there I lay close to the captain's fire.

Barren fields, a barren plain, behind mists the pallid green of the moon.

He leaves the house, he finds himself in the street, a horse is waiting, a servant is holding the stirrup, the ride takes him through an echoing wilderness.

LETTER TO HIS FATHER

Letter to His Father [30]

DEAREST FATHER:

You asked me recently why I maintain that I am afraid of you. As usual, I was unable to think of any answer to your question, partly for the very reason that I am afraid of you, and partly because an explanation of the grounds for this fear would mean going into far more details than I could even approximately keep in mind while talking. And if I now try to give you an answer in writing, it will still be very incomplete, because even in writing this fear and its consequences hamper me in relation to you and because [anyway] the magnitude of the subject goes far beyond the scope of my memory and power of reasoning.

To you the matter always seemed very simple, at least in as far as you talked about it in front of me, and, without discrimination, in front of many other people. It looked to you more or less as follows: you have worked hard all your life, have sacrificed everything for your children, above all for me, consequently I have lived "like a fighting-cock," have been completely at liberty to learn whatever I wanted, and have had no cause for material worries, which means worries of any kind at all. You have not expected any gratitude for this, knowing what "children's gratitude" is like, but have expected at least some sort of obligingness, some sign of sympathy. Instead I have always dodged you and hidden from you, in

138

my room, among my books, with crazy friends, or with extravagant ideas. I have never talked to you frankly, I have never come to you when you were in the synagogue, never visited you at Franzensbad, nor indeed ever shown any family feeling, I have never taken any interest in the business or your other concerns, I left the factory on your hands and left you in the lurch, I encouraged Ottla in her obstinacy, and never lifted a finger for you (never even got you a theater ticket), while I do everything for my friends. If you sum up your judgment of me, the result you get is that although you don't charge me with anything downright improper or wicked (with the exception perhaps of my latest marriage plan), you do charge me with coldness, estrangement, and ingratitude. And, what is more, you charge me with it in such a way as to make it seem my fault, as though I might have been able, with something like a touch on the steering wheel, to make everything quite different, while you aren't in the slightest to blame, unless it be for having been too good to me.

This, your usual way of representing it, I regard as accurate only in so far as I too believe you are entirely blameless in the matter of our estrangement. But I am equally entirely blameless. If I could get you to acknowledge this, then what would be possible is—not, I think, a new life, we are both much too old for that—but still, a kind of peace; no cessation, but still, a diminution of your unceasing reproaches.

Oddly enough you have some sort of notion of what I mean. For instance, a short time ago you said to me: "I have always been fond of you, even though outwardly I didn't act towards you as other fathers generally do, and this precisely because I can't pretend as other people can." Now, Father, on the whole I have never doubted your goodness towards me, but this remark is one I consider wrong. You can't pretend, that's a fact, but merely for that reason to maintain that other fathers pretend is either mere opinionatedness, and as such beyond discussion, or on the other hand—and this in my view is what it really is—a veiled expression of the fact that something is wrong in our relationship and that you have played your part in causing it to be so, but without its being your fault. If you really mean that, then we are in agreement.

I'm not going to say, of course, that I have become what I am only as a result of your influence. That would be very much exaggerated (and I am indeed inclined to this exaggeration). It is indeed quite possible that even if I had grown up entirely free from your influence I still could not have become a person after your own heart. I should probably have still become a weakly, timid, hesitant, restless person, neither Robert Kafka nor Karl Hermann, but yet quite different from what I really am, and we might have got on with each other excellently. I should have been happy to have you as a friend, as a chief, an uncle, a grandfather, even indeed (though this rather more hesitantly) as a father-in-law. Only as what you are, a father, you have been too strong for me, particularly since my brothers died when they were small and my sisters only came along much later, so that I had to bear the whole brunt of it all alone, something I was much too weak for.

Compare the two of us: I, to put it in a very much abbreviated form, a Löwy with a certain basis of Kafka, which, however, is not set in motion by the Kafka will to life, business, and conquest, but by a Löwyish spur that urges more secretly, more diffidently, and in another direction, and which often fails to work entirely. You, on the other hand, a true Kafka in strength, health, appetite,

loudness of voice, eloquence, self-satisfaction, worldly
dominance, endurance, presence of mind, knowledge of
human nature, a certain way of doing things on a grand
scale, of course also with all the defects and weaknesses
that go with all these advantages and into which your
temperament and sometimes your hot temper drive you.
You are perhaps not wholly a Kafka in your general out-
look, in so far as I can compare you with Uncle Philipp,
Ludwig, and Heinrich. That is odd, and here I don't see
quite clearly either. After all, they were all more cheerful, fresher, more informal, more easygoing, less severe
than you. (In this, by the way, I have inherited a great
deal from you and taken much too good care of my inheritance, without, admittedly, having the necessary
counterweights in my own nature, as you have.) Yet you
too, on the other hand, have in this respect gone through
various phases. You were perhaps more cheerful before
your children, in particular I, disappointed you and depressed you at home (when other people came in, you
were quite different) and perhaps have become more
cheerful again since then, now that your grandchildren
and your son-in-law again give you something of that
warmth which your children, except perhaps Valli[31] could
not give you. However it was, we were so different and
in our difference so dangerous to each other that, if anyone had tried to calculate in advance how I, the slowly
developing child, and you, the full-grown man, would
stand to each other, he could have assumed that you
would simply trample me underfoot so that nothing was
left of me. Well, that didn't happen. Nothing alive can be
calculated. But perhaps something worse happened. And
in saying this I would all the time beg of you not to forget that I never, and not even for a single moment, believe any guilt to be on your side. The effect you had on

me was the effect you could not help having. But you should stop considering it some particular malice on my part that I succumbed to that effect.

I was a timid child. For all that, I am sure I was also obstinate, as children are. I am sure that Mother[32] spoilt me too, but I cannot believe I was particularly difficult to manage; I cannot believe that a kindly word, a quiet taking of me by the hand, a friendly look, could not have got me to do anything that was wanted of me. Now you are after all at bottom a kindly and softhearted person (what follows will not be in contradiction to this, I am speaking only of the impression you made on the child), but not every child has the endurance and fearlessness to go on searching until it comes to the kindliness that lies beneath the surface. You can only treat a child in the way you yourself are constituted, with vigor, noise, and hot temper, and in this case this seemed to you, into the bargain, extremely suitable, because you wanted to bring me up to be a strong brave boy.

Your educational methods in the very early years I can't, of course, directly describe today, but I can more or less imagine them by drawing retrospective conclusions from the later years and from your treatment of Felix.[33] What must be considered as heightening the effect is that you were then younger and hence more energetic, wilder, more untrammeled and still more reckless than you are today and that you were, besides, completely tied to the business, scarcely able to be with me even once a day, and therefore made all the more profound an impression on me, never really leveling out into the flatness of habit.

There is only one episode in the early years of which I have a direct memory. You may remember it, too. Once in the night I kept on whimpering for water, not, I am certain, because I was thirsty, but probably partly to be annoying, partly to amuse myself. After several vigorous threats had failed to have any effect, you took me out of bed, carried me out onto the *pavlatche*[34] and left me there alone for a while in my nightshirt, outside the shut door. I am not going to say that this was wrong—perhaps at that time there was really no other way of getting peace and quiet that night—but I mention it as typical of your methods of bringing up a child and their effect on me. I dare say I was quite obedient afterwards at that period, but it did me inner harm. What was for me a matter of course, that senseless asking for water, and the extraordinary terror of being carried outside were two things that I, my nature being what it was, could never properly connect with each other. Even years afterwards I suffered from the tormenting fancy that the huge man, my father, the ultimate authority, would come almost for no reason at all and take me out of bed in the night and carry me out onto the *pavlatche*, and that therefore I was such a mere nothing for him.

That then was only a small beginning, but this sense of nothingness that often dominates me (a feeling that is in another respect, admittedly, also a noble and fruitful one) comes largely from your influence. What I would have needed was a little encouragement, a little friendliness, a little keeping open of my road, instead of which you blocked it for me, though of course with the good intention of making me go another road. But I was not fit for that. You encouraged me, for instance, when I saluted and marched smartly, but I was no future soldier, or you encouraged me when I was able to eat heartily or even drink beer with my meals, or when I was able to repeat songs, singing what I had not understood, or prattle to you using your own favorite expressions, imitating you, but nothing of this had anything to do with my future. And it is characteristic that even today you really only encourage me in anything when you yourself are involved in it, when what is at stake is your own sense of self-importance, which I damage (for instance by my intention of marrying) or which is damaged in me (for instance when Papa[35] is abusive to me). Then I receive encouragement, I am reminded of my worth, the matches I would be entitled to make are pointed out to me, and Pepa is condemned utterly. But apart from the fact that at the age I have now reached I am almost quite unsusceptible to encouragement, what help could it be to me anyway, when it only comes where it isn't primarily a matter of myself at all?

At that time, and at that time everywhere, I would have needed encouragement. I was, after all, depressed even by your mere physical presence. I remember, for instance, how we often undressed together in the same bathing hut. There was I, skinny, weakly, slight; you strong, tall, broad. Even inside the hut I felt myself a miserable specimen, and what's more, not only in your eyes but in the eyes of the whole world, for you were for me the measure of all things. But then when we went out of the bathing hut before the people, I with you holding my hand, a little skeleton, unsteady, barefoot on the boards, frightened of the water, incapable of copying your swimming strokes, which you, with the best of intentions, but actually to my profound humiliation, always kept on showing me, then I was frantic with desperation and all my bad experiences in all spheres at such moments fitted magnificently together. What made me feel best was when you sometimes undressed first and I was able to stay behind in the hut alone and put off the disgrace of showing myself in public until at length you came to see what I was doing and drove me out of the hut. I was grateful to you for not seeming to notice my extremity, and besides, I was proud of my father's body.

For the rest, this difference between us remains much the same to this very day.

In keeping with that, furthermore, was your intellectual domination. You had worked your way up so far alone, by your own energies, and as a result you had unbounded confidence in your opinion. For me as a child that was not yet so dazzling as later for the boy growing up. From your armchair you ruled the world. Your opinion was correct, every other was mad, wild, *meshugge*, not normal. With all this your self-confidence was so great that you had no need to be consistent at all and yet never ceased to be in the right. It did sometimes happen that you had no opinion whatsoever about a matter and as a result all opinions that were at all possible with respect to the matter were necessarily wrong, without exception. You were capable, for instance, of running down the Czechs, and then the Germans, and then the Jews, and what is more, not only selectively but in every respect, and finally nobody was left except yourself. For me you took on the enigmatic quality that all tyrants have whose rights are based on their person and not on reason. At least so it seemed to me.

Now where I was concerned you were in fact astonishingly often in the right, which was a matter of course in talk, for there was hardly ever any talk between us, but also in reality. Yet this too was nothing particularly incomprehensible: in all my thinking I was, after all, under the heavy pressure of your personality, even in that part of it—and particularly in that—which was not in accord with yours. All these thoughts, seemingly independent of you, were from the beginning loaded with the burden of your harsh and dogmatic judgments; it was almost impossible to endure this, and yet to work out one's thoughts with any measure of completeness and permanence. I am not here speaking of any sublime thoughts, but of every little enterprise in childhood. It was only necessary to be happy about something or other, to be filled with the thought of it, to come home and speak of it, and the answer was an ironical sigh, a shaking of the head, a tapping of the table with one finger: "Is that all you're so worked up about?" or "I wish I had your worries!" or "The things some people have time to think about!" or "What can you buy yourself with that?" or "What a song and dance about nothing!" Of course, you couldn't be expected to be enthusiastic about every childish triviality, toiling and moiling as you used to. But that wasn't the point. The point was, rather, that you could not help always and on principle causing the child such disappointments, by virtue of your antagonistic nature, and further that this antagonism was ceaselessly intensified through accumulation of its material, that it finally became a matter of established habit even when for once you were of the same opinion as myself, and that finally these disappointments of the child's were not disappointments in ordinary life but, since what it concerned was your person, which was the measure of all things, struck to the very core. Courage, resolution, confidence, delight in this and that, did not endure to the end when you were against whatever it was or even if your opposition was merely to be assumed; and it was to be assumed in almost everything I did.

This applied to thoughts as well as to people. It was enough that I should take a little interest in a person—which in any case did not happen often, as a result of my nature—for you, without any consideration for my feelings or respect for my judgment, to butt in with abuse, defamation, and denigration. Innocent, childlike people, such as, for instance, the Yiddish actor Löwy, had to pay for that. Without knowing him you compared him, in a dreadful way that I have now forgotten, to vermin and as was so often the case with people I was fond of you were automatically ready with the proverb of the dog and its fleas.[36] I here particularly recall the actor because at that time I made a note of your pronouncements about him, with the comment: "This is how my father speaks of my friend (whom he does not even know), simply because he is my friend. I shall always be able to bring this up against him whenever he reproaches me with the lack of a child's affection and gratitude." What was always incomprehensible to me was your total lack of feeling for the suffering and shame you could inflict on me with your words and judgments. It was as though you had no notion of your power. I too, I am sure, often hurt you with what I said, but then I always knew, and it pained me, but I could not control myself, could not keep the words back, I was sorry even while I was saying it. But you struck out with your words without more ado, you weren't sorry for anyone, either during or afterwards, one was utterly defenseless against you.

But that was what your whole method of upbringing was like. You have, I think, a gift for bringing up children; you could, I am sure, have been of use to a human being of your own kind with your methods; such a person would have seen the reasonableness of what you told him, would not have troubled about anything else, and would quietly have done things the way he was told. But for me as a child everything you shouted at me was positively a heavenly commandment, I never forgot it, it remained for me the most important means of forming a judgment of the world, above all of forming a judgment of you yourself, and there you failed entirely. Since as a child I was together with you chiefly at meals, your teaching was to a large extent teaching about proper behavior at table. What was brought to the table had to be eaten up, there could be no discussion of the goodness of the food—but you yourself often found the food uneatable, called it "this swill," said "that brute" (the cook) had ruined it. Because in accordance with your strong appetite and your particular habit you ate everything fast, hot and in big mouthfuls, the child had to hurry, there was a somber silence at table, interrupted by admonitions: "Eat first, talk afterwards," or "faster, faster, faster," or "there you are, you see, I finished ages ago." Bones mustn't be cracked with the teeth, but you could. Vinegar must not be sipped noisily, but you could. The main thing was that the bread should be cut straight. But it didn't matter that you did it with a knife dripping with gravy. One had to take care that no scraps fell on the floor. In the end it was under your chair that there were most scraps. At table one wasn't allowed to do anything but eat, but you cleaned and cut your fingernails, sharpened pencils, cleaned your ears with the toothpick. Please, Father, understand me rightly: these would in themselves have been utterly insignificant details, they only became depressing for me because you, the man who was so tremendously the measure of all things for me, yourself did not keep the commandments you imposed on me. Hence the world was for me divided into three parts: into one in which I, the slave, lived under laws that had been invented only for me and which I could, I did not know why, never completely comply with; then into a second world, which was infinitely remote from mine, in which you lived, concerned with government, with the issuing of orders and with annoyance about their not being obeyed; and finally into a third world where everybody else lived happily and free from orders and from having to obey. I was continually in disgrace, either I obeyed your orders, and that was a disgrace, for they applied, after all, only to me, or I was defiant, and that was a disgrace too, for how could I presume to defy you, or I could not obey because, for instance, I had not your strength, your appetite, your skill, in spite of which you expected it of me as a matter of course; this was the greatest disgrace of all. What moved in this way was not the child's reflections, but his feelings.

My situation at that time becomes clearer, perhaps, if I compare it with that of Felix. You do, of course, treat him in a similar way, even indeed employing a particularly terrible method against him in his upbringing: whenever at meals he does anything that is in your opinion uncleanly, you are not content to say to him, as you used to say to me at that time: "What a swine you are," but add: "a thorough Hermann" or "just like your father." Now this may perhaps—one can't say more than "perhaps"—not really harm Felix in any essential way, for where he is concerned you are actually no more than a grandfather, an especially important one, of course, but still, not everything, as you were for me; and besides, Felix is of a quiet, even at this stage to a certain extent manly character, one who may perhaps be disconcerted by a great voice thundering at him, but not conditioned permanently by it, but above all he is, of course, only comparatively seldom together with you, and apart from that he is also under other influences, you are for him more something of an endearing curiosity from which he can pick and choose whatever he likes. For me you were nothing in the least like a curiosity, I couldn't pick and choose, I had to take everything.

And this, besides, without being able to produce any arguments against any of it, for it is fundamentally impossible for you to talk calmly about a subject you don't approve of or which simply is not suggested by you; your hectoring temperament doesn't allow of that. In recent years you have been explaining this as due to your nervous heart condition. I don't know that you were ever essentially different. At the most, the nervous heart condition is a means by which you exert your domination more severely, since the thought of it necessarily chokes off the least opposition from others. This is, of course, not a reproach, only a statement of fact. Rather as in Ottla's case, what you say is: "One simply can't talk to her at all, she flies straight in your face," but in reality she does not begin by flying out at all. You mistake the person for the thing. The thing under discussion is what flies in your face and you immediately make up your mind about it without listening to the person; whatever is brought forward afterwards merely serves to irritate you further, never to convince you. Then all one gets from you is: "Do whatever you like. So far as I'm concerned you have a free hand. You're of age, I've no advice to give you," and all this with that frightful hoarse undertone of anger and utter condemnation that only makes me tremble less today than in my childhood because the child's exclusive sense of guilt has been partly replaced by insight into our helplessness, yours and mine.

The impossibility of getting on calmly together had one more result, actually a very natural one: I lost the capacity to talk. I dare say I would never have been a very eloquent person in any case, but I would, after all, have had the usual fluency of human language at my command. But at a very early stage you forbade me to talk. Your threat: "Not a word of contradiction!" and the raised hand that accompanied it have gone with me ever since. What I got from you—and you are, as soon as it is a matter of your own affairs, an excellent talker—was a hesitant, stammering mode of speech, and even that was still too much for you, and finally I kept silent, at first perhaps from defiance, and then because I couldn't either think or speak in your presence. And because you were the person who really brought me up, this has had its repercussions throughout my life. It is altogether a remarkable mistake for you to believe I never fell in with your wishes. "Always agin you" was really not my basic principle where you were concerned, as you believe and as you reproach me. On the contrary: if I had obeyed you less, I am sure you would have been much better pleased with me. As it is, all your educational measures hit the mark exactly. There was no hold I tried to escape. As I now am, I am (apart, of course, from the fundamentals and the influence of life itself) the result of your upbringing and of my obedience. That this result is nevertheless distressing to you, indeed that you unconsciously refuse to acknowledge it as the result of your methods of upbringing, is due to the fact that your hand and the material I offered were so alien to each other. You would say: "Not a word of contradiction!" thinking that that was a way of silencing the oppositional forces in me that were disagreeable to you, but the effect of it was too strong for me, I was too docile, I became completely dumb, cringed away from you, hid from you, and only dared to stir when I was so far away from you that your power could no longer reach me, at any rate directly. But you were faced with all that, and it all seemed to you to be "agin," whereas it was only the inevitable consequence of your strength and my weakness.

Your extremely effective rhetorical methods in bringing me up, which never failed to work with me anyway, were: abuse, threats, irony, spiteful laughter and—oddly enough—self-pity.

I can't recall your ever having abused me directly and in downright abusive terms. Nor was that necessary; you had so many other methods, and besides, in talk at home and particularly at business the words of abuse went flying around me in such swarms, as they were flung at other people's heads, that as a little boy I was sometimes almost stunned and had no reason not to apply them to myself too, for the people you were abusing were certainly no worse than I was and you were certainly not more displeased with them than with me. And here again, too, was your enigmatic innocence and inviolability; you cursed and swore without the slightest scruple about it; indeed you condemned cursing and swearing in other people and would not have it.

You reinforced abusiveness with threats, and this applied to me too. How terrible for me was, for instance, that "I'll tear you apart like a fish," in spite of knowing, of course, that there was nothing worse to follow (admittedly, as a little child I didn't know that), but it was almost exactly in accord with my notions of your power and I saw you as being capable of doing this too. What was also terrible was when you ran round the table, shouting, to grab one, obviously not really trying to grab, but still pretending to, and Mother (in the end) had to rescue one, as it seemed. Once again one had, so it seemed to the child, remained alive through your mercy and bore one's life henceforth as an undeserved gift from you. This too is the place to mention the threats about the consequences of disobedience. When I began to do something you did not like and you threatened me with the prospect of failure, my veneration for your opinion was so great that the failure then became inevitable, even though perhaps it happened only at some later time. I lost confidence in my own actions. I was wavering, doubtful. The older I became the more material there was for you to bring forward against me as evidence of my worthlessness; gradually you began really to be right in a certain respect. Once again I am careful not to assert that I became like this solely through you;

you only intensified what was already there, but you did greatly intensify it, simply because where I was concerned you were very powerful and you employed all your power to that end.

You put special trust in bringing children up by means of irony, and this was most in keeping with your superiority over me. An admonition from you generally took this form: "Can't you do it in such-and-such a way? That's too hard for you, I suppose. You haven't the time, of course?" and so on. And each such question would be accompanied by malicious laughter and a malicious face. One was so to speak already punished before one even knew that one had done something bad. What was also maddening were those rebukes when one was treated as a third person, in other words accounted not worthy even to be spoken to angrily: that is to say, when you would speak in form to Mother but in fact to me, sitting there at the same time. For instance: "Of course, that's too much to expect of our worthy son" and the like. (This then produced a corollary in that, for instance, I did not dare to ask, and later from habit did not even really much think of asking, you anything directly when Mother was there. It was much less dangerous for the child to put questions to Mother, sitting there beside you, and to ask Mother: "How is Father?"—so guarding oneself against surprises.) There were, of course, also cases when one was entirely in agreement with even the worst irony, namely when it referred to someone else, for instance Elli, with whom I was on bad terms for years. There was an orgy of malice and spiteful delight for me when such things were said of her, as they were at almost every meal: "She has to sit six feet away from the table, the great fat lump" and when you, morosely sitting on your chair without the slightest trace of pleasantness of humor, a bitter enemy, would exagger-

atedly imitate the way she sat, which you found utterly
loathsome. How often such things happened, over and
over again, and how little you really achieved as a result
of them! I think the reason was that the expenditure of
anger and malice seemed to be in no proper relation to
the subject itself, one did not have the feeling that the
anger was caused by this trifle of sitting some way back
from the table, but that the whole bulk of it was already
there to begin with then only by chance happened to
settle on this matter as a pretext for breaking out. Since
one was convinced that a pretext would be found anyway, one did not bother particularly, and anyway one's
feelings became dulled by these continual threats. One
had gradually become pretty sure of not getting a beating, anyway. One became a glum, inattentive disobedient
child, always trying to escape from something and in the
main to escape within oneself. So you suffered, and so we
suffered. From your own point of view you were quite
right when, clenching your teeth and with that gurgling
laughter that gave the child its first notions of hell, you
used bitterly to say (as you did only just recently in connection with a letter from Constantinople): "A *nice*
crowd that is!"

What seemed to be quite incompatible with this attitude to your children was, and it happened very often,
that you complained in public. I confess that as a child
(though doubtless this was rather later) I was completely callous about this and could not understand how
you could possibly expect to get any sympathy from anyone. You were so huge, a giant in every respect. What
could you care for our pity or even our help? Our help,
indeed, you could not but despise, as you so often despised us ourselves. Hence I did not take these complaints at their face value and looked for some hidden
motive behind them. Only later did I come to understand

that you really suffered a great deal because of your children, but at that time, when these complaints might in other circumstances still have met with a childish candid sympathy that would not have counted the cost but would have been ready to offer any help it could, to me they could only seem to be overemphatic means of drilling me and humiliating me, as such not in themselves very intense, but with the harmful accompanying effect that the child became used to not taking very seriously the very things it should have taken seriously.

Fortunately there were, I admit, exceptions to all these things, mostly when you suffered in silence, and affection and kindliness by their own strength overcame all obstacles, and moved me immediately. Admittedly this was rare, but it was wonderful. For instance, when in earlier times, in hot summers, when you were tired after lunch, I saw you having a nap at the office, your elbow on the desk; or when you joined us in the country, in the summer holidays, on Sundays, worn out from work at the office; or the time when Mother was gravely ill and you stood holding on to the bookcase, shaking with sobs; or when, during my last illness, you came tiptoeing to Ottla's room to see me, stopping in the doorway, craning your neck to see me, and out of consideration for me only waved your hand to me. At such times one would lie back and weep for happiness, and one weeps again now, writing it down.

You have a particularly beautiful, very rare way of quietly, contentedly, approvingly smiling, a way of smiling that can make the person for whom it is meant entirely happy. I can't recall its ever having expressly been my lot in my childhood, but I dare say it may have happened, for why should you have refused it to me at that time when I still seemed blameless to you and was your great hope? For the rest, such friendly impressions in the

long run brought about nothing but an increase in my
sense of guilt, making the world still more incomprehensible to me.

I would rather keep to the practical and permanent. In
order to assert myself a very little in relation to you, and
partly too from a kind of vengefulness, I soon began to
observe little ridiculous things about you, collecting them
and exaggerating them. For instance, there was the way
you so easily let yourself be dazzled by people who
were, for the most part, only seemingly your social superiors; you would keep on talking about them, as of
some Imperial Councilor or other and the like (on the
other hand such things pained me too, to see you, my
father, believing you had any need of such trifling con-
firmations of your own value, and boasting about them).
Or I would observe your taste for indecent expressions,
which you would produce in the loudest possible voice,
laughing about them as though you had said something
particularly good, while in point of fact it was only a
banal little obscenity (at the same time this again was
for me a humiliating manifestation of your vitality).
There were, of course, plenty of such observations. I
was happy about them; they were for me an occasion
for whispering and joking; you sometimes noticed it
and were angry about it, taking it to be malice and
lack of respect for you, but believe me it was for me
nothing other than a means—moreover, a useless one—of
attempted self-preservation; they were jokes of the kind
that is made everywhere about gods and kings, jokes that
are not only compatible with the profoundest respect but
which are indeed part and parcel of it.

Incidentally, you too, in keeping with your similar position where I was concerned, tried a similar form of self-
defense. You were in the habit of pointing out how ex-
aggeratedly well off I was and how well I had in fact

been treated. That is correct, but I don't believe it was of any real use to me in the circumstances that actually prevailed.

It was true that Mother was illimitably good to me, but all that was for me in relation to you, that is to say, in no good relation. Mother unconsciously played the part of a beater during a hunt. Even if your method of upbringing might in some unlikely case have set me on my own feet by means of producing defiance, dislike, or even hate in me, Mother canceled that out again by kindness, by talking sensibly (in the maze and chaos of my childhood she was the very pattern of good sense and reasonableness), by pleading for me, and I was again driven back into your orbit, which I might perhaps otherwise have broken out of, to your advantage and to my own. Or it was so that no real reconciliation ever came about, that Mother merely shielded me from you in secret, secretly gave me something, or allowed me to do something, and then where you were concerned I was again the furtive creature, the cheat, the guilty one, who in his worthlessness could only pursue backstairs methods even to get the things he regarded as his right. Of course, I then became used to taking such courses also in quest of things to which, even in my own view, I had no right. This again meant an increase in the sense of guilt.

It is also true that you hardly ever really gave me a whipping. But the shouting, the way your face got red, the hasty undoing of the braces and the laying of them ready over the back of the chair, all that was almost worse for me. It is like when someone is going to be hanged. If he is really hanged, then he's dead and it's all over. But if he has to go through all the preliminaries to being hanged and only when the noose is dangling before his face is told of his reprieve, then he may suffer from it all his life long. Besides, from so many occasions when I had, as you clearly showed you thought, deserved to be beaten, when you were however gracious enough to let me off at the last moment, here again what accumulated was only a huge sense of guilt. On every side I was to blame, I was in debt to you.

You have always reproached me (and what is more either alone or in front of others, you having no feeling for the humiliation of this latter, your children's affairs always being public affairs) for living in peace and quiet, warmth, and abundance, lacking for nothing, thanks to your hard work. I think here of remarks that must positively have worn grooves in my brain, like: "When I was only seven I had to push the barrow from village to village." "We all had to sleep in one room." "We were glad when we got potatoes." "For years I had open sores on my legs from not having enough clothes to wear in winter." "I was only a little boy when I was sent away to Pisek to go into business." "I got nothing from home, not even when I was in the army, even then I was sending money home." "But for all that, for all that—Father was always Father to me. Ah, nobody knows what that means these days! What do these children know of things? Nobody's been through that! Is there any child that understands such things today?" Under other conditions such stories might have been very educational, they might have been a way of encouraging one and strengthening one to endure similar torments and deprivations to those one's father had undergone. But that wasn't what you wanted at all; the situation had, after all, become quite different as a result of all your efforts, and there was no opportunity to distinguish oneself in the world as you had done. Such an opportunity would first of all have had to be created by violence and revolution, it would have meant breaking away from home (assuming one had had the resolution and strength to do so and that Mother wouldn't have worked against it, for her part, with other means). But all that was not what you wanted at all, that you termed ingratitude, extravagance, disobedience, treachery, madness. And so, while on the one hand you tempted me to it by means of example, story, and humiliation, on the other hand you forbade it with the utmost severity. Otherwise you ought, for instance, really to have been delighted, apart from the accompanying circumstances, with Ottla's Zürau escapade.[37] She wanted to get back to the country from which you had come, she wanted work and hardship such as you had had, she did not want to batten on the results of your work, just as you yourself were independent of your father. Were those such dreadful intentions? Was that so remote from your example and your precept? Well, Ottla's intentions came to nothing finally in practice, were indeed perhaps carried out in a somewhat ridiculous way, with too much fuss, and she did not have enough consideration for her parents. But was that exclusively her fault and not also the fault of the circumstances and above all of the fact that you were so estranged from her? Was she any less estranged from you (as you later tried to convince yourself) in the business than afterwards at Zürau? And would you not quite certainly have had the power (assuming you could have brought yourself to do so) to turn that escapade into something very good by means of encouragement, advice and supervision, perhaps even merely by means of toleration?

In connection with such experiences you were in the habit of saying, in bitter jest, that we were too well off. But this joke is in a certain sense no joke at all. What you had to fight for we received from your hand, but the fight for external life, a fight that was instantly open to you and which we were naturally not spared either, we have to fight for only late in life, in our maturity but with only childish strength. I do not say that our situation is therefore inevitably less favorable than yours was, on the contrary, it is probably no better and no worse (although this is said without reference to our different natures), only we have the disadvantage of not being able to boast of our wretchedness and not being able to humiliate anyone with it as you have done with your wretchedness. Nor do I deny that it would have been possible for me really to enjoy the fruits of your great and successful work, that I could have turned them to account and continued to work with them, so giving you joy, but what stood in the way of this was, here again, our estrangement. I could enjoy what you gave, but only in humiliation, weariness, weakness, and with a sense of guilt. That was why I could be grateful to you for everything only as a begger is, and never show it by doing the right things.

The next external result of this whole method of up-bringing was that I fled from everything that even remotely reminded me of you. First there was the business. In itself, particularly in my childhood, so long as it was a shop, I ought to have liked it very much, it was so animated, the lights lit at evening, so much to see and hear, being able to help now and then and to distinguish oneself, but above all to admire you for your magnificent commercial talents, the way you sold things, managed people, made jokes, were untiring, knew the right decision to make at once in doubtful cases, and so forth; even the way you wrapped up a parcel or opened a crate was a spectacle worth watching, and all this was certainly not the worst school for a child. But since you gradually began to terrify me on all sides and the business and you became one for me, the business too made me feel uneasy. Things that had at first been a matter of course for me there now began to torment and shame me, particularly the way you treated the staff. I don't know, perhaps it was like that in most businesses (in the Assecurazioni Generali, for instance, in my time it was really similar, and the explanation I gave the director for my resignation was, though not strictly in accordance with the truth, still not entirely a lie, my not being able to bear the cursing and swearing, which incidentally had not actually been directed at me; it was a matter about which I was too painfully sensitive from home), but in my childhood other businesses did not concern me. But you I heard and saw shouting, cursing and raging in the shop, in a way that in my opinion at that time had not its equal anywhere in the world. And not only cursing, but other sorts of tyrannizing. For instance, the way you would push goods you did not want to have mixed up with others, knocking them off the counter—only the thoughtlessness of your rage was some slight excuse—and the assistant had to pick them up. Or your constant mode of referring to an assistant with t.b. lungs: "Sooner he dies the better, the mangy dog." You called the employees "paid enemies," and that was what they were too, but even before they became such you seemed to me to be their "paying enemy." There, too, I learnt the great lesson that you could be unjust; in my own case I would not have noticed it so soon, for here was too much accumulated sense of guilt, ready to admit that you were right; but there, in my childish view, later of course a little but not overmuch corrected, were strangers, who were after all working for us and because of that had to live in constant dread of you. Of course, there I exaggerated, and this because I simply assumed you had as terrible an effect on these people as on me. If it had been so, they could not have lived at all; since however they were grown-up people, most of them with excellent nerves, they shook off this abuse without any trouble and in the end it did you much more harm than it did them. But it made the business insufferable to me, reminding me far too much of my relations with you: quite apart from your proprietary interest and apart from your mania for domination even as a businessman, you were so greatly superior to all those who ever came to learn the business from you that nothing they ever did could satisfy you, and you must, as I assumed, in the same way be forever dissatisfied with me too. That was why I could not but side with the staff, incidentally also because, from sheer nervousness, I could not understand how anyone could be so abusive to a stranger, and hence from sheer nervousness tried somehow to reconcile the staff, which in my opinion must be in a terrible state of indignation, with you, with our family, if for no other reason than that of my own security. To this end it was not sufficient to behave in an ordinary decent way to the staff, not even modestly; on the contrary, I had to be humble, not only to be first in saying "good morning" or "good evening" but if it was at all possible also to prevent any return of the greeting. And even if I, insignificant creature that I was, had licked their feet down below, it would still have been no compensation for the way that you, the master, were lashing out at them up above. This relationship that I came to have towards my fellow men extended beyond the limits of the business and on into the future (something similar, but not so dangerous and deep-going as in my case is for instance Ottla's taste for associating with poor people, sitting together with the maids, which annoys you so much, and the like). In the end I was almost afraid of the business and, in any case, it had long ceased to be any concern of mine even before I went to the Gymnasium and hence was taken even further away from it. Besides, it seemed to be entirely beyond my resources and capacities, since, as you said, it exhausted even yours. You then tried (to me this today seems touching and shaming) to extract, nevertheless, some little sweetness for yourself from my dislike of the business, of your handiwork—a dislike that was after all very distressing to you—by asserting that I had no business sense, I had loftier ideas in my head, and the like. Mother was, of course, delighted with this explanation that you wrung from yourself, and I too, in my vanity and wretchedness, let myself be influenced by it. But if it had really been only or mainly "loftier ideas" that turned me against the business (which I now, but only now, have come really and honestly to hate), they would have had to express themselves differently, instead of letting me float quickly and timidly through my schooling and my law studies until finally I landed up at a clerk's desk.

If I was to flee from you, I had to flee from the family as well, even from Mother. True, one could always get protection from her, but only in relation to you. She loved you too much and was too devoted and loyal to you to have been able to constitute an independent spiritual force, in the long run, in the child's struggle. It was, incidentally, a true instinct the child had, for with the passing of the years Mother became ever more closely allied to you; while, where she herself was concerned, she always kept her independence, within the narrowest limits, delicately and beautifully, and without ever essentially hurting you, still, with the passing of the years she did more and more completely, emotionally rather than intellectually, blindly adopt your judgments and your condemnations with regard to the children, particularly in the case—certainly a grave one—of Ottla. Of course, it must always be borne in mind how tormenting and utterly wearing Mother's position in the family was. She toiled in the business and in the house, and suffered doubly in watching all the family illnesses, but the culmination of all this was what she suffered in her position midway between us and you. You were always affectionate and considerate to her, but in this respect you spared her exactly as little as we spared her. We all hammered ruthlessly away at her, you from your side, we from ours. It was a diversion, nobody meant any harm, thinking of the battle that you were waging with us and that we were waging with you, and it was Mother on whom we relieved our wild feelings. Nor was it at all a good contribution to the children's upbringing the way you—of course, without being in the slightest to blame for it yourself—tormented her on our account. It even seemed to justify our otherwise unjustifiable behavior towards her. How much she suffered from us on your account and from you on our account, quite without counting those cases where you were in the right because she was spoiling us, even though this "spoiling" may sometimes have been only a quiet, unconscious counterdemonstration against your system. Of course, Mother could not have borne all this if she had not drawn the strength to bear it from her love for us all and her happiness in that love.

My sisters were only partly on my side. The one who was happiest in her relation to you was Valli. Being closest to Mother, she fell in with your wishes in a similar way, without much effort and without suffering much harm. But, just because she reminded you of Mother, you did accept her in a more friendly spirit, although there was little Kafka material in her. But perhaps precisely that was what you wanted; where there was nothing of the Kafka, even you could not demand anything of the sort; nor had you the feeling, as with the rest of us, that here something was getting lost which had to be saved by force. For the rest, it may be that you were never particularly fond of the Kafka element as it manifested itself in women. Valli's relationship to you would perhaps even have become still more friendly if the rest of us had not slightly interfered with it.

Elli is the only example of the almost complete success of a breaking out from your orbit. When she was a child she was the last person I should have expected it of. For she was such a clumsy, tired, timid, bad-tempered, guilt-ridden, overmeek, malicious, lazy, greedy, miserly child, I could hardly bring myself to look at her, far from speaking to her, so much did she remind me of myself, in so very much the same way was she under the same spell of our upbringing. Her miserliness in particular was abhorrent to me, since I had it to an, if possible, even greater extent. Miserliness is, after all, one of the most reliable signs of profound unhappiness; I was so unsure of everything that, in fact, I possessed only what I actually had in my hands or in my mouth or what was at least on the way there, and this was precisely what she, being in a similar situation, most enjoyed taking away from me. But all this changed when, at an early age—this is the most important thing—she left home, married, had children, and became cheerful, carefree, brave, generous, unselfish, and hopeful. It is almost incredible how you actually did not notice this change at all, or at any rate did not give it its due, blinded as you were by the grudge you have always borne Elli and at bottom still bear her to this day; only this grudge matters much less now, since Elli no longer lives with us and, besides, your love for Felix and affection for Karl have made it less important. It is only Gerti who sometimes has to suffer for it still.[38]

Of Ottla I scarcely dare write; I know by doing so I

risk ruining the whole effect I hope for from this letter. In ordinary circumstances, that is, so long as she is not in particular need of danger, all you feel for her is hatred; you have yourself confessed to me that in your opinion she is always intentionally causing you suffering and annoyance, and while you are suffering on her account she is satisfied and pleased. In other words, a sort of fiend. What an immense estrangement, greater still than that between you and me, must have come about between you and her, for such an immense misunderstanding to be possible. She is so remote from you that you scarcely see her any more, but set a specter in the place where you suppose her to be. I grant you that you have had a particularly difficult time with her. I don't, of course, quite see to the bottom of this very complicated case, but at any rate here was something like a kind of Löwy, equipped with the best Kafka weapons. Between us there was no real struggle; I was soon finished off; what remained was flight, embitterment, melancholy, and inner struggle. But you two were always in fighting position, always fresh, always energetic. A sight as magnificent as it was desperate. At the very beginning you were, I am sure, very close to each other, for even today Ottla is, of the four of us, perhaps the purest representation of the marriage between you and Mother and of the forces there combined. I don't know what it was that deprived you both of the happiness of the harmony between father and child, but I can't help believing that the development in this case was similar to that in mine. On your side there was the tyranny of your own nature, on her side the Löwy defiance, touchiness, sense of justice, restlessness, and all that, backed up by the consciousness of Kafka vigor. Doubtless I too influenced her, but scarcely of my own doing, simply through the fact of my existence. Besides, as the last to arrive, she found herself in a situation where the balance of power was already established and was able to form her own judgment from the large amount of material at her disposal. I can even imagine that she may, in her inmost being, have wavered for some time as to whether she should fling herself into your arms or into those of the enemies, and it is obvious that at that time there was something you failed to do and that you rebuffed her, but if it had been possible, the two of you would have become a magnificently harmonious pair. In that way, of course, I should have lost an ally, but the sight of the two of you would have richly compensated me, and besides, as a result of the unforeseeable happiness of finding complete contentment at least in one child you would have altered greatly to my advantage. All this, however, is today only a dream. Ottla has no contact with her father and has to seek her way alone, like me, and the degree of confidence, self-confidence, health, and ruthlessness by which she surpasses me makes her in your eyes more wicked and treacherous than I seem to you. I understand that. From your point of view she can't be different. Indeed she is herself capable of regarding herself with your eyes, of feeling what you suffer and of being—not desperate, despair is my business—but very sad. You do see us together often enough, in apparent contradiction to this, whispering and laughing, and now and then you hear us talking of you. The impression you get is that of impudent conspirators—strange conspirators. You are, admittedly, a chief subject of conversation between us, as of our thoughts ever since we can remember, but truly it is not in order to plot something against you that we sit together, but in order to discuss—with all our might and main, jokingly and seriously, in affection, defiance, anger, revulsion, submission, consciousness of guilt, with all the resources of our heads and hearts—this terrible trial that is pending between us and you, to discuss it in all its details, from all sides, on all occasions, from far and near—a trial in which you keep on claiming to be the judge, whereas, at least in the main (here I leave a margin for all the mistakes I may naturally make) you are a party too, just as weak and deluded as we are.

An example of the effect of your methods of upbringing, one that is very instructive in the context of the whole situation, is the case of Irma. On the one hand, she was, after all, a stranger, already grown up when she entered your business, and had to do with you mainly as her employer, so that she was only partially exposed to your influence and this at an age when she had already developed powers of resistance; yet, on the other hand, she was also a blood relation, venerating you as her father's brother, and the power you had over her was far greater than that of a mere employer. And for all this she, who, with her frail body, was so efficient, intelligent, hard-working, modest, trustworthy, unselfish, and loyal, who loved you as her uncle and admired you as her employer, she who stood the test in previous and in subsequent situations, was not a very good clerk to you. The fact was that, under pressure from us too of course, she came near to being in the relation, to you, of one of your own children, and the power of your personality to bend others was, even in her case, so great that what developed in her (admittedly only in relation to you and, it is to be hoped, without the deeper suffering a child experiences) was forgetfulness, carelessness, a grim sardonic sort of humor, and perhaps even a shade of defiance, in so far as she was capable of that at all, and in all this I am not taking any account whatsoever of the fact that she was inclined to be ailing, and not very happy in other respects either, and that she was burdened by the bleakness of her life at home. What was so illuminating to me in your relation to her, you yourself summed up in a remark that became classical for us, one that was almost blasphemous, but at the same time extraordinary evidence of the *naïvety* of your way of treating people: "The late lamented in the Lord has left me a damned mess to clear up."

I might go on to describe further orbits of your influence and of struggle against it, but there I would be entering uncertain ground and would have to construct things, and apart from that, the further you are at a remove from your business and your family the pleasanter you have always become, easier to get on with, better mannered, more considerate, and more sympathetic (I mean outwardly, too), in exactly the same way as for instance an autocrat, when he happens to be outside the frontiers of his own country, has no reason to go on being tyrannical and is able to associate good-humoredly even with the lowest of the low. In point of fact, in the group photographs taken at Franzensbad, for instance, you always looked as big and jolly, among those sulky little people, as a king upon his travels. This was something, I grant you, from which your children might have benefited too, only they would have had to be capable of recognizing this even as little children, which was impossible, and I, for instance, would have had not to live constantly in, as it were, the inmost, strictest, strangling ring of your influence, as I did, of course, in reality.

In this way, did I lose my family feeling, as you say? On the contrary, I tended, rather, to preserve my feeling for the family, although mainly in a negative sense, in the sense of breaking away (which, of course, could never be completed) from you. Relations to people outside the family, however, suffered if possible still more as a result of your influence. You are entirely mistaken if

you believe I do everything for other people out of affection and loyalty, and for you and the family nothing,
out of coldness and treachery. I repeat for the tenth
time: even in other circumstances I should probably
have become a shy and nervous person, but it is a long
dark road from there to where I have really come to.
(Up to this point there is in this letter relatively little I
have intentionally passed over in silence, but now and
later I shall have to be silent on certain matters that it
is still too hard for me to confess—to you and to myself.
I say this in order that, if the picture as a whole should
be somewhat blurred here and there, you should not believe that what is to blame is any lack of evidence; on
the contrary, there is evidence that might well make the
picture unbearably stark. It is not easy to strike a
median position.) Here, it is enough to remind you of
early days. I had lost my self-confidence where you were
concerned, and in its place had developed a boundless
sense of guilt. (In recollection of this boundlessness I
once wrote of someone, accurately: "He is afraid the
shame will outlive him, even.") I could not suddenly undergo a transformation when I came into the company
of other people; on the contrary, with them I came to
feel an even deeper sense of guilt, for, as I have already
said, in their case I had to make good the wrongs done
them by you in the business, wrongs in which I too had
my share of responsibility. Besides, you always, of
course, had some objection to make, frankly or covertly,
to everyone I associated with, and for this too I had to
beg his pardon. The mistrust that you tried to instill into
me, at business and at home, towards most people (tell
me of any single person who was of importance to me in
my childhood whom you didn't at least once tear to
shreds with your criticism), this mistrust, which oddly
enough was no particular burden to you (the fact was

that you were strong enough to bear it, and besides, it was in reality perhaps only a token of the autocrat), this mistrust, which for me as a little boy was nowhere confirmed in my own eyes, since I everywhere saw only people excellent beyond all hope of emulation, in me turned into mistrust of myself and into perpetual anxiety in relation to everything else. There, then, I was in general certain of not being able to escape from you. The fact that you were mistaken on this point was perhaps due to your actually never learning anything about my association with other people, and to your mistrustful and jealous (I don't deny, do I? that you are fond of me) assumption that I had to get compensation elsewhere for what was missing in life at home, since it was after all impossible that outside my home I should live in the same way. Incidentally, it was precisely in my childhood that I found a certain comfort, in this respect, in my very mistrust of my own judgment. I would say to myself: "Oh, you're exaggerating, you tend too much to feel trivialities as great exceptions, the way young people always do." But this comfort was one that I later lost almost entircly, with an increasing perspective of the world.

I found equally little means of escape from you in Judaism. Here some escape would, in principle, have been thinkable, but more than that, it would have been thinkable that we might both have found each other in Judaism or even that we might have begun from there in harmony. But what sort of Judaism was it I got from you? In the course of the years I have taken roughly three different attitudes to it.

As a child I reproached myself, in accord with you, for not going to the synagogue enough, for not fasting, and so on. I thought that in this way I was doing a wrong not to myself but to you, and I was penetrated by a sense of guilt, which was, of course, always ready to hand.

Later, as a boy, I could not understand how, with the insignificant scrap of Judaism you yourself possessed, you could reproach me for not (if for no more than the sake of piety, as you put it) making an effort to cling to a similar insignificant scrap. It was indeed really, so far as I could see, a mere scrap, a joke, not even a joke. On four days in the year you went to the synagogue, where you were, to say the least of it, closer to the indifferent than to those who took it seriously, patiently went through the prayers by way of formality, sometimes amazed me by being able to show me in the prayer book the passage that was being said at the moment, and for the rest, so long (and this was the main thing) as I was there in the synagogue I was allowed to hang about wherever I liked. And so I yawned and dozed through the many hours (I don't think I was ever again so bored, except later at dancing lessons) and did my best to enjoy the few little bits of variety there were, as, for instance, when the Ark of the Covenant was opened, which always reminded me of the shooting galleries where a cupboard door would open in the same way whenever one got a bull's-eye, only with the difference that there something interesting always came out and here it was always just the same old dolls with no heads. Incidentally, it was also very frightening for me there, not only, as goes without saying, because of all the people one came into close contact with, but also because you once mentioned, by the way, that I too might be called up to read the Torah. That was something I went in dread of for years. But otherwise I was not fundamentally disturbed in my state of boredom, unless it was by the *bar mizvah*, but that meant no more than some ridiculous learning by heart, in other words, led to nothing but something like the ridiculous passing of an examination, and then, so far as you were concerned, by little, not very significant incidents, as when you were called up to read the Torah and came well out of the affair, which to my way of feeling was purely social, or when you stayed on in the synagogue for the prayers for the dead, and I was sent away, which for a long time, obviously because of being sent away and lacking, as I did, any deeper interest, aroused in me the more or less unconscious feeling that what was about to take place was something indecent.—That was how it was in the synagogue, and at home it was, if possible, even more poverty-stricken, being confined to the first evening of Passover, which more and more developed into a farce, with fits of hysterical laughter, admittedly under the influence of the growing children. (Why did you have to give way to that influence? Because you brought it about in the first place.) And so there was the religious material that was handed on to me, to which may be added at most the outstretched hand pointing to "the sons of the millionaire Fuchs," who were in the synagogue with their father at the high holidays. How one could do anything better with this material than get rid of it as fast as possible was something I could not understand; precisely getting rid of it seemed to me the most effective act of "piety" one could perform.

But later on still I did see it again differently and came to realize why it was possible for you to think that in this respect too I was showing ill will and betraying you. You had really brought some traces of Judaism with you from that ghetto-like little village community; it was not much and it dwindled a little more in town and while you were doing your military service, but still, the impressions and memories of your youth did just about suffice to make some sort of Jewish life, especially since you did not, after all, need much of that kind of help, coming as you did of a vigorous stock and being personally scarcely capable of being shaken by religious scruples if they were not very much mixed up with social scruples. At bottom the faith that ruled your life consisted in your believing in the unconditional rightness of the opinions prevailing in a particular class of Jewish society, and hence actually, since these opinions were part and parcel of your own nature, in believing in yourself. Even in this there was still Judaism enough, but it was too little to be handed on to the child; it all dribbled away while you were passing it on. In part it was youthful memories of your own, of a kind that could not be conveyed to others; in part it was your dreaded personality. It was also impossible to make a child, over-acutely observant from sheer nervousness, understand that the few flimsy gestures you performed in the name of Judaism, and with an indifference in keeping with their flimsiness, could have any higher meaning. For you they had their meaning as little souvenirs of earlier times, and that was why you wanted to pass them on to me, but this, since after all even for you they no longer had any value in themselves, was something you could do only by means of persuasion or threats; this could, on the one hand, not be successful and could not, on the other hand, but make you, since you utterly failed to recognize your weak position here, very angry with me on account of my apparent obstinacy.

The whole thing is, of course, not an isolated phenomenon. It was much the same with a large section of this transitional generation of Jews, which had migrated from the still comparatively devout countryside to the towns. The situation arose automatically; only it did, as it happened, bring one more source of acrimony, and a fairly painful one, into our relationship, which was already far from lacking in sources of acrimony. On the other hand, although you ought, on this point too, just like myself, to believe in your own blamelessness, you ought, however, to explain this blamelessness by your personality and the conditions of the time, but not merely by external circumstances, that is, not by saying for instance that you had too much other work and too many other worries to be able to give your mind to such things as well. This is the manner in which you are in the habit of twisting your undoubted innocence into an unjust reproach to others. That can be very easily refuted everywhere and here too. It was not a matter of any sort of instruction you ought to have given your children, but of an exemplary life. Had your Judaism been stronger, then your example would have been compelling too; this goes without saying and is, again, by no means a reproach, but only a refutation of your reproaches. You have recently been reading Franklin's memoirs of his youth. I did, in fact, give you this book to read on purpose, but not, as you ironically commented, because of a little passage on vegetarianism, but because of the relationship between the author and his father, as it is there described, and of the relationship between the author and his son, as it is spontaneously revealed in these memoirs written for that son. I do not wish to dwell here on matters of detail.

I have received a certain retrospective confirmation of this view of your Judaism from your attitude in recent years, when it seemed to you that I was taking more interest in Jewish things. As you have a dislike in advance of every one of my activities and particularly of the nature of my interest, so you have had it here too. But in spite of this general attitude, one would really have expected that here you would make a little exception. It was, after all, Judaism of your Judaism that was here stirring, and thus with it the possibility too of the start

of new relations between us. I do not deny that if you
had shown interest in them these things might, for that
very reason, have become suspect in my eyes. For I do
not dream of asserting that I am in this respect in any
way better than you. But it never came to putting it to
the test. Through my mediation Judaism became abhorrent to you and Jewish writings unreadable; they
"nauseated" you.—This may have meant that you were
insisting that only that Judaism which you had shown me
in my childhood was the right one, and beyond that
there was nothing. But that you should insist on that
was, after all, scarcely thinkable. But then the "nausea"
(apart from the fact that it was directed primarily not
against Judaism but against me personally) could only
mean that unconsciously you did acknowledge the weakness of your Judaism and of my Jewish upbringing, did
not wish to be reminded of it in any way, and reacted to
all reminder with frank hatred. Incidentally, your negative high esteem of my new Judaism was much exaggerated; first of all, it bore your curse within it, and secondly, in its development the fundamental relationship to
one's fellow men was decisive, in my case that is to say
fatal.

You struck nearer home with your dislike of my writing and all that, unknown to you, was connected with it.
Here I had, in fact, got some distance away from you by
my own efforts, even if it was slightly reminiscent of the
worm that, as a foot tramples on the tail end of it,
breaks loose with its top end and drags itself aside. To
a certain extent I was in safety; there was a chance to
breathe freely. The dislike that you naturally and immediately had of my writing too was, by way of exception,
welcome to me. My vanity and my ambition did suffer,
it is true, under your soon proverbial way of hailing the
arrival of my books: "Put it on my bedside table!" (as it

happened, you were usually playing cards when a book came), but fundamentally I was thoroughly glad of it, not only out of rebellious malice, not only out of delight at a new confirmation of my view of our relationship, but quite spontaneously, because to me that formula sounded something like: "Now you are free!" Of course it was a delusion; I was not, or, to put it most optimistically, was not *yet*, free. My writing was all about you; all I did there, after all, was to bemoan what I could not bemoan upon your breast. It was an intentionally long-drawn-out leave-taking from you, only although it was brought about by force on your part, it did not take its course in the direction determined by me. But how little all this amounted to! It is all only worth talking about at all because it has happened in my life; otherwise it would not be worthy of remark at all; and then too for the reason that in my childhood it ruled my life as a premonition, later as a hope, and still later often as despair, dictating—it may be said, yet again in your shape—my few little decisions to me.

For instance, the choice of a career. True, here you gave me complete freedom, in your magnanimous and, in this regard, even indulgent manner. Admittedly, here too you were conforming to the general method of treating sons in the Jewish middle class, which was the measure of things for you, or at least with the values of that class. Finally, what also played a part in this was one of your misunderstandings with respect to my person. The fact is, for reasons of paternal pride, ignorance of my real life, and conclusions drawn from my feebleness, you have always regarded me as a particularly keen worker. As a child, in your view I was always at my lessons, and later always at my writing. Now this does not even remotely correspond to the facts. It would be correct, and much less exaggerated, to say that I paid little atten-

tion to my lessons and learnt nothing; the fact that
something did stick in my mind after those many years,
seeing that I had a moderately good memory and a capacity for learning that was not of the most inferior kind,
is after all not very remarkable, but, be that as it may,
the total sum of knowledge and particularly of a solid
basis for knowledge are extremely pitiable in comparison
with the expenditure of time and money in the course
of an outwardly untroubled, quiet life, particularly too
in comparison with almost all the people I know. It is
pitiable, but to me understandable. As far as I can think
I have had such anxieties, of the very deepest kind,
about asserting my spiritual existence that everything
else was a matter of indifference to me. Jewish school-
boys in our country often tend to be odd; among them
one finds the most unlikely things; but something like
my cold indifference, scarcely disguised, indestructible,
childishly helpless, approaching the ridiculous, and brut-
ishly complacent, the indifference of a self-sufficient but
coldly imaginative child, I have never found anywhere
else, but admittedly here it was the sole defense against
destruction of the child's nerves by fear and a sense of
guilt. All that occupied my mind was worry about myself, and this in various ways. There was, for instance,
the worry about my health; it began imperceptibly
enough, with now and then a little anxiety about digestion, hair falling out, a spinal curvature, and so on, this
intensifying in innumerable gradations, finally end-
ing with a real illness. But since there was nothing at all
I was certain of, since I needed to be provided at every
instant with a new confirmation of my existence, since
nothing was in my very own, undoubted, sole possession,
determined unequivocally only by me—in sober truth a
disinherited son—naturally even the thing nearest at
hand, my own body, became insecure; I shot up, tall and

lanky, without knowing what to do with my lankiness, the burden being too heavy, the back becoming bent; I scarcely dared to move or, least of all, to do gymnastics, and so I remained weakly: I was amazed by everything (that did not trouble me) as by a miracle, for instance my good digestion; that sufficed to make me lose it, and so now the way was open to every sort of hypochondria, until finally under the strain of the superhuman effort of wanting to marry (of this I shall speak later) blood came from the lung, something in which, of course, the apartment in the Schönbornpalais—which, however, I needed only because I believed I needed it for my writing, so that even that comes under the same heading—may have quite a fair share. Well, so all this did not originate in excessive work, as you always imagine. There were years in which, being in perfectly good health, I lazed away more time on the sofa than you in all your life, including all your illnesses. When I rushed away from you, frightfully busy, it was generally in order to lie down in my room. My total achievement in work done, both at the office (where, admittedly, laziness is nothing particularly striking, and mine, furthermore, was kept in bounds by my timidity) and at home as well, is minute; if you had any real idea of it, you would be aghast. Probably I am constitutionally not lazy at all, but there was nothing for me to do. In the place where I lived I was spurned, condemned, fought to a standstill, and although I did make the utmost endeavors to escape to some other place, that was not work, for there it was a matter of something impossible, something that was, apart from small exceptions, unattainable for one of my resources.

This then was the state in which I was given the liberty to choose my career. But was I still at all capable of really making use of such liberty? Had I still any confidence in my own capacity to achieve a real career? My

valuation of myself was much more dependent on you
than on anything else, say for instance some external success. *That* was strengthening for a moment, noth-
thing more, but on the other side your weight always dragged me down much more strongly. Never, I
thought, should I pass out of the first class at elementary
school, but I succeeded, I even got a prize; but I should
certainly not pass the entrance exam for the Gymnasium, but I succeeded in that; but now I should certainly
fail in the first class at the Gymnasium, no, I did not fail,
and I went on and on succeeding. What this produced,
however, was not confidence; on the contrary, I was always convinced—and I positively had the proof of it in
your forbidding expression—that the more things I was
successful in, the worse the final outcome would inevitably be. Often in my mind's eye I saw the terrible assem-
bly of the masters (the Gymnasium is only the most integral example, but it was the same all around me), as
they would meet, when I had passed out of the first class,
and then in the second class, when I had passed out of
that, and then in the third, and so on, meeting in order
to examine this unique, outrageous case, to discover how
I, the most incapable and, in any case, the most igno-
rant of all, had succeeded in creeping up so far as this
class, which now, when everybody's attention had at last
been focused on me, would of course instantly spew me
out, to the high delight of all the righteous, now liberated from this nightmare. Living with such fantasies is
not easy for a child. In these circumstances, what could
I care about my lessons? Who was capable of striking a
spark of real interest out of me? Lessons, and not only
lessons but everything round about me, at that decisive
age, interested me pretty much as a defaulting bank
clerk, still holding his job and trembling at the thought
of discovery, is interested in the small current business of

the bank, which he still has to deal with as a clerk. That was how small and faraway everything was in comparison to the main thing. So it went on up to matriculation, which I passed really, this time, partly only by means of cheating, and then everything stagnated, for now I was free. If I had been concerned only with myself up to now, in spite of the discipline of the Gymnasium, how much more now that I was free. So there was actually no such thing for me as liberty to choose my career, for I knew: compared to the main thing everything would be exactly as much a matter of indifference to me as all the subjects taught at school, and so it was a matter of finding a profession that would be most likely to allow me to indulge this indifference without overmuch injuring my vanity. So the law was the obvious choice. Little contrary attempts on the part of vanity, of senseless hope, such as a fortnight's study of chemistry, or six months' German studies, only reinforced that fundamental conviction. So I studied law. This meant that in the few months before the exams, and in a way that told severely on my nerves, I was positively living, in an intellectual sense, on sawdust, which had, moreover, already been chewed for me in thousands of other people's mouths. But in a certain sense this very thing was to my taste, as in a certain sense too the Gymnasium had previously been and later my job as a clerk was, for all this was utterly appropriate to my situation. At any rate I here showed astonishing foresight; even as a small child I had had fairly clear premonitions with regard to my studies and career. This was something from which I expected no rescue; here I had long ago given up.

But I showed no foresight at all with regard to the significance and possibility of a marriage for me; this up to now the greatest terror of my life has come upon me almost completely unexpectedly. The child had developed

so slowly, these things were outwardly all too remote
from him; now and then the necessity of thinking
of them did arise; but that here a permanent, decisive
and indeed the most grimly bitter ordeal was imminent
was something that could not be recognized. In reality,
however, the plans to marry became the most large-scale
and hopeful attempt at escape, and then the failure was
on a correspondingly large scale, too.

I am afraid that, because in this sphere everything I
try is a failure, I shall also fail to make these attempts
to marry comprehensible to you. And yet on this depends
the success of this whole letter, for in these attempts
there was, on the one hand, concentrated everything I
had at my disposal in the way of positive forces, and, on
the other hand, here there also accumulated, and with
downright fury, all the negative forces that I have described as being the result in part of your method of upbringing, that is to say, the weakness, the lack of self-
confidence, the sense of guilt, and they positively drew
a cordon between myself and marriage. The explanation
will be hard for me also because I have spent so many
days and nights thinking and burrowing through the
whole thing over and over again that now even I myself
am bewildered by the mere sight of it. The only thing
that makes the explanation easier for me is your—in
my opinion—complete misunderstanding of the matter;
slightly to correct so complete a misunderstanding does
not seem excessively difficult.

First of all you rank the failure of the marriages with
the rest of my failures; I should have nothing against
this, provided you accepted my previous explanation of
my failure as a whole. It does, in fact, form part of the
same series, only you underrate the importance of the
matter, underrating it to such an extent that whenever

we talk of it we are actually talking about quite different things. I venture to say that nothing has happened to you in your whole life that had such importance for you as the attempts at marriage have had for me. By this I do not mean that you have not experienced anything in itself as important; on the contrary, your life was much richer and more care-laden and more concentrated than mine, but for this very reason nothing of this sort has happened to you. It is like when one person has to climb five low steps and another person only one step, but one that is, at least for him, as high as all the other five put together; the first person will not only manage the five, but hundreds and thousands more as well, he will have led a great and very strenuous life, but none of the steps he has climbed will have been of such importance to him as for the second person that one, first, high step, that step which it is impossible for him to climb even by exerting all his strength, that step which he cannot get up and which he naturally cannot get past either.

Marrying, founding a family, accepting all the children that come, supporting them in this insecure world and even guiding them a little as well, is, I am convinced, the utmost a human being can succeed in doing at all. That seemingly so many succeeded in this is no evidence to the contrary, for, first, there are not many who do, in fact, succeed, and secondly, these not-many usually don't "do" it, it merely "happens" to them; although this is not that Utmost, yet it is still very great and very honorable (particularly since "doing" and "happening" cannot be kept clearly distinct). And finally, it is not a matter of this Utmost at all, anyway, but only of some distant but decent approximation; it is, after all, not necessary to fly right into the middle of the sun, but it is necessary to crawl to a clean little spot on the earth where the sun sometimes shines and one can warm oneself a little.

How, now, was I prepared for this? As badly as possible. This is apparent even from what has been said hitherto. But in so far as there is a direct preparing of the individual and a direct creating of the general basic conditions, you did not intervene much outwardly. Nor is it otherwise possible; what is decisive here is the general sexual morality of class, nation, and time. All the same, you did intervene here too—not much, for the precondition for such intervention can only be great mutual trust, and both of us had been lacking in this even long before the decisive time came—and not very happily, because our needs were, after all, quite different; what grips me need hardly touch you at all, and vice versa, what is innocence in you may be guilt in me, and vice versa, what has no consequences for you may be the last nail in my coffin.

I remember going for a walk one evening with you and Mother; it was on the Josefsplatz near where the Länderbank is today; and I began talking about these interesting things, in a stupidly boastful, superior, proud, cool (that was spurious), cold (that was genuine) and stammering manner, as indeed I usually talked to you, reproaching the two of you for my having been left uninstructed, for the fact that it was my schoolmates who first had to take me in hand, that I had been in the proximity of great dangers (here I was brazenly lying, as was my way, in order to show myself brave, for as a consequence of my timidity I had, except for the usual sexual misdemeanors of city children, no very exact notion of these "great dangers"), but finally hinted that now, fortunately, I knew everything, no longer needed any advice, and that everything was all right. I had begun talking about this, in any case, mainly because it gave me pleasure at least to talk about it, and then too out of curiosity, and finally too in order somehow to avenge myself on the two of you for something or other. In keeping with your nature you took it quite simply, only saying something to the effect that you could give me some advice about how I could go in for these things without danger. Perhaps it was just such an answer that I had wanted to lure out of you, for it was in keeping with the pruriency of a child overfed with meat and all good things, physically inactive, everlastingly occupied with himself, but still, my outward sense of shame was so hurt by this, or I believed it must be so hurt, that against my will I could not go on talking to you about this and, with arrogant impudence, cut the conversation short.

It is not easy to judge the answer you gave me then; on the one hand, there was, after all, something staggeringly frank, in a manner of speaking, primeval, about it; on the other hand, however, as regards the instruction itself, it was uninhibited in a very modern way. I don't know how old I was at the time, certainly not much over sixteen. It was nevertheless a very remarkable answer for such a boy to be given, and the distance between the two of us is also shown in the fact that this was actually the first direct instruction bearing on real life that I ever received from you. But its real meaning, which sank into my mind even then, but only much later came partly to the surface of my consciousness, was this: what you were advising me to do was, after all, in your opinion and, still far more, in my opinion at that time, the filthiest thing possible. The fact that you were prepared to see to it that physically speaking I should not bring any of the filth home with me was incidental, for in that way you were only protecting yourself, your own household. The main thing was, rather, that you remained outside your

own advice, a married man, a pure man, exalted above
these things; this was intensified for me at that time
probably even more through the fact that marriage too
seemed to me to be shameless and hence it was impossible for me to refer the general information I had picked
up about marriage to my parents. In this way you became still more pure, rose still higher. The thought that
you might perhaps have given yourself similar advice too
before marriage was to me utterly unthinkable. So there
was almost no smudge of earthly filth on you at all. And
precisely you were pushing me, just as though I were
predestined to it, down into this filth, with a few frank
words. And so if the world consisted only of me and you,
a notion I was much inclined to have, then this purity of
the world came to an end with you and, by virtue of your
advice, the filth began with me. In itself it was, of course,
incomprehensible that you should thus condemn me;
only old guilt and profoundest contempt of your side
could explain it to me. And so this again was something
that struck home to my innermost being, and very hard
too.

Here is perhaps where it becomes most clear how we
were both not to blame. A gives B a piece of advice that
is frank, in keeping with his attitude to life, not very
lovely but still even today perfectly usual in town, a
piece of advice that might prevent damage to health.
This piece of advice is for B morally not very invigorat-
ing—but why should he not be able to work his way out
of this, and repair the damage, in the course of the years?
—besides, he does not even have to take the advice at all,
and, in any case, in the advice itself there is no occasion for B's whole future world, say, to come tumbling
down upon him. And yet something of this kind does
happen, but only for the very reason that A is you and
B is myself.

The extent to which we are both not to blame is something I can get a particularly good general view of because a similar clash between us took place in quite different circumstances some twenty years later, as a fact horrible, in itself, however, much less damaging—for where was there anything in me, the thirty-six-year-old, that could still be damaged? I am referring to a little discussion on one of the few agitated days after I had informed you of my last marriage project. What you said to me was more or less as follows: "She probably put on some specially chosen blouse, the thing these Prague Jewesses are good at, and straightaway, of course, you made up your mind to marry her. And, what's more, as fast as possible, in a week, tomorrow, today. I can't make you out, after all, you're a grown man, here you are in town, and you can't think of any way of managing but going straight off and marrying the next best girl. Isn't there anything else you can do? If you're frightened, I'll go along with you myself." You put it in more detail and more plainly, but I can no longer recall the particular points, perhaps too things became a little misty before my eyes, I was almost more interested in Mother, as she, though perfectly in agreement with you, nevertheless took something from the table and left the room with it.

You have, I suppose, scarcely ever humiliated me more deeply with words and have never more clearly shown me your contempt. When you spoke to me in a similar way twenty years earlier, looking at it through your eyes one might even have seen in it some respect for the precocious city boy, who in your opinion could already be initiated into life without more ado. Today this consideration could only intensify the contempt, for the boy who was about to take his first leap into life got stuck halfway and seems to you today to be richer by no experience but only more pitiable by twenty years. My de-

ciding on a girl meant nothing at all to you. You had
(unconsciously) always kept down my power of decision and now believed (unconsciously) that you knew
what it was worth. Of my attempts at escape in other
directions you knew nothing, thus you could not know
anything, either, of the thought processes that had led
me to this attempt to marry, and had to try to guess at
them, and your guess was in keeping with your total
judgment of me, a guess at the most abominable, crude,
and ridiculous thing possible. And you did not for a moment hesitate to say this to me in just such a manner.
The shame you inflicted on me with this was nothing to
you in comparision to the shame that I would, in your
opinion, inflict on your name by this marriage.

Now, as it happens, with regard to my attempts at
marriage there is much you can say in reply, and you
have indeed done so: you could not have much respect
for my decision since I had twice broken the engagement
to F. and twice renewed it again, since I had dragged
you and Mother to Berlin to celebrate the engagement,
and all for nothing, and the like. All this is true—but how
did it come about?

The fundamental idea of both attempts at marriage
was quite a right and proper one: to set up house, to
become independent. It is an idea that does after all appeal to you, only then in reality it always turns out like
the children's game where one holds and even presses
the other's hand, calling out: "Oh, go away, go away,
why don't you go?" Which in our case, of course, is complicated by the fact that you have always honestly meant
this "go away!" since you have always, without knowing
it, held me, or rather, held me down, only by virtue of
your personality.

Both girls were chosen by chance, it is true, but extraordinarily well. Here again is a sign of your complete misunderstanding, in that you can believe that I, the timid, hesitant, suspicious person, can make up my mind to marry all of a sudden, with a jerk, say out of delight over a blouse. Both marriages would, on the contrary, have been marriages of common sense, in so far as that means that day and night, the first time for years, the second time for months, all my power of thought was concentrated on the plan.

Neither of the girls disappointed me, only I disappointed both of them. My judgment on them is today exactly the same as at the time when I wanted to marry them.

Neither is it the case that in my second attempt at marriage I disregarded the experiences gained from the first attempt, that is to say, was rash and careless. The cases were, as it happens, quite different from each other; it was precisely the early experiences that were able to give me hope in the second case, which was altogether much more promising. I don't want to go into details here.

Why then did I not marry? There were individual obstacles, as there are everywhere, but, after all, life consists in taking such obstacles in one's stride. The essential obstacle, however, which was unfortunately independent of the individual case, was that I am obviously intellectually incapable of marrying. This manifests itself in the fact that from the moment when I make up my mind to marry I can no longer sleep, my head burns day and night, life can no longer be called life, I stagger about in despair. It is not actually worries that bring this about; true, in keeping with my sluggishness and pedantry there are countless worries that are involved in all this, but they are not the decisive thing; true, they are like worms completing the work on the corpse, but the decisive blow comes from elsewhere. It is the general pressure of anxiety, of weakness, of self-contempt.

I will try to explain it in more detail. Here, in the attempt to marry, two seemingly antagonistic elements in my relations with you unite more intensely than anywhere else. Marriage is certainly the pledge of the most acute form of self-liberation and independence. I should have a family, the highest thing that one can achieve, in my opinion, and so too the highest thing you have achieved; I should be your equal; all old and everlastingly new shame and tyranny would now be mere history. That would, admittedly, be like a fairy tale, but precisely there does the questionable element lie. It is too much; so much cannot be achieved. It is as if a person were a prisoner and he had not only the intention of escaping, which would perhaps be attainable, but also, and indeed simultaneously, the intention of rebuilding the prison as a pleasure seat for himself. But if he escapes, he cannot do any rebuilding, and if he rebuilds, he cannot escape. If I want to become independent in the particular unhappy relationship in which I stand to you, I must do something that will have, if possible, no relation to you at all; marrying is, it is true, the greatest thing of all and provides the most honorable independence, but it is also at the same time in the closest relation to you. To try to get out at this point therefore has a touch of madness about it, and every attempt is almost punished with it.

Precisely this close relation does indeed partly lure me towards marrying. I picture this equality that would then arise between us, and which you would be able to understand better than any other form of equality, as so beautiful precisely because I could then be a free, grateful, guiltless, upright son, and you could be an untroubled, untyrannical, sympathetic, contented father. But to this end it would be necessary to make all that has happened be as though it had never happened, which means, we ourselves should have to be cancelled out.

But we being what we are, marrying is barred to me through the fact that it is precisely and peculiarly your most intimate domain. Sometimes I imagine the map of the world spread out flat and you stretched out diagonally across it. And what I feel then is that only those territories come into question for my life that either are not covered by you or are not within your reach. And, in keeping with the conception that I have of your magnitude, these are not many and not very comforting territories, and above all marriage is not among them.

This very comparision proves that I am far from wishing to say that you, by your example, drove me out of marriage as you did, for instance, out of the business. On the contrary, in spite of all the remote similarity. In your and Mother's marriage I had before me an, in many ways, model marriage, a model as regards constancy, mutual help, number of children, and even when the children grew up and increasingly disturbed the peace, the marriage as such remained untouched by this. It was perhaps precisely from this example that I formed my high idea of marriage; the desire for marriage was powerless simply for other reasons. These lay in your relation to your children, which is, after all, what this whole letter is about.

There is a view according to which fear of marriage sometimes has its source in a fear that one's children would some time pay one out for the sins one has oneself committed against one's own parents. This, I believe, in my case has no very great significance, for my sense of guilt actually originates, of course, in you, and goes so much with the deep conviction of its uniqueness, indeed this feeling of uniqueness is an essential part of

its tormenting nature, that a repetition is unthinkable. All
the same I must say that I should find such a mute, glum,
dry, doomed son unbearable; I dare say, if there were no
other possibility, I should flee from him, emigrate, as you
at first meant to do on account of my marriage. And so
there may be some influence of this too in my incapacity
to marry.

What is however much more important in all this is
the anxiety about myself. This is to be understood as follows: I have already indicated that in writing and in
what is connected with it I have made some attempts at
independence, attempts at escape, with the very smallest of success; they will scarcely lead any further; much
confirms this for me. Nevertheless it is my duty to watch
over them, or, rather, my life consists in this, letting no
danger that I can avert, indeed no possibility of such a
danger, approach them. Marriage is the possibility of
such a danger, admittedly also the possibility of the
greatest advancement, for me however it is enough that
it is the possibility of a danger. What should I do if it
turned out to be a danger after all! How could I go on
living in matrimony in the perhaps undemonstrable, but
nevertheless irrefutable sense of this danger! Faced with
this I can, indeed, waver, but the final outcome is certain: I must renounce. The simile of the bird in the hand
and the two in the bush has only a very remote application here. In my hand I have nothing, in the bush there
is everything, and yet—so it is decided by the conditions
of battle and the exigency of life—I must choose the
nothing. I had, after all, to make a similar choice in
choosing my profession too.

The most important obstacle to marriage however is
the no longer eradicable conviction that what is essential to supporting a family and, more, to guiding it is
what I have recognized in you, and indeed everything

rolled into one, good and bad, as it is organically combined in you, that is to say, strength, and scorn of the
other, health and a certain immoderation, eloquence and
inadequacy, self-confidence and dissatisfaction with everyone else, a superior attitude to the world and tyranny,
knowledge of human nature and mistrust of most people,
then also good qualities without any drawback, such as
industry, endurance, presence of mind, and fearlessness.
Of all this I had by comparison almost nothing or only
very little, and was it with this I wanted to risk marrying, while I could see for myself that even you had to
fight hard in your marriage and where the children were
concerned even failed? This question I did not, of course,
put to myself in so many words and did not answer in so
many words; otherwise everyday thinking would, after
all, have taken the matter over and shown me other men
who are different from you (to name one, near at hand,
who is very different from you: Uncle Richard) and yet
have married and at least have not collapsed under the
strain, which is in itself a great deal and would have been
quite enough for me. But there it is, I did not ask this
question, but experienced it from childhood on. I tested
myself, after all, not only then when I was faced with
marriage, but in the face of every little thing; in the face
of every little thing you by your example and your method
of upbringing convinced me, as I have tried to describe,
of my incapacity, and what turned out to be right in the
case of every little thing, proving you to be in the right,
naturally could not but turn out to be tremendously right
when it came to the greatest thing of all, that is to say,
when it came to marriage. Up to the time of the attempts
at marriage I grew up more or less like a businessman
who lives from day to day, it is true with worries and
forebodings, but still without keeping any proper books.
He makes a few small profits, which as a consequence of

their rarity he keeps on pampering and exaggerating in his imagination, and for the rest only daily losses. Everything is entered, but never balanced. Now comes the necessity of drawing a balance, that is, the attempt at marriage. And with the large sums that have to be taken into account here it is as though there had never been even the smallest profit, everything one single great liability. And now marry without going mad!

That is what my life with you has been like up to now, and these are the prospects inherent in it for the future.

Surveying my reasoned account of the fear I have of you, you might answer: "You maintain I make things easy for myself by explaining my relation to you simply as being your fault, but I believe that in spite of outward effort you make things at least no more difficult for yourself, only much more profitable. First, you too repudiate all guilt and responsibility in this; then, our method is the same. But whereas I then attribute the sole guilt to you as frankly as I mean it, you are at the same time trying to be 'too clever' and 'too affectionate' and to acquit me too of all blame. Of course, in this latter you only apparently succeed (and you do not want more, either), and what appears between the lines, in spite of all the 'turns of phrase' about character and nature and antagonism and helplessness, is that actually I have been the aggressor, while everything you were up to was only self-defense. And so for the time being, by means of your insincerity, you would have achieved enough, for you have proved three things, first that you are blameless, secondly that I am to blame, and thirdly that out of sheer magnanimity you are prepared not only to forgive me but, what is both more and less, also to prove, into the bargain, and to try to believe it yourself, that I, contrary to the truth, am also blameless. One would think that would be enough for you now, but it is still not enough.

What you are, in fact, set upon is living entirely on me. I admit that we fight with each other, but there are two kinds of fighting. There is chivalrous fighting, in which the forces of independent opponents are measured against each other, each one remaining alone, losing alone, winning alone. And there is the fighting of vermin, which not only sting but at the same time suck the blood too to sustain their own life. That is, after all, what the professional soldier really is, and that is what you are. You are unfit for life; but in order to be able to settle down in it comfortably, without worries and without self-reproaches, you prove that I have deprived you of all your fitness for life and put it into my pockets. What does it matter to you now if you are unfit for life, now it is my responsibility, but you calmly lie down and let yourself be hauled along through life, physically and mentally, by me. For example: when you recently wanted to marry, you wanted—and this you do, after all, admit in this letter—at the same time not to marry, but in order not to have to exert yourself you wanted me to help you with this not-marrying, through my forbidding you to make this marriage on account of the 'disgrace' that this union would bring upon my name. Now as it happened I did not dream of doing this. First of all, here as elsewhere, I never wanted 'to be an obstacle to your happiness,' and secondly, I never want to have to hear such a reproach from my own child. But was my having overcome my own feelings, and so leaving your way open to this marriage, any help to me? Not in the slightest. My dislike of the marriage would not have prevented it; on the contrary, it would in itself have been for you an added stimulus to marry the girl, for the 'attempt at escape,' as you put it, would thus, of course, have become complete. And my consent to the marriage did not prevent your reproaching me, for you do prove that I am, in any case, to blame for your not marrying. At bottom, however, here and in everything else, you have to my way of thinking proved nothing but that all my reproaches were justified and that among them there was indeed one especially justified reproach missing, namely the charge of insincerity, obsequiousness, and parasitism. If I am not very much mistaken, you are preying upon me even now with this letter as such."

To this I answer that first of all this whole rejoinder, which can also be partly turned against you, does not originate in you but, in fact, in me. Not even your mistrust of yours, after all, is as great as my self-mistrust, which you inculcated in me. A certain justification for the rejoinder, which in itself also contributes new material to the characterization of our relationship, I do not deny. Naturally things cannot in reality fit together in the way the evidence does in my letter; life is more than a Chinese puzzle. But with the correction that results from this rejoinder—a correction that I neither can nor will elaborate in detail—in my opinion something has yet been achieved that is so closely approximate to the truth that it may be able to reassure us both a little and make our living and our dying easier.

FRANZ

FRAGMENTS FROM NOTEBOOKS
AND LOOSE PAGES

Fragments from Notebooks and
Loose Pages

AMONG MY SCHOOLMATES I was stupid, but still, not the stupidest. And even if the latter contention was not infrequently made by some of my teachers to my parents and to myself, it was done only in the same state of delusion as that of many people who believe they have conquered half the world if they have dared to make such an extreme judgment.

But it was generally and really believed that I was stupid; there was good evidence for it, which was easily passed on if, for instance, enlightenment was required for a stranger who had begun by getting not at all a bad impression of me and did not hide this from others.

This was something I was often annoyed about and which I often wept over too. And at that time those were the only moments when I felt insecure in the tumult of the present and desperate about the future, theoretically insecure, I must say, theoretically desperate, for once it was a matter of some work I was instantly sure of myself and confident, that is to say, I was almost like the actor who comes rushing out of the wings, pulls up short a long way from the center of the stage, his hands, let us say, pressed to his brow, while the passion, which he will need an instant later, has grown so big within him that he cannot hide it, although he stands there with his eyes screwed up, biting his lips. The present, half-vanished insecurity heightens the passion that is about to break forth, and the passion reinforces the insecurity. Irresistibly a sense of insecurity begins forming all over again, enclosing both and us too.

That is why it vexes me to make the acquaintance of strangers. I used to be uneasy even at being looked at by so many people down their noses, as one gazes through a telescope out of a little house and across the lake, or even into the mountains and the empty air. Then ridiculous assertions would be made, statistical lies, geographical errors, heresies, as outrageous as they were senseless, or sound political views, respectable opinions on topical events, laudable ideas that surprised him to whom they occurred almost as much as they surprised the rest of the company, and everything was proved all over again by the way people looked at me, by the way someone grasped the edge of the table, or jumped up from a chair. No sooner had they begun doing that sort of thing than they stopped again, looking at one long and hard, for the upper part of their bodies would of its own accord bend forwards or backwards out of its normal position. Some of them went so far as to forget their clothes (bending their legs sharply at the knees, in order to support themselves only on their toes, or crumpled their jackets, clutching them to their chests), others did not, many held on, by their fingers, to a pince-nez, a fan, a pencil, a lorgnon, or a cigarette, and most of them, even if they had a firm skin, grew hot in the face. Their gaze slid off us, as a raised arm drops.

I was admitted into my natural condition, it was open to me to wait and then to listen, or to go away and go to bed, a thing I always looked forward to, for I was often sleepy, being timid as I was. It was like a long interval between dances, when only a few people make up their minds to leave, and most stand or sit about here and there, while the musicians, to whom nobody gives a thought, are having refreshments somewhere before they continue playing. Only it was not so peaceful, and not everyone necessarily noticed that there was an interval at all, since there were many balls going on in the ballroom at the same time. Could I go away if someone became excited, even if only faintly, through me, through a memory, through much else, and fundamentally, through everything together, by me, and now undertook to hasten through this excitement from its very beginning, borne up perhaps by a story or a patriotic idea? His eyes, indeed his whole body, with the clothes upon it, became gloomy, and words broke. . . . [Lacuna of approximately 2 pages.]

Through all this I still sensed my fear, this fear of a man to whom I had held out my hand quite without emotion, whose name I did not know, if one of his friends had not perhaps ejaculated his christian name, and whom I had, after all, been sitting opposite here for hours on end, in perfect calm, only a little exhausted, as young people are, by even the rare glances this grown-up person cast upon me.

I had—let us assume this—I had several times allowed my gaze to meet his and, unoccupied as I was, since after all nobody reckoned with me, I had tried to look into his kindly blue eyes for rather longer, whether it was . . . that in this way one positively quits the company. And if this had not been successful, that proved every bit as little as the fact of the attempt. All right then, I did not succeed in doing so, I showed this incapacity from the very beginning and even later could not conceal it even for a moment, just as unskilled skaters' feet try to go in different directions and both feet try to get away from the ice. If there were an otherwise sound. . . . [lacuna] and a shrewd person, who was, however, neither in front of nor beside nor behind these hundred, where he might have been noticed at once, easily, but in the very midst of the others, so that he could be seen only from some very elevated position, and even then one saw him only as he disappeared. That was how I was thought of by my father, who was a very much respected and successful man particularly in the world of politics in my native country. I heard this dictum by chance when, being perhaps seventeen years old, I was reading a book about Red Indians in the room with the door open. The words struck me at the time, I registered them mentally, but they did not make the slightest impression on me. As it usually happens that general criticisms, of themselves, have no effect on young people. For, either still completely quiescent and self-contained, or at any rate still constantly flung back upon themselves, they feel their own nature as something loud and strong as the music of a military band. To them, however, the general judgment seems to be based on unknown assumptions, on unknown intentions, as a result of which it is inaccessible from all sides; it assumes the character of a person strolling about on the island in the pool, where there are neither boats nor bridges, hearing the music, but not being heard.

By this I do not mean, however, to attack young people's logic. . . .

Every human being is peculiarly, and by virtue of his peculiarity, called to play his part in the world, but he must have a taste for his own peculiarity. So far as my experience went, both in school and at home the aim was to erase all trace of peculiarity. In this way they made the work of education easier, but also made life easier for the child, although, it is true, he first had to go through the pain caused him by discipline. A boy, for instance, who is in the middle of reading an exciting story in the evening will never be made to realize, merely by an argument bearing solely upon himself, that he must stop reading and go to bed. When in such a case I was told such things as that it was getting late, I was damaging my eyesight, I would be sleepy in the morning and find it hard to get up, and that the rubbishy, silly story wasn't worth it, although I could not specifically refute this, it was actually only because it all did not even come anywhere near beginning to be worth thinking about. For everything was endless, or streamed away into vagueness in such a way that it could be equated with what was endless, time was endless, and so it could not be too late, my eyesight was endless, and so I could not damage it, even the night was endless, and so there was no need to worry about getting up in the morning, and where books were concerned I did not discriminate according to whether they were silly or sensible, but according to whether they were thrilling or not, and this one was thrilling. All this I could not express in these terms, but the result was that I made a nuisance of myself with my pleas to be allowed to go on reading, or I resolved to go on reading even without permission. That was my peculiarity. It was suppressed by means of turning off the gas and leaving me without a light. By way of explanation they said: Everyone is going to bed, so you must go to bed too. I saw this and could not but believe it, although it made no sense to me. Nobody wants to carry out so many reforms as children do. Apart from this, in a certain respect, praiseworthy oppression, still, here, as almost everywhere, there remained a sting that no amount of reference to generality could make even a little blunter. The fact was, I continued to believe that precisely on that evening nobody in the world wanted to read as much as I wanted to. This was something that, for the time being, no reference to general principles

could refute, all the more since I saw that nobody believed in my irresistible desire to read. Only gradually,
and much later, perhaps indeed when the desire was di-
minishing, did I begin to have a sort of belief that many
people enjoyed reading as much as I did and yet managed
to control themselves. At that time, however, all I felt
was the injustice done to me, I went to bed sadly, and
here were the beginnings of that hatred which has in a
certain respect determined my life in relation to my family and hence my life as a whole. Although being forbidden to read is only an example, it is a characteristic one,
for this prohibition went deep. My peculiarity was not
accorded any recognition; but since I felt it, I could not
fail—being very sensitive on this score and always suspicious—to recognize adverse criticism in this attitude to
me. But if even this openly displayed peculiarity met
with condemnation, how much worse then must those
peculiarities be which I kept concealed for the reason
that I myself recognized something a little wrong in
them. For instance, I had been reading in the evening
even though I had not yet learnt my lesson for school
the next day. That was perhaps in itself, as a dereliction
of duty, something very bad indeed, but I was not concerned with an absolute judgment, all I cared about was
a comparative judgment of the matter. Yet on such a
judgment this negligence was doubtless no worse than
the sheer fact of reading for a long time, particularly
since it was very much restricted, in its consequences, by
my great dread of school and authority generally. What
I now and then neglected through reading I easily made
good in the morning, or at school, having a very good
memory at that time. But the main thing was that the
condemnation with which my peculiarity of reading for
a long time had met I myself now extended, by my own
means, to the peculiarity, which I kept concealed, of

dereliction of duty, and in this way I came to the most depressing of results. It was as though someone were touched, simply by way of warning, with a fagot that was not intended to hurt him, and he then undid the bundle, drew the individual tips of the twigs into himself and began pricking and scratching his inner being according to a plan of his own, while the other person's hand was still calmly holding the other end of the fagot. But even though I did not punish myself very severely in such cases at that time, there is no doubt that I did not profit from my peculiarities with that true gain which finally manifests itself as permanent self-confidence. On the contrary, the consequences of displaying any peculiarity were such that I either hated the person who suppressed it or recognized the peculiarity as nonexistent, two consequences that were also capable of being associated in a hypocritical manner. But if I kept a peculiarity concealed, the result was that I hated myself or my destiny, regarding myself as wicked or damned. The relationship between these two groups of peculiarities underwent a very marked external change in the course of the years. The peculiarities I displayed increased more and more the nearer I came to the life to which I had access. Yet this brought me no liberation, it did not cause the quantity of what was concealed to diminish, and on more refined inspection it appeared that it would never be possible to confess everything. Even the seemingly complete admissions made in the earlier period later turned out to have their root in my inner being. But even if that had not been so—with the loosening up of the entire psychic organization that I had undergone, without decisive interruptions, even *one* concealed peculiarity was enough to upset me so much that, however much I adapted myself in other respects, I still could not hold on anywhere at all. But there was still worse. Even if I had not kept any secret to myself, but had flung everything so far away from me that I would have stood there in complete purity, in the next instant I would again have been choked with the old muddle and confusion, for in my opinion the secret would not have been completely recognized and assessed, and in consequence would have been restored to me by the generality and imposed upon me anew. That was no delusion, but only a particular form of the recognition that, at any rate among living human beings, nobody can rid himself of himself. If, for instance, someone confesses to a friend that he is miserly, for that moment and in relation to his friend, that is to say, in relation to a person whose judgment is authoritative, he has seemingly freed himself from his miserliness. For this moment it is, besides, of no account how his friend takes the confession, that is, whether he denies that there is such miserliness in him or gives advice about how to get rid of miserliness, or even defends miserliness. It might not even be decisive if the friend were to break off the friendship as a result of this confession. What is decisive, however, is that one has confided one's secret to the generality, perhaps not as a penitent sinner, but at least as an honest one, and in this way hopes to have reconquered one's good and—this is the most important element of all—free childhood. But one has only made the conquest of a brief folly and much subsequent bitterness. For somewhere on the table between the miserly person and his friend there lies the money that the miserly one must take and put in his pocket and towards which he is moving his hand ever faster. When his hand is about half-way the confession is, of course, already less effective, but it is still having a liberating influence on him; beyond that point it no longer does so, on the contrary, all it does then is to cast a glaring light upon the forward-moving hand. Effective confessions are possible only be-

fore or after the act. The act does not permit anything
else to exist alongside itself; for the hand scooping up the
money there can be no liberation by means of words or
penitence. Either the act, that is, the hand, must be destroyed, or in avarice one must . . . oneself. . . .

Emphasis of peculiarity—desperation.

I have never discovered what the rule is.

May the Evil that is in a half-circle about you, as the
brow is over the eye, radiate downwards into inactivity.
While you sleep, may it watch over you without being
permitted to advance even in the very slightest.

The thought that judges works its way self-tormentingly
upwards through the pain, heightening the torment and
helping not at all. As if the fundamental architectural
problem were raised for the first time in the house that is
burning down to the ground.

I was able to die, but not to bear pain; through my attempts to avoid it I increased it markedly; I could yield
submissively to death, but not to suffering, I lacked
scope for spiritual movement, just as, when everything
is packed, the tightened straps are agonizingly tightened
yet again and again and the departure is not taken. The
worst thing: pain that does not kill.

Striving to level out. I said: "It's not so bad, they're
all like this," but in this way only made it worse.

Necessity of the errors in my upbringing, I could not
tell how it should be done differently.

Leveling out is right, perhaps, but such a far-reaching
objectivization cancels out any chance of life.

There are many waiting. A throng reaching further than the eye can see, extending away into darkness. What does it want? It is evidently definite demands that it is making. I shall listen to these demands and then answer. But I shall not go out onto the balcony; nor could I do so even if I wanted to. In the winter the door to the balcony is locked and the key is not available. But neither shall I go to the window. I do not want to see anyone, I am not going to let myself be confused by the sight of anything. At my desk—that is my place. My head in my hands—that is my attitude.

There is a door in my apartment to which I hitherto paid no attention. It is in the bedroom, in the party wall between this and the next house. I have never thought about it, indeed I did not even know about it. And yet it can be seen quite plainly, though the lower part of it is concealed by the beds; it extends to a great height, almost not a door but a gate. Yesterday it was opened. I happened to be in the dining-room, which is separated from the bedroom by yet another room. I had come home very late for lunch, there was nobody left in the house, only the maid was busy in the kitchen. Then the noise began in the bedroom. I instantly hurried into the room and saw the door being slowly opened, the beds being pushed aside by some gigantic force. I called out: "Who is that? What is wanted? Careful! Look out!" and expected to see a gang of brutal and violent men bursting in, but it was only a slim young man who slipped in, as soon as there was a crack just wide enough for him to get through, and hailed me joyfully.

Nothing of the sort, nothing of the sort.

When I come along the water at night, from the direction of the tower, now, every night, the tough, dark

water is slowly moved, almost like a body, under the light
of the lantern. As if I were slowly passing the lantern over
a sleeper and, simply from the effect of the light, he were
to stretch and turn over without awakening.

At midnight I am always to be met with by the river,
either I am on night duty and am on my way to the
prison, or I was on day duty and am going home. Use was
once made of this opportunity. Tired after work, and at
the same time in a state of almost unendurable, suffocating rage with B., a colleague of mine, on account of an incident in the course of duty, something of which there
will be more to say later, there I was, on my way home.
Turning round once, looking up at the little window
with the light burning high up in the prison tower, where
B. was now sitting at supper, the bottle of rum between
his legs, it seemed to me I saw him sitting quite close in
front of me for an instant, all high and mighty, indeed I
even smelt him, but then I spat on the ground and walked
on.

A shout arises out of the river.

My sister is keeping a secret from me. She has a little
calendar, which indeed she received partly only through
me, for I have known the gentleman who gave each of us
one of these calendars much longer than she has known
him, and it was for my sake that he brought the calendars. Well then, she has written or entered the secret
into this calendar, but the calendar itself she has locked
into her pen case, and the key. . . .

Someone pulled at my clothes, but I shook him off.

Restless.

Once at a spiritualist séance a new spirit announced its presence, and the following conversation took place:

THE SPIRIT: Excuse me.

THE SPOKESMAN: Who are you?

SPIRIT: Excuse me.

SPOKESMAN: What do you want?

SPIRIT: To go away.

SPOKESMAN: But you've only just come.

SPIRIT: It's a mistake.

SPOKESMAN: No, it isn't a mistake. You've come and you'll stay.

SPIRIT: I've just begun to feel ill.

SPOKESMAN: Badly?

SPIRIT: Badly.

SPOKESMAN: Physically?

SPIRIT: Physically?

SPOKESMAN: You answer with questions. That will not do. We have ways of punishing you, so I advise you to answer, for then we shall soon dismiss you.

SPIRIT: Soon?

SPOKESMAN: Soon.

SPIRIT: In one minute?

SPOKESMAN: Don't go on in this miserable way. We shall dismiss you when it seems to us. . . .

Evening was falling, in the country, I was sitting in my room under the gables, with the window shut, and was watching the cowherd, who was standing on the mown field, his pipe in his mouth, his stick rammed into the ground, seemingly taking no notice of the cattle, which were grazing near and far, though indeed in profound tranquillity. There came a knock at the window, I started up out of my doze, pulled myself together, and said aloud: "It's nothing, the wind is shaking the window." When there came another knock, I said: "I know it's only the

wind." But at the third knock a voice asked to be let in.
"But it's only the wind," I said, took the lamp from the
cupboard, lit it, and drew the curtains over the window.
Then the whole window began to tremble, and there began a humble, wordless lamentation.

For what are you lamenting, desolate soul? Why do
you flutter round the house of life? Why don't you gaze
into the distance, which belongs to you, instead of here
struggling for what is alien to you? Better the live pigeon
on the roof than the half dead, agonizing, and resistant
sparrow in the hand.

Wrap your cloak, O sublime dream, around the child.

There came two soldiers and seized me. I struggled, but
they held firm. They conducted me to their master, an
officer. How gay his uniform was! I said: "What do you
want with me, I am a civilian." The officer smiled and
said: "You are a civilian, but that does not prevent us
from seizing you. The army has power over everything."

Evaluation in the variety trade.
It is very difficult to make even approximately correct evaluations and even for a very short time in the
sphere of variety productions. The best experts, with a
long life of experience behind them, have failed to do so.
A good example of this is the Iron King's career.

Belvedere slope.
How he walked, the man with the cloak falling in long
folds, a briefcase in his hand, bareheaded, the gold wire of
his spectacles over his ears, on that sunny morning of the
first of May, on the quiet path amid the greenery.

Karpfengasse (Carp Street).

The ugly young man in the evening, alone, a crude, vigorous, resistant nature.

The two old gentlemen near the Rudolfinum, tranquil, long-winded, dignified narrative, the women following.

August 20, 1916. How this madness suddenly leaps upon me again, it always happens when there is some gain in confidence in my state of health, such as happened the day before yesterday after the visit to Dr. Mühlstein.

Remaining pure	Being married
bachelor	Married man
I remain pure	Pure?
I hold all my vigor together	You remain outside the context, become a fool, fly to all four quarters of the sky, but you don't get any further, I draw all strength that is at all available to me out of the bloodstream of human life.
Only responsible for myself	All the more infatuated for (with) you.
	(Grillparzer, Flaubert)
No worry. Concentration on work.	Since I grow in vigor, I carry more.
	Here is nevertheless a certain truth.

The huntsman's cabin was not far from the lumbermen's cabins. The lumbermen, twelve in number, were

living there in order now, when there was good snow, to
prepare the trunks that were dragged down into the
valley by the sledges in the daytime. It was hard work,
but it would not have been too much for the workers if
they had only been given enough beer. But they had only
a medium-sized barrel, and it was meant to be shared out
over a week, which was an impossible task. They always
complained about this to the huntsman when he came
over to see them in the evening. "You men have a hard
time," the huntsman said in agreement, and they poured
out their woes to him. The huntsman's cabin is in a lonely
place in the forest on the mountain. There he spends the
winter with his five dogs. But how long the winter lasts
in this country! One might almost say it lasts a lifetime.

The huntsman is of good cheer, he lacks for nothing of
any importance, he does not complain of hardship, indeed
he considers himself all too well equipped. "If a huntsman
came to me," he thinks, "and saw the way my cabin is
fitted up and my stores, it would, I dare say, be the end
of huntsmanship. But isn't it the end even so? There are
no huntsmen." He goes to the corner where the dogs are
asleep on blankets and covered with blankets. The way
gun dogs sleep. They are not asleep, they are only waiting
to go hunting, and that looks like sleep.

Peter is betrothed to a rich girl in the next village. One
time, in the evening, he went to see her, there was a
great deal to discuss, for the wedding was to take place
in a week. The discussion turned out well. Everything
had been arranged to his satisfaction; at peace with the
world, his pipe in his mouth, he was walking home about
ten o'clock, paying no attention at all to the road,
which he knew so well. And so it happened that as he
was in a little wood, without at first quite knowing
why, he started back in fear. Then he found himself look-

ing into two golden, gleaming eyes, and a voice said: "I am the wolf." "What do you want?" Peter asked, standing there, in his agitation, with outspread arms, his pipe in one hand, his stick in the other. "You," said the wolf, "all day long I've been looking for something to eat." "Please, wolf," Peter said, "spare me for today, in a week I am to be married, let me live long enough to have my wedding." "I don't like that," the wolf said. "What advantage will it be to me to wait?" "Then take both of us, me and my wife," Peter said. "And what is to be done till the wedding?" the wolf asked. "After all, I can't go on starving till then. I'm feeling sick and faint with hunger even now, and if I don't get something to eat very soon, I shall eat you up now even against my will." "Please," Peter said, "come with me, I live not far away, I shall feed you on rabbits over the week." "I must also get at least one sheep." "All right, one sheep." "And five hens."

Outside the city gate there was no one, and under the archway of the gate there was no one. One walked on clean-swept gravel towards it; through a square hole in the wall one could see into the gatekeeper's cell, but the cell was empty. Although that was very strange, for me it was very advantageous, for I had no identity papers, in fact the whole of my property was one garment made of leather and the stick in my hand.

Today I had a talk with the captain in his cabin. I complained about my fellow passengers. It couldn't be called a passenger ship, I said, at least half the people on board were the worst sort of riffraff. My wife, I said, hardly dared to leave the cabin, but even inside, with the door locked, she did not feel safe, and I had to stay with her.

A race began in the woods. The whole place was full of animals. I tried to establish order.

It was now evening. The cool breath of it was wafted towards us, refreshing in its coolness, fatiguing in its lateness. We sat down on a bench by the old tower. "It was all in vain," you said, "but it is over now, it is time to draw breath, and this is the right place."

She is asleep. I do not wake her. Why don't you wake her? It is my misfortune and my happiness. I am unhappy at not being able to wake her, at not being able to set foot upon the burning threshold of her house, at not knowing the road to her house, at not knowing the direction in which the road runs, at always moving further and further away from her, strengthless as the leaf on the autumn wind, moving always further away from its tree, and then too: I was never on that tree, I am a leaf on the autumn wind, but from no tree.—I am happy at not being able to wake her. What would I do if she were to arise, if she were to get up from her bed, if I were to get up from my bed, the lion from its lair, and my roaring were to burst upon my terrified ears?

I asked a traveler whom I met on the highway whether the seven deserts lay beyond the seven seas, and beyond them the seven mountains, on the seventh mountain the castle and. . . .

Climbing. *Senait*.[39] It was a squirrel, it was a squirrel, a wild cracker of nuts, leaper, climber, and her bushy tail was famous in the woods. This squirrel, this squirrel was always traveling, always searching, it could not say anything about it, not because it lacked the power of speech, but because it had simply no time at all.

Scenes from the Defense of a Courtyard

It was a plain wooden fence, without a single gap, not quite so high as a man. Behind it there were standing three men, whose faces could be seen rising up over the top of the fence, the one in the middle was the tallest, the other two, more than a head smaller, were thrusting up against him, it was a unified group. These three men were defending the fence, or rather the whole courtyard that was surrounded by it. There were other men there too, but they were not directly taking part in the defense. One was seated at a little table in the middle of the courtyard; as it was warm, he had taken off his uniform jacket and hung it over the arm of the chair. He had before him some little slips of paper on which he was writing, in a large, broad handwriting that used up a great deal of ink. Now and then he glanced at a little drawing that was fixed to the table, farther away from him, with drawing pins, it was a plan of the courtyard, and this man, who was the commandant, was writing out instructions for the defense on the basis of this plan. Sometimes he would half rise from his chair in order to glance over at the three defenders and across the fence into the open country. Whatever he saw there was also turned to account in his instructions. He worked rapidly, as was necessary in this critical situation. A little barefoot boy who was playing in the sand nearby would deliver the slips whenever they were ready and the commandant called him. Yet the commandant, first of all, always had to clean his hands, which were dirty with damp sand, on his uniform jacket before giving him the slips. The sand was damp from the water that splashed out of a big tub in which a man was washing army underclothes, he had also hung a line from one board in the fence to a weak lime tree that stood forlornly in the courtyard. On this line there was washing hung up to dry, and now when the commandant suddenly pulled his shirt, which was by now sticking to his sweating body, over his head and took it off, with a curt exclamation throwing it to the man at the tub, the latter took a dry shirt from the line and handed it to his superior officer. Not far from the tub, in the shade of the tree, a young man sat on a chair, rocking to and fro, taking no notice of all that was going on round about, gazing absently into the sky and at the flight of the birds, and practicing military signals on a hunting horn. That was as necessary as anything else, but sometimes it was too much for the commandant, and then, without looking up from his work, he could make a sign to the bugler to stop, and when that had no effect he would turn round and shout at him, then for a little while there was silence, until softly, only as an experiment, the bugler began to blow again and, as he was carried away by his enthusiasm, gradually let the volume increase to what it had been before. The curtain had been let down over the gable window, which was not in itself striking, for all the windows on this side of the house had been covered up in some way in order to prevent the enemy from seeing in and attacking them, but crouching behind this curtain was the smallholder's daughter, gazing down on the bugler, and the notes of the hunting horn delighted her so much that sometimes she could only bear to listen to them with closed eyes, her hand on her heart. Really she ought to have been supervising the maids in the large parlor at the back of the house, where they were preparing lint, but she had not been able to make herself stay there any longer, where the notes had come only faintly, never quite satisfyingly, always merely awakening yearning, and she had stolen through the deserted, gloomy house and made her way up here. Sometimes, too,

she bent a little further forward to see whether her father
was still sitting at his work or had perhaps gone to in-
spect the servants, for then she could not have stayed
there any longer either. No, he was still sitting on the
stone step outside the front door, puffing away at his
pipe and cutting shingles; there was a big pile of finished
and half-finished shingles, as also of raw material, lying
around him. The house and the roof, alas, would suffer
in the battle, and one had to prepare for the future.
Through the window next to the front door, which was
boarded up except for one small chink, there came smoke
and noise; that was the kitchen, and the smallholder's wife
was just finishing the midday meal together with the
army cooks. The big stove was not big enough for the
job, and so two cauldrons had been set up as well, but
even they were not sufficient, as now became apparent:
the commandant attached great importance to the
men's having plentiful food. So it had been decided to
help things out with a third cauldron, but since it was
slightly damaged, a man on the garden side of the house
was busy soldering it. He had originally tried to do it in
front of the house, but the commandant had not been
able to endure the hammering and the cauldron had had
to be rolled away. The cooks were very impatient and
kept on sending someone to see whether the cauldron was
ready yet, but it was always not yet ready, there was
no prospect of having it for that day's lunch, and they
would have to go short. First the commandant was
served. In spite of his having several times insisted, very
gravely, that nothing was to be cooked specially for him,
the housewife had not been able to bring herself to give
him the ordinary food provided for the soldiers, nor would
she entrust anyone else with the job of waiting on him,
but put on a beautiful white apron, set a plate full of
strong chicken soup on a silver tray, and carried it out to

the commandant in the courtyard, since it could not be
expected that he would interrupt his work and go into
the house to eat. He rose at once, very politely, when he
saw the mistress of the house herself approaching, but
had to tell her that he had no time to eat, neither time
nor peace of mind; the mistress of the house pleaded, her
head inclined, tears in her upturned eyes, and in this way
contrived to get the commandant, still standing, smilingly
to take one spoonful of soup from the plate still in the
housewife's hands. With this, however, the extreme of
politeness had been given its due, the commandant bowed
and sat down to his work, probably scarcely noticing
that the housewife stood beside him for a little while
longer and then, sighing, went back to the kitchen. But
it was quite a different matter with the men's appetite.
Scarcely had the bearded face of a cook appeared in the
opening at the kitchen window, and scarcely had he blown
a signal on a whistle to indicate that the midday meal was
going to be distributed, things everywhere became lively,
livelier than was to the commandant's liking. From a
wooden shed two soldiers pulled out a handcart, which
was actually nothing but a large barrel, into which
soup was poured in a broad stream out of the kitchen
window for those of the men who were not allowed
to leave their posts and to whom the food was therefore taken. First of all the little cart went to the defenders at the fence, which would doubtless have been
done anyway, even if the commandant had not made
a sign with his finger, for these three were at the moment
those most exposed to the enemy, and this was something
that even the plain man could appreciate, perhaps more
than the officer, but the commandant was mainly concerned with getting the distribution done quickly and
making as short as possible the tiresome interruption of
the work on the defenses which was caused by the meal,

for he could see how even these three otherwise model soldiers were now taking more interest in the courtyard and the little cart than in the area in front of the fence. They were quickly served from the little cart, which was then pulled farther along the fence, for about every twenty paces there were three soldiers squatting down by the fence, ready, whenever it should be necessary, to stand up like those first three and show themselves to the enemy. In the meantime the reserve came out of the house in a long file and went to the kitchen window, each man with his bowl in his hand. The bugler also approached, and to the regret of the smallholder's daughter, who was now returning to join the maids, took his bowl out from under his chair and put his hunting horn there in place of it. And a rustling began in the top of the lime tree, for there a soldier sat who had to observe the enemy through a telescope and who, in spite of his important, indispensable work, had at least for the time being been forgotten by the man in charge of the soup cart. This made him all the more resentful since some soldiers, idle, good-for-nothing reservists, had sat down round the tree trunk in order to enjoy their meal better, and the steam and smell of the soup rose up to him. He did not dare to shout, but he lashed about in the branches and several times pushed the telescope down through the foliage in order to draw attention to himself. All in vain. He was one of those to be served from the little cart and he had to wait until it came to him at the end of the round. Now this, of course, took a long time, for the courtyard was a big one, there were something like forty groups of three men to be served, and when the little cart, drawn by the now exhausted soldiers, at last came to the lime tree, there was only a little left in the barrel and especially the pieces of meat were few and far between. Although the lookout gladly accepted what was left, when it was handed up to him in a bowl by means of a hooked pole, he then slid a short way down the trunk and—this was his thanks—furiously kicked the face of the soldier who had served him. This man, understandably beside himself with excitement, had himself hoisted up by his comrade and was up in the tree in a twinkling; and now, invisible from below, there began a fight that manifested itself only in the swaying of the branches, muffled groans, and flying of leaves, until in the end the telescope fell to the ground and everything at once became quiet. The commandant, being very much taken up with other matters—there seemed to be various things going on out there in the field—had fortunately noticed nothing; quietly the soldier climbed down; in the friendliest way the telescope was handed up, and all was well again; there had not even been anything worth mentioning lost of the soup, for before beginning the fight the lookout had carefully fastened the bowl to the topmost twigs where it was safe from the wind.

I now again write what I have heard, what was confided to me. But it was not confided to me as a secret that I must keep, all that was directly confided to me was that voice that spoke, the rest is no secret, on the contrary, it is mere chaff; and what flies in all directions when work is being done is what can be communicated and what implores the boon of being communicated, for it has not the strength to remain lonely and quiet when whatever gave it life has slipped away forever.

Now the following is what I heard.

Somewhere in Southern Bohemia, on a wooded hill, about two kilometers away from a river that would easily be seen from here if the forest did not block the view, there stands a little house. There an old man dwells. The outer dignity of old age has not been granted him. He is small, one leg is straight, but the other is markedly bowed. His face is sparsely but entirely overgrown with a beard that is white, yellow, and in places probably even blackish, his nose is squashed flat and rests on the slightly pouting upper lip, which almost closes it. His eyelids droop low over his little. . . .

Those savages of whom it is recounted that they have no other longing than to die, or rather, they no longer have even that longing, but death has a longing for them, and they abandon themselves to it, or rather, they do not even abandon themselves, but fall into the sand on the shore and never get up again—those savages I much resemble, and indeed I have fellow clansmen round about, but the confusion in these territories is so great, the tumult is like waves rising and falling by day and by night, and the brothers let themselves be borne upon it. That is what, in this country, is called "giving someone a leg up"; everyone here is always ready with such help. Anyone who might collapse without cause and remain lying on the ground is dreaded as though he were the Devil, it is because of the example, it is because of the stench of truth that would emanate from him. Granted, nothing would happen; one, ten, a whole nation might very well remain lying on the ground and nothing would happen; life in all its might would go on just the same; the attics are still chockablock with flags that were never unfurled; this barrel organ can play only one tune, but it is eternity in person that turns the handle. And yet the fear! How people do always carry their own enemy, however powerless he is, within themselves. On his account, on account of this powerless enemy, they are. . . .

"Well, how about it?" the gentleman said, gazing at me smilingly and straightening his tie. I was able to meet his gaze, but then of my own accord turned a little to one side and stared into the surface of the table, straining my eyes ever harder, as though there were a cavity opening up and growing deeper, drawing the gaze down into it. At the same time I said: "You want to test me, but you have not hitherto provided any evidence of your right to do so." Now he laughed aloud: "My right is my existence, my right is my sitting here, my right is my question, my right is the fact that you understand me." "Very well," I said, "let us assume it is so." "So then I shall test you," he said, "only I would beg you to shift your chair back a little; you leave me too little room here. I should also like you not to look downwards, but into my eyes. Perhaps it is more important to me to see you than to hear your answers." When I had done as he required, he began: "Who am I?" "My examiner," I said. "True enough," he said. "What else am I?" "My uncle," I said. "Your uncle," he exclaimed, "what a crazy answer." "My uncle," I said emphatically. "Nothing better."

I was standing on the balcony outside my room. It was very high, I counted the rows of windows, it was on the sixth floor. Down below there were lawns, it was a little square enclosed on three sides, I dare say it was in Paris. I went into the room, leaving the door open; although it seemed to be only March or April, the day was warm. In one corner there was a small, very light desk, I could have lifted it with one hand and swung it round in the air. But now I sat down at it, ink and pen were there ready, I was going to write a picture postcard. I put my hand in my pocket, uncertain whether I had a postcard, then I heard a bird and, when I glanced round, noticed a bird cage on the balcony, against the wall of the house. I went straight out again, I had to rise on my toes in order to see the bird, it was a canary. This possession delighted me. I pushed in farther a scrap of lettuce that was squeezed between the wires and let the bird peck at it. Then I turned to the square again, rubbed my hands and bent over the balcony railing for an instant. In an attic on the far side of the square someone seemed to be watching me through opera glasses, probably because I was a new tenant; this was petty, but perhaps it was an invalid for whom the view from his window was the whole world. Since I had, after all, found a postcard in my pockets, I went into the room in order to write; on the card, however, there was not a view of Paris but only a picture, it was called "Evening Prayer," there was a quiet lake, in the foreground a very few rushes, in the middle a boat, and in it a young mother with her child on her arm.

We were playing "Blocking the Road"; we fixed a certain distance on the path, which one had to defend and one had to pass. The attacker was blindfolded, but the defender had no means of preventing him from passing except that in the instant of passing over he touched the attacker on the arm; if he did it earlier or later he had lost. Anyone who has never played this game will think that the track is made very difficult and the defense very easy, but the fact is the very opposite, or at any rate it is more frequent to find people good at attacking. There was only one of us who could defend, and it must be confessed that he was practically infallible at it. I often watched him, but that was hardly any fun, for without running about much he was always in the right place, nor indeed could he have run very well, for he had a slight limp, but apart from that he was not very lively anyway; others, when they were defending, were always crouching, on the alert, peering wildly around; his dim blue eyes then had as calm a gaze as ever. What such a defense meant was something one realized only when one was the attacker.

I love her and cannot talk to her, I lie in wait for her in order not to meet her.

I loved a girl who loved me, but I had to leave her. Why?

I don't know. It was as though she were surrounded by a circle of armed men holding their lances pointing outwards. Whenever I approached I ran into the points, was wounded, and had to fall back. I suffered much.

Was the girl not to blame for this?

I think not, or rather, I know she was not. The previous simile was not complete, I was also surrounded by armed men, holding their lances pointing inwards, that is to say, against me. When I pushed towards the girl I was first of all caught on the lances of my own armed men and even at this stage could not get any farther. Perhaps I never got as far as the girl's armed men, and if I did get there, then already bleeding from my lances and unconscious. Did the girl remain alone?

No, another got through to her, easily and without hindrance. I, exhausted by my efforts, looked on as indifferently as though I were the air through which their faces moved, meeting in the first kiss.

Two men were sitting at a crudely made table. A flickering oil lamp hung over them. It was far from my native country.

"I am in your hands," I said.

"No," said the one man, who held himself very straight and clutched his long beard with his left hand. "You are free and that is why you are lost."

"So I can go?" I asked.

"Yes," the man said and whispered something to his neighbor, while he stroked his hand in a friendly way. The other was an old man; true, he too was still upright and very vigorous. . . .

It was an extremely low, small door that opened into the garden, not much higher than the wire hoops that one sticks in the ground for croquet. For this reason we could not go into the garden side by side, but one had to crawl in after the other. Marie made it yet more difficult for me by beginning to pull me by the feet just as my shoulders were almost wedged tight in the little doorway. Finally I did manage to do it after all, and Marie, astonishingly enough, also got through, though I must say it was only with my help. We had been so busy with all this that we had not noticed at all the host who had evidently been standing nearby from the very beginning and watching us. That was very embarrassing for Marie, for her thin dress had become quite crumpled from crawling. . . . But nothing could be done about that now, for the host was already welcoming us, shaking me cordially by the hand, patting Marie on the cheek. I could not remember how old Marie was, probably she was a small child, since she was greeted in this way, but I am sure I was not much older. A servant ran past, almost flying along; in his raised right hand—the left he held against his hip—he carried a large dish, filled to the brim, the contents of which I could not recognize in the brief moment I had; all I saw was long ribbons or leaves or seaweed hanging down all round the dish and fluttering in the air behind the servant. I drew Marie's attention to the servant, she nodded to me, but was not so surprised as I had expected. Yet actually it was her first entry into smart society; her origins, after all, were of a small lower-middle-class kind; it could not but be for her as for a person who has always lived in the plain and suddenly the curtain before him tears apart and he is standing at the foothills of a mountain range. But even in her behavior to the host she showed nothing of the kind, quietly listening to his words of greeting and at the same time slowly drawing on the gray gloves that I had bought her the day before. At bottom it really pleased me very much that she passed the text in this way. The host then invited us to follow him; we walked in the direction in which the servant had disappeared; the host was always one pace ahead of us, but always half-turning back to us.

Who is it? Who walks under the trees on the quay? Who is quite lost? Who is past saving? Over whose grave does the grass grow? Dreams have arrived, upstream they came, they climb up the wall of the quay on a ladder. One stops, makes conversation with them, they know a number of things, but what they don't know is where they come from. It is quite warm this autumn evening. They turn towards the river and raise their arms. Why do you raise your arms instead of clasping us in them?

You are always hanging around the door, enter vigorously. Inside there are two men sitting at a crudely made table, waiting for you. They exchange views about the causes of your delay. They are knightly men in medieval dress.

He is very strong and is becoming ever stronger. He seems to live at other people's expense. One could imagine him as an animal in the wilderness, going down to the water to drink in the evening, alone, slowly, thoughtfully, with loping tread. His eyes are dim, one doesn't often get the impression that he really sees the person on whom he turns his eyes. But it is then not absent-minded-ness, preoccupation, that prevents him from doing so, but a certain dullness. They are the dim drinker's eyes of a man who is obviously not a drinker. Perhaps some wrong is done him, perhaps that has made him so taciturn, per-haps wrong has always been done him. It seems to be that sort of undefined wrong which young people so often feel weighing on themselves, but which they finally throw off while they still have the strength to do so; he, of course, is old by now, though perhaps not so old as he looks with his heavy, unwieldy build, the almost obtru-sive, downward furrows in his face, and the paunch over which the waistcoat bulges.

It was the first cut of the spade, it was the first cut of the spade, there the earth lay in crumbs, crumbled before my feet, there a bell rang, there a door trem-bled. . . .

It was a political meeting. How odd it is that most meetings are held in the square of the stables, on the bank of the river, over the roaring of which the human voice can scarcely make itself heard. In spite of the fact that I was sitting on the balustrade of the quay near the speakers—they were speaking from up on a bare, rec-tangular pedestal made of ashlars—I understood but little. Of course, I knew in advance what it was about, and everybody knew. Besides, everyone was agreed, I have never seen more complete unanimity, and I too was com-pletely of their opinion, the case was all too clear, how often it had been talked over and still it was as clear as on the first day; both the unanimity and the clarity were suffocating, one's power of thought was paralyzed by so much unanimity and clarity, sometimes one would have wished to hear only the river and nothing else.

If today I try to render an account to myself of my friend and my relationship to him, that is one of those many, usually hopeless fresh starts that one makes over and over again in the course of a long life, starts like the run for a jump of which one does not know whether it leads forward into life or away out of life. But it is hopeless, and so it is without danger.

I have known him since my early youth. He is about seven or eight years older than I, but this difference in age, great as it is in itself, did not make itself very noticeable, today indeed I even seem to be the elder, he himself does not regard it otherwise. Yet this is something that only developed slowly. I remember our first meeting. I had just come out of school, it was a dark winter afternoon, I was a little boy in the bottom class at elementary school. When I came round a corner of the street, I saw him; he was sturdily built, thickset, and had a face that was at once bony and yet fleshy, he looked quite different from what he looks like today, since his childhood his physical appearance has changed so greatly that he is unrecognizable as the same person.

He was pulling a shy little puppy along on a lead. I stopped and watched, not out of spitefulness, only from curiosity. I was very inquisitive, everything fascinated me. But he resented my looking on and said: "Mind your own business, stupid."

Many people say he is lazy, others say he is afraid of work. These latter judge him rightly. He is afraid of work. When he begins a job, he feels like someone who has to leave his home country—not a home country that he loves, but still, a place that is accustomed, familiar, and safe. Where will the work lead him? He feels himself dragged away, like a shy little puppy being tugged along a city street. It is not the noise that upsets him; if he could hear the noise and differentiate between the various elements in it, it would certainly occupy him entirely from the very first instant, but he does not hear it, while he is being pulled along through the midst of the noise he hears nothing, only a special quietness, which seems to be turned on him from all sides, listening to him, a quietness that is trying to feed on him, and this is all he hears. This is uncanny, this is at once exciting and boring, this is scarcely to be borne. How far will he get? Two, three paces, no further. And then, wearied by the journey, he will do nothing but stagger back to his home country, that gray, unloved home. This makes every sort of work hateful to him.

He has locked himself up in the second room, I have knocked and rattled at the door, but he has kept quiet. He is angry with me, he won't have anything to do with me. But then I am angry too, and I don't bother about him any more. I push the table up to the window and now I shall write the letter concerning which we have quarreled. How petty all this squabbling is, how closely and constrictedly we must live together for such a bone of contention ever to become noticeable at all, no third person would be able to understand it, it can't be conveyed to anyone else, everyone would think we were completely at one with each other, and indeed we are at one.

It is a letter to a girl, I am writing to say goodbye to her, as is sensible and right. There is nothing that could be more sensible and right. One can recognize this particularly clearly by imagining a letter to the opposite effect; such a letter would be terrible and impossible. Perhaps I shall write such a letter and read it aloud outside the locked door, and then he will have to admit that I am right. True, he does admit that I am right anyway,

he too considers the letter of farewell to be right, but
he is angry with me. This is what he is like most of the
time, he is hostile to me, but helpless; when he gazes at
me out of his quiet eyes, it is as though he were demanding
that I should give him grounds for his hostility. "Fellow," I think, "what do you want of me? And what
have you made of me already!" And I get up, just as I
always do, go to the door, and knock again. No answer,
but it turns out that the door is open this time, yet the
room is empty, he has gone out, this is the real punishment with which he likes to punish me, after such a quarrel he goes out, does not come back for days, for nights.

I was a visitor among the dead. It was a large, clean
vault, there were some coffins there, but there was still
plenty of room, two coffins were open, inside they
looked like rumpled beds from which people had just got
up. A desk stood a little to one side, so that I did not
notice it at once; a man of powerful build sat at it. In
his right hand he held a pen, it was as though he had been
writing and had only just stopped, his left hand was toying with a shining watch chain on his waistcoat and his
head was bent low towards it. A charwoman was sweeping the place, but there was nothing to be swept up.
    In some sort of curiosity I tugged at her kerchief,
which entirely shaded her face. Only now did I see her. It
was a Jewish girl I had once known. She had a voluptuous
white face and narrow dark eyes. When she now looked
at me, laughing, out of the rags in which she was
wrapped, which made an old woman of her, I said: "I suppose you are play-acting here?" "Yes," she said, "a little.
How well you know your way about!" But then she
pointed to the man at the desk and said: "Now go and
greet him, over there, he's the master here. So long as
you haven't greeted him, I'm actually not supposed to

talk to you." "And who is he?" I asked, lowering my voice. "A French nobleman," she said, "de Poitin is his name." "And how does he come to be here?" I asked. "That I don't know," she said, "it's all a great jumble here. We're waiting for someone to come and clear things up. Is it you?" "No, no," I said. "That's very sensible," she said, "but now go to the master."

So I went over to him and bowed. As he did not raise his head—I could see only his tousled white hair—I said "Good evening," but he still did not stir, a little cat ran round the edge of the table, it had jumped right out of the gentleman's lap and vanished back there again, perhaps he was not looking at his watch chain at all, but down under the table. I wanted to explain now how I had come here, but my girl acquaintance tugged at my jacket from behind, whispering: "That'll be enough."

I was very well satisfied with this, I turned to her and the two of us walked arm in arm farther into the vault. The broom disturbed me. "Throw the broom away," I said. "No, please," she said, "let me keep it. You do see that sweeping this place out can't be any trouble to me, don't you? Well then, but I do get certain benefits from it, which I don't want to give up. By the way, are you going to stay here?" she asked, changing the conversation. "For your sake I should like to stay here," I said slowly. We were now walking close together, pressing up against each other like a couple of lovers. "Stay, oh, stay," she said, "how I have longed for you. It isn't so bad here as you may fear. And what do the two of us care what it is like all around us?" We walked for a little while in silence, we had unlinked our arms and now had them round each other's shoulders, holding each other tight. We were walking on the main path, to right and to left there were coffins, the vault was very large, or at least very long. Although it was dark, it was not completely so, it was a kind of twilight, but it became a little lighter still in the place where we were and in a little circle around us. Suddenly she said: "Come, I'll show you my coffin." That surprised me. "But you're not dead," I said. "No," she said, "but to tell you the truth: I don't know my way about here, and that's why I'm so glad you've come. In a short time you will understand everything, even now you probably see everything more clearly than I do. Anyway: I *have* a coffin." We turned to the right into a side path, again between two rows of coffins. In its general layout the place reminded me of a large wine cellar that I had once seen. On this path we also crossed a small, fast-flowing stream, scarcely three feet wide. Then we soon reached the girl's coffin. It was lined with beautiful lace-edged pillows. The girl sat down in it and tried to entice me down, less with her beckoning forefinger than with her gaze. "You dear girl," I said, pulled her kerchief away and laid my hand on her soft thick hair. "But I can't stay with you yet. There is someone here in the vault whom I have to talk to. Won't you help me to look for him?" "You have to talk to him? But no obligations are binding here," she said. "But I don't belong here." "Do you believe you'll ever get away from here now?" "Certainly," I said. "That's all the more reason for not wasting your time," she said. Then she groped under the pillow and pulled out a shift. "This is my shroud," she said and handed it up to me, "but I don't wear it."

I went into the house, shutting after me the little postern door in the big barred gate. Through the long vaulted hall the gaze fell on a well-tended little garden in a courtyard with a flower-entwined pedestal in the center. On my left was a glass-fronted compartment in which the porter sat, resting his forehead on his hand, bowed over a newspaper. Pasted on one pane of glass in front, slightly concealing the porter, was a large picture cut out of an illustrated magazine, I went closer, it was evidently a little Italian town, the largest part of the picture was taken up by a wild mountain stream with an immense waterfall, the houses of the little town were on its banks, pressed close up to the edge of the picture.

I said good day to the porter and, pointing to the picture, said: "A beautiful picture, I know Italy, what is the name of the little town?" "I don't know," he said, "the children from the second floor pasted it up here in my absence in order to annoy me. What is it you wish?" he then asked.

We had a little quarrel. Karl maintained he had definitely given the little opera glasses back to me; although he had had a great longing for them and had for a long time turned them this way and that in his hands, had perhaps even borrowed them for a few days, he had definitely given them back. I, for my part, tried to make him remember the situation, named the street in which it had happened, the inn opposite the monastery that we had just been passing, described how he had at first wanted to buy the opera glasses from me, how he had then offered me various things in exchange, and how then, after all, he had come out with the request that I should make him a present of the glasses. "Why did you take them away from me?" I said lamentingly. "My dear Josef," he said, "look, that was all over and done with long ago. True, I'm convinced I gave you back the opera glasses, but even if you did make me a present of them, why are you tormenting yourself about it now, and me as well? Do you happen to feel the need of the glasses at the moment? Or has the loss had a great effect on your life?" "Neither one thing nor the other," I said, "only I am sorry that you took the glasses away from me at that time. I had been given them as a present, I was very pleased with them, they were slightly gilded, do you remember? And they were so small that one could carry them round in one's pocket all the time. And yet the lenses were powerful, one saw better through them than through many large glasses."

I was standing near the door of the large hall; far away from me, against the wall at the back, was the king's couch; a fragile, young, extremely nimble nun was busying herself about him, straightening the pillows, pushing up a little table with refreshments on it, from which she selected some for the king, and all the time she had under her arm the book out of which she had been reading aloud. The king was not ill, otherwise, of course, he would have retired into his bedroom, but he did have to remain lying down, some agitation or other had cast him down and upset his sensitive heart. A servant had just announced the king's daughter and her husband, and that was why the nun had interrupted her reading aloud. It was very embarrassing for me to find that now I was perhaps going to overhear private conversations, but since here, after all, I was, and nobody ordered me to go away, perhaps intentionally, perhaps because, unimportant as I was, I had been forgotten, I considered myself under an obligation to remain there and only withdrew to the far end of the hall. A little door in the wall quite close to the king was opened and, stooping, one after the other, the princess and the prince came out of it; in the room then the princess linked her arm with the prince's, and thus united they approached the king.

"I cannot go on doing it," the prince said. "You solemnly took the obligation upon yourself before the wedding," the king said. "I know," the prince said, "nevertheless I cannot do it any longer." "Why not?" the king asked. "I cannot breathe the air outside," the prince said, "I cannot endure the noise there, I am not immune from dizziness, I am overcome by nausea at that height, in short, I cannot do it any more." "The last point has some sense, though, of course, a bad one," the king said, "all the rest is empty talk. And what does my daughter say?" "The prince is right," the princess said, "a life such as he is leading now is a burden, a burden to him and to me. Perhaps you have not a quite clear picture of it, Father. You see, he has to be perpetually in readiness, in reality it happens about once a week, but he has to be in readiness all the time. It may happen at the most absurd times of day. For instance, we may be sitting at a meal, with a small company, one forgets all sorrow for a while and is innocently gay. Then the watchman bursts in and calls the prince, now of course everything has to be done with the greatest of speed, he has to take off his clothes, squeeze himself into the tight regulation uniform, repulsively bright, almost theatrical, almost dishonorable as it is, and now, poor fellow, out he hurries. The company is dispersed, the guests take themselves off, fortunately, for when the prince comes back he is incapable of speaking, incapable of enduring anyone with him but me, sometimes he can only just get in through the door and the next instant he collapses on the carpet. Father, is it possible to go on living like this?" "Women's talk," the king said, "nor does it surprise me, but that you, prince, have let women's talk—and this now becomes clear to me —persuade you to refuse to serve me—that distresses me."

That is the area, fifteen feet long, fifteen five wide, that is to say, not large, but still, it is one's own ground. Who has arranged it thus? That is not exactly known. Once there came a strange man, he had a great deal of leather harness over his garment, belts, shoulder straps, halters, and pouches. From one pouch he drew forth a note pad, made a note, and then asked: "Where is the petitioner?" The petitioner stepped forward. Half the occupants of the house were gathered around him in a great semicircle; at that time I was a little boy of about five, I saw and heard everything, but if I had not had it all precisely recounted to me much later I would know hardly anything about it. It was too unintelligible for me to have been very attentive at that time; nevertheless other people's accounts of it afterwards was much more vivid from my having my own vague memory of it. So I positively see before me to this day how the strange man sharply surveyed the petitioner. "It is no small matter that you demand," the stranger said, "are you aware of that?"

It was especially in the lower forms at the grammar school that I did very badly. For my mother, that silent, proud woman who always exerted the utmost strength to keep her restless nature under control, this was torment. She had great notions of my abilities, but out of shame she did not admit this to anyone and therefore she had no confidante with whom she could have talked it over and gained reassurance; all the more tormenting to her were my failures, which could not be hushed up, of course, but as it were confessed themselves, producing a repellent crowd of confidants, namely the whole teaching staff and all my schoolmates. I became a sad puzzle to her. She did not punish me, she did not scold; she could see for herself that I at least did not completely fail to try hard; at first she thought there was a conspiracy against me among the masters, and she never quite lost this belief, but my transfer to another grammar school and my doing almost even worse there did somewhat shake her belief in the hostility of the masters, though I must say it did not shake her belief in me. And I went on living my untrammeled childish life followed by her sadly questioning glances. I had no ambition; if I did not fail in the examinations I was content, and if I had failed, a threat that did not cease all through the school year. . . .

There is building continually going on in the town. Not in order to extend the town, which is adequate for our needs, its limits have remained unaltered for a long time; indeed there seems to be a certain reluctance to enlarge it, we prefer to restrict ourselves, building over squares and gardens, putting more stories on old buildings; but actually these new constructions are not the main part of the continual building operations, either. The work is concerned rather, if it may provisionally be so expressed, with safeguarding what already exists. Not that people built worse in earlier times than they do nowadays and that the old deficiencies have to be continually made good now. Although there is a certain carelessness—it is difficult to distinguish how much of it is frivolity and how much is lethargic restlessness—that always prevails among us, in the matter of building it actually has least chance of manifesting itself. We are, after all, in the land of quarries, we build almost exclusively in stone, there is even marble available, and whatever people may neglect in the work of building is made up for by the permanence and solidity of the material. Besides, with regard to building there is no difference between the ages, the same rules of architecture have been valid from the earliest times, and if, owing to the national character, they are not always strictly observed, this too is quite traditional and is as true of the most ancient buildings as of the most modern. Thus, for instance, on

the Roman Hill outside the town there is a ruin, the remains of a country villa that is said to have been built
there more than a thousand years ago. It is said that it
was built for a rich merchant who had grown old and
solitary; they say it began to decay as soon as he died, for
we are not the sort of people among whom one is likely to
find someone who would want to live so far outside the
town. So the building was abandoned to decay through
the centuries, and the work of decay is certainly more
thorough than that of the builders. If today, on a quiet
Sunday—and one is scarcely likely to be bothered with
meeting anyone on the way through the scrub on the
hillside—one strolls up there and contemplates the remains, one finds only a few foundation walls, the highest
of them no longer as high as a man; then somewhere
there, embedded in the hard ground, crushed by the
pressure of passing time, there are little smashed columns, and, overgrown with old, almost black ivy, the
worthless torso of a statue gleams forth, guessed at
rather than recognized for what it is. That is about all,
except for two or three little piles of rubble, positively
grown together and hard as rock, and here and there on
the hillside a few stones sunk into the ground. Everything else has been cleared away. And yet even today
one can recognize from the layout—and tradition confirms this—that it was a spacious, palatial edifice, and
where one can scarcely squeeze through the low-growing
but dense briars, scratching oneself on thorns till the
blood runs, there was once a beautiful park, with trees
and terraces, which is said to have survived long after the
house itself was gone.

I had utterly lost my way in a forest. It was incomprehensible how I had lost my way, for only a short time
earlier I had been walking, true, not on a track, but

near the track, which had always been visible to me. But now I had lost my way, the track had vanished, and all attempts to find it again had failed. I sat down on a tree stump and wanted to think my situation over, but my mind was distracted, I kept on thinking of something other than what was most important, dreaming away over my worries. Then I suddenly noticed the heavily laden bilberry bushes round about; I picked some of the berries and ate.

I was staying in the Edthofer Hotel, Albian or Cyprian Edthofer, or something like that, I can't remember the whole name now, and I dare say I wouldn't find it again now, either, in spite of the fact that it was a very big hotel, one, incidentally, that was extremely well furnished and well run. Nor do I remember now why, in spite of the fact that I stayed there for scarcely more than a week, I changed my room almost every day; as a result I often did not know the number of my room and, when I came home during the day or in the evening, would have to ask the chambermaid what was the number of the room I happened to be occupying. However, all the rooms that came in question for me on one floor and, what was more, in one corridor. There were not many rooms, so I did not have to wander round. Was perhaps only this one corridor meant for hotel purposes and the rest of the building for apartments to let, or something else? I don't remember, perhaps I did not know even then, I did not bother about it. But that was nevertheless improbable, the large building bore the word "hotel" and the name of the proprietor in large, widely spaced metal lettering, which did not shine very brightly, indeed was of a rather dim reddish color. Or was it only the proprietor's name that was there, without the word "hotel"? That is possible, and that would, of course, then explain a good deal. But to this very day, from my vague memory of it, I would on the whole be inclined to decide that it said "hotel." The place was much frequented by officers. I was, naturally, usually in town all day, having all sorts of things to do and so much to see, and hence I had not much time to observe what went on in the hotel, but I did often see officers there. True, there was a barracks next door, or rather, it was not really next door, the connection between the hotel and the barracks must have been somehow different, it was both looser and closer. Today that is not easy to describe, indeed even in those times it would not have been easy, I did not seriously exert myself to establish this, in spite of the fact that the lack of clarity sometimes caused me difficulties. That is to say, sometimes, when I came home in an absent-minded state, distracted by the din of the metropolis, I could not immediately find the entrance to the hotel. It is true that the entrance to the hotel seems to have been very small, indeed it is possible—in spite of the fact that this would really have been strange—that there was no proper entrance at all, and that if one wanted to get into the hotel one had to go through the door of the restaurant. Well, and so it may have been like that; but I could not always find even the door of the restaurant. Sometimes, when I thought I was standing in front of the hotel, I was in fact standing in front of the barracks, although it was quite a different square, quieter and clearner than that in front of the hotel, quite deathly quiet and elegantly clean, and yet it was such that the two could be mistaken one for the other. One had first to go round a corner and only then was one in front of the hotel. But it seems to me now that at times, though, admittedly, only at times, it was different, that even from that quiet square—say with the help of an officer who was going the same way—one could find the hotel door at once, and by this I mean not any other, second door, but simply the same door that formed the entrance to the restaurant, a narrow, extremely high door, the inside of it concealed by a beautiful white curtain adorned with ribbons. Yet the hotel and the barracks were two fundamentally different buildings; the hotel built in the usual hotel style, though certainly with some trace of the tenement about it; the barracks, on the other hand, a small Romanesque castle, low-built but spacious. The barracks explained the continual presence of officers; on the other hand, I never saw any other ranks. How I discovered that what seemed to be a castle was a barracks I do not remember now; but, as I have previously mentioned, I frequently had cause to think about it, when, irritably searching for the door to the hotel, I wandered about the quiet square. But once I was upstairs in the corridor, I was safe. I felt very much at home there and was happy to have found such a pleasant spot in the large, strange city.

Why do you reproach me, wicked man? I don't know you, this is the first time I have seen you. You say you gave me money to fetch sweets for you from that shop? No, that is certainly a mistake, you did not give me any money. Aren't you confusing me with my friend Fritz? Not that he looks like me, of course. I am not at all afraid of your telling the teacher at school. He knows me and will not believe the accusation. And my parents are sure not to restore the money to you—why should they, anyway? After all, I did not get anything from you. But if they should want to give you anything, I shall ask them not to do so. And now let me go. No, you mustn't follow me, if you do I'll tell a policeman. Ah, so you don't want to go to the policeman. . . .

Away from here, simply away from here! You need not tell me where you are taking me. Where is your hand, ah I grope for it in vain in the dark. If I only had got hold of your hand, I think then you wouldn't spurn me. Do you hear me? Are you in the room at all? Perhaps you are not here at all. And what should lure you here, into the ice and mist of the North, where no one would expect to find human beings at all? You are not here. You have shunned these realms. But I stand or fall with the decision whether you are here or not.

That people who limp think they are nearer to flying than people who walk. And indeed there is a good deal to be said in favor of their opinion. Is there anything that there is nothing to be said in favor of?

Poor deserted house! Were you ever inhabited? Tradition says nothing of it. No one inquires into your history. How cold it is in you. How the wind blows through your gray entrance hall, nothing preventing it. If you were ever inhabited, then the traces of it have been removed with incomprehensible thoroughness.

I have buried my reason in my hand; my head I carry straight, cheerfully, but my hand dangles wearily, my reason draws it earthwards. Just look at the small, calloused, five-fingered hand, streaked with blood vessels, much wrinkled and with protruding veins, how good that I was able to rescue my reason by putting it into this unassuming container. What is particularly excellent is that I have two hands. As in a children's game I ask: In which hand am I holding my reason? No one can guess, for by clasping my hands I can in a twinkling convey my reason from one hand to the other.

Yet again, yet again, exiled far away, exiled far away. Mountains, wilderness, a wide country it is that has to be traveled through.

I am a gun dog. Karo is my name. I hate everyone and everything. I hate my master, the huntsman, hate him in spite of the fact that, dubious person that he is, he is simply not worth it.

Dreaming, the flower hung upon the tall stem. Evening twilight gathered around it.

There was no balcony, only instead of the window a door, here on the third floor, opening straight into the open air. It was now open, on this spring evening. A student was walking up and down the room, learning; whenever he came to the window-door he would scrape his sole over the threshold outside, as one fleetingly licks at something sweet that one has put aside for some later occasion.

The manifold things that revolve, in manifold ways, in the manifoldness of the one moment in which we live. And still the moment is not over, just see!

Far, far away world history takes its course, the world history of your soul.

Nevermore, nevermore will you return to the cities, nevermore will the great bell peal over your head.

Tell me, how are you getting on in that world?
The question as to how I am getting on I shall answer, contrary to custom, frankly and objectively. I am get-

ting on well, for, contrary to the way it was in previous times, I now move in a large society, with manifold connections, and am capable of satisfying the crowd that throngs to consort with me, by means of my knowledge, by means of my answers, at any rate they keep on coming as enthusiastically as they came the first time. And I for my part repeat: Come, you will always find me ready. Admittedly, I do not always understand what you want to know, but that is probably not at all necessary. My existence is important to you and so is, therefore, what I say, since that lends emphasis to my existence. I dare say I do not err in these assumptions, and therefore I let myself go in giving my answers, and hope in this way to please you.

In your answer there is a certain amount that is not clear to us. Will you explain it to us point for point?

You timid ones, you polite ones, you children, ask, just ask!

You speak of a large society in which you move—what society is this?

Why, you—you yourselves. The little company of you all round the table, and in another town another, and so on in many towns.

So that is what you call: moving in society. But wait: you are, as you say, our old schoolfellow Kriehuber. Are you, or are you not?

Certainly, I am.

Very well then, as our old friend you visit us and we, being unable to forget your loss, draw you to us by means of our longing and make your path easier for you. Is it so?

Yes, yes, of course.

But you have, after all, led a retired life; we don't believe that you have ever had any friends or acquaintances outside our town at all. So whom do you visit in those towns and who calls you thither?

We lay alongside. I stepped ashore, it was a small harbor, a small place. Some people were lounging about on the marble pavement, I addressed them, but did not understand their speech. It was doubtless an Italian dialect. I called the mate over, he understands Italian, but he too could not understand the people here, he denied that it was Italian. Yet all this did not seriously worry me, my sole desire was to rest a little, for once, from the endless voyage, and for that purpose this place was as good as another. I went on board again in order to give the necessary instructions. Everyone was to remain on board for the time being, only the mate was to go with me, I had been out of the habit of being on solid ground for all too long and, together with my yearning for it, there was also a certain dread of it in me, which I could not shake off, and that was why the mate was to accompany me. I also went down once again to the women's cabin. There my wife was suckling our youngest child, I stroked her gentle, flushed face and informed her of my intentions. She smiled up at me in agreement.

[40] Much as I should like to avoid it, I must nevertheless continue with the annoyance that I began causing you with my intrusive disagreement—it was not a disagreement, I don't get so far as that, it was only resistance —about Schweiger; I must take the matter up once more. That conversation that evening was too much of a weight on my mind afterwards, all night long, and if it had not been that the next morning I was slightly distracted by an unexpected chance happening, I am sure I would have had to write to you at once.

The tormenting thing about that evening for me—I saw the conversation becoming imminent from the very beginning, from the moment of opening the door; that was bad, it almost spoilt the whole pleasure of your visit

for me—lay for me in the fact that I really did not say
anything against Schweiger, only chatted a little and,
for the rest, was only stubborn, while what you said in
defense of certain details was excellent, for me unexpected, and completely to the point. But it could not
convince me; on this score I am completely impervi-
ous to conviction, even long before I come to the details.
If, however, I nevertheless cannot make my objections
comprehensible, even to myself, this is explained by my
weakness, which manifests itself not only in thinking and
talking, but also in attacks of a sort of waking swoon.
I try, for instance, to say something against the play, and
when I have got no further than the second sentence,
the swoon begins pushing its way in with questions such
as: "What are you talking about? What is it all about?
What *is* literature? Where does it come from? What use
is it? What questionable things! Add to this questionableness the further questionableness of what you say,
and what you get is a monstrosity. How did you get on
to these sublime and futile paths? Does all this deserve
serious questioning and a serious answer? Perhaps, but not
yours, all that is a matter for higher authorities. Withdraw quickly!" And this "Withdraw" means that I [am]
instantly in complete darkness, out of which I cannot be
led by the aid of my opponent in argument or by anyone's
aid. You don't seem to have any experience whatsoever
of this sort of thing in your own case, in spite of the fact
that you wrote *Spiegelmensch*. Certainly, even in a state
of repose I grant that the interpolator is right, you
were sometimes too stern with him, he is nothing but
the wind, after all, playing with airy existences, length-
ening the life of falling leaves.

But, in spite of everything, I do want to make yet
another attempt not to remain quite mute, but to say
briefly in what way Schweiger affronts me.

Above all I feel there is obscurantism in the fact that
Schweiger is degraded to an individual case, though it is
admittedly a tragic one: the immediacy of the whole play
forbids that. If one tells a fairy tale, then everyone knows
that one has confided oneself to alien powers and excluded the jurisdiction of our own day. Here, however,
one does not know that. The play sets out to arouse the
feeling that only today, on this very evening, and more
by chance than by deliberate purpose, is the case of
Schweiger being treated, that these happenings might
equally well have taken place, for instance, in a neighboring house that is quite differently constituted. But
this assertion on the part of the play is something I cannot believe; if in the other houses in this Catholic Austrian town that is constructed all round Schweiger, there
is anyone living at all, then it is Schweiger who lives in
each house, and no one else. The other characters in the
play also have no home of their own, they all live with
Schweiger and are his attendant circumstances. Schweiger
and Anna do not even have a chance to refer to a happily
married couple anywhere, that is honestly admitted by
implication; perhaps what they want is generally impossible, nobody in the play would have the strength to refute
that; where the many children on the Danube steamer
come from is an enigma. And so why the little town, why
Austria, why the little individual case submerged in all
that?

But you make it even more individual and isolated. It is
as though you simply could not make it individual and
isolated enough. You invent the story of the child-
murder. This I consider a debasing of the sufferings of a
whole generation. Anyone who has no more to say about
this than psychoanalysis has ought not to meddle with
the subject. There is no pleasure in spending any time on
psychoanalysis, and I keep as aloof from it as I possibly

can, but it does at least exist every bit as much as this
generation does. Jewry has always produced its sufferings
and joys almost simultaneously with the appropriate
Rashi[41] commentary, and thus it is in this case too.

Recently I was in M. I had to have a conference with K.
It was not actually an urgent matter, it could probably
have been dealt with quite well by letter, even though
more slowly—but since it was not urgent, that would
not have done any harm—but it chanced that I had some
free time and suddenly felt like clearing the whole thing
up with K. without much fuss; besides, I had never been
in M., which I had once been told was a place worth
seeing; and so I decided on the spur of the moment that
I would go there, unfortunately—there was no time to do
so—without first making sure that I could find K. in M.
at this time.

In fact K. was not at home. He almost never leaves the
little town; he is, as was recounted to me in M., a person
of particularly settled habits, who likes to stay where
he is, but for this very reason various matters had piled
up, which had to be discussed on the spot, even though
they took him no farther than the environs of M. Journeys of this kind that had been overdue for a long time
now simply had to be undertaken without more ado, and
so on the very day before my arrival K., in a frightful
temper, as his sister half sighingly, half smilingly, told me,
had at last had to call for his carriage. In order to save
himself from having to make any more journeys for as
far ahead as he could see, K. had resolved that this time
he would tackle everything that had to be dealt with in
one big round-journey, even if it should last a few days,
and that he would leave out nothing, indeed that he
would, in so far as he could, even anticipate journeys that
were only a threat for the future; and he was also fitting

into this trip attendance at the wedding of a niece. When K. would be back could not be said with certainty; true, it was only a matter of a trip through the farther environs of M., but his program was very full and besides, when he had once set out on a trip, K. was incalculable. It might be that after the first or second night spent in the villages he would be so utterly disgusted with traveling that he would break the journey short, let business go, no matter how urgent it was, and return today or tomorrow. It was, however, equally possible that once he got going he would enjoy the change and that the many friends and relatives round about would even compel him to prolong his trip beyond its unavoidably necessary duration, for at bottom he is a talkative, cheerful man who loves to have a large company around him and who enjoys the regard he has earned by honest work; and in some villages especially he will be welcomed in a positively magnificent fashion; besides, he has the capacity, as a result of his personal influence and of his knowledge of human nature, to achieve things—by means of a few words and in a twinkling—that no exertions could accomplish from a distance. When he notices that he is having such successes, he naturally feels a desire for still more of them; and this too may prolong his journey.

[Second version:] In fact K. was not at home. I discovered this at his shop and then went straight to his house in order to inquire further into the matter. By provincial standards it was an amazingly large apartment, at least the first room was, into which I was shown by the maid. It was almost a hall, yet at the same time cosy, but not by any means overloaded with knick-knacks; all the furniture was arranged with enough space between, clearly and distinctly, all of it forming a unified whole, and there was also a certain respectable sense of family tradition expressed in it. And the next room, of which one got a glimpse through the twinkling panes of a glass door, seemed to be similar. There too K.'s sister soon appeared, quickly, almost breathlessly, tying on a pleated white afternoon apron before she came into the room where I was. She was a small, frail, elderly spinster, very polite and obliging, who much regretted the unfortunate coincidence of my arrival and her brother's departure—he had left the very previous day—considered this and that, did not know what to do, would naturally have informed her brother at once, but this was impossible, since he was making a little business trip, intended to last only a few days, round the villages of the farther environs, was working out his route according to the needs of the moment, and for this reason had not been able to give any definite address. It was, furthermore, as she added smilingly, in keeping with her brother's character that from time to time he enjoyed driving around the country for a little while, out of everybody's reach.

On the handle of Balzac's walking-stick: I break all obstacles.

On mine: All obstacles break me.

The common factor is "all."

Confession, unreserved confession, door bursting open, in the interior of the house the world appears, its dim reflection having hitherto been outside.

The fact that there are fear, grief, and desolation in the world is something he understands, but even this only in so far as they are vague, general feelings that only graze the surface. All the other feelings he denies, saying that what we call by that name is only an appearance, fairy tale, a mirror-image of experience and of the memory.

How can it be otherwise, he asks, since, after all, real

events can never be caught up with by our feelings, far less overtaken by them? We experience them only before and after the real event, which flits by at an elementally incomprehensible speed; they are dreamlike fictions, relevant only to ourselves. We live in the stillness of midnight and experience the sunrise and the sunset by turning ourselves towards the East or the West.

Little vitality, mistaken upbringing, bachelordom, produce the sceptic, but not necessarily: in order to save his scepticism many a sceptic marries, at least ideally, and becomes a believer.

In the darkness of the street under the trees on an autumn evening. I ask you; you do not answer me. Oh, if you would answer me, if your lips would open, the dead eye become animated and the word meant for me ring out!

The door opened and what entered the room, fat and succulent, its sides voluptuously swelling, footless, pushing itself along on its entire underside, was the green dragon. Formal salutation. I asked him to come right in. He regretted that he could not do that, as he was too long. This meant that the door had to remain open, which was rather awkward. He smiled, half in embarrassment, half cunningly, and began:

"Drawn hither by your longing, I come pushing myself along from afar off, and underneath am now scraped quite sore. But I am glad to do it. Gladly do I come, gladly do I offer myself to you."

With a hard blow the light streamed down, tearing the fabric, which fled in all directions, mercilessly burning through the remains of the empty, wide-meshed net. Down below, like an animal caught by surprise, the earth twitched and stood still. Mutually spellbound, they gazed at each other. And the third, shunning this encounter, dodged to one side.

Once I broke my leg, it was the most wonderful experience I ever had in my life.

A half-moon, a sycamore leaf, two rockets.

All I inherited from my father was a small silver *spice box*.

When the fight began and five heavily armed men leapt from the scarp onto the road, I slipped under the carriage and got away, running through the pitch-darkness towards the forest.

It was after supper, we were still sitting round the table, father leaning far back in his armchair, one of the largest pieces of furniture I have ever seen, dozing and smoking his pipe; mother was mending a pair of my trousers, bending over her work and taking no notice of anything else, and uncle was sitting straight up, stretching towards the lamp, his *pince-nez* on his nose, reading the newspaper. I had been playing in the street all the afternoon, only after supper had remembered that I still had some work to do for school, and now had taken my book and copybook, but I was too tired, had only just enough strength left to ornament the cover of the copybook with wavy lines, sinking down farther and farther until I was almost lying on top of the copybook, forgotten by the grownups. Then Edgar, the boy from next door, who actually should have been in bed long before that, came soundlessly through the door, through which, oddly enough, I saw, not our dark entrance hall, but the clear moon over the expanse of wintry landscape. "Come on, Hans," Edgar said, "the teacher's waiting outside, in the sledge. How do you think you're going to do your homework without the teacher's help?" "Oh, will he help me?" I asked. "Yes," Edgar said, "this is the best chance, he's just on his way to Kummerau, he's in the best of moods because of the sledge trip, he won't refuse anything one asks." "Will my parents let me?" "But surely you're not going to ask them. . . ."

It was very difficult homework and I was afraid I wouldn't be able to manage it. Besides, it was now late in the evening, I had set about it much too late, having wasted the long afternoon playing in the street, and having concealed my omission from father, who might have been able to help me, and now everyone was asleep and I was sitting alone with my copybook in front of me. "Who will help me now?" I said in a low voice. "I will," said a strange man, slowly sitting down on a chair on my right, at the narrow end of the table, just as in the office of my father, the advocate, the clients crouch down at the side of his desk, and he propped his elbows on the table and stretched his legs out, a long way into the room. I had been about to start up, but it was just my teacher; he would, of course, be the best person to solve the problem that he himself had set. And in confirmation of this view of mine he nodded, amiably or haughtily or ironically, I could not decipher which. But was it really my teacher? Outwardly and as a whole he seemed to be completely so, but if one went on to consider details, it became doubtful. For instance, he had my teacher's beard, that stiff, thin, protruding, grizzled black, long beard, which grew over his upper lip and his whole chin. But if one leaned forward towards him, one got the impression that there was something artificial about it, and the suspicion was not diminished by the fact that the alleged teacher bent forward towards me, put his hand under his beard and held it out to me for inspection.

The master of dreams, great Isachar, was sitting before the mirror, his back pressed hard against the glass, his head bent a long way back and sunk deep into the mirror. Then there came Hermana, the master of twilight, and plunged into Isachar's breast until he disappeared right into it.

In our little town we are entirely among ourselves, it lies lost amid the high mountains, almost impossible to find. There is only one narrow track leading up to where we are, and even this is often interrupted by bare boulders with no path leading through them, and only those who are at home in the mountains can ever find the track again.

When I had to go to confession, I did not know what to say. All my worries had vanished; cheerful, calm, without any tremor of the radiant patches of sunlight, there, glimpsed through the half-open church door, the square lay. All I could remember was the sufferings of the immediate past, I wanted to penetrate further to their evil roots, but it was impossible, I could not remember any sufferings, and they had no roots in me. I could hardly understand the confessor's questions; though I understood the words, however hard I strained I could not extract from them even the slightest application to myself. Many of the questions I asked him to repeat, but it was of no avail, they were only like seeming acquaintances about whom one's memory deceives one.

In the gale, folly of the leaves, heavy door, light tapping at it, assimilation of the world, introduction of the guests, great amazement, what babbling, queer mouth, impossibility of coming to terms with this, work of various kinds with retrospective gaze, hammer blow upon hammer blow, are the engineers coming now? No, there is some sort of delay, the director is entertaining them, there is a shout of Hurrah, the young men, in the midst of it the brook purls, an old man is looking on, how it lives and how sweetly it smells; but have supermundane, divine youth to feel this, sublime gnat fluttering round the table lamp, yet, my little, my tiny, grasshopper-like table-companion, squatting on the chair, drawn up so high. . . .

Our director is young, there are great projects under way, he is always urging us on, there is no limit to the time he gives to that, and each one of us is of as much account to him as all are. He is capable of spending whole days with some little person of no importance on whom our gaze has scarcely lighted, he sits down with him on one chair, he holds him in an embrace, he puts his knee on the other's knee, he requisitions his ear, to which no one else is any longer permitted to have access, and now he begins the work.

Our chief holds very much aloof from the staff; there are whole days during which we do not set eyes on him at all, and then he is in his office, which, although it is also in the shop, has frosted glass panes up to the height of a man and can be entered not only through the shop but also through the entrance hall of the building. There is probably no particular intention in this aloofness, nor does he feel that he is a stranger to us, but it is completely in keeping with his nature. He considers it neither necessary nor useful to stimulate the staff to be particularly hard-working; anyone whose own common sense does

not make him do his best cannot, in his view, be a good
shop assistant and will simply not be able to keep his job
in a steadily run shop that exploits the obvious possibilities, but exploits them to the full; indeed he himself will
feel how little he belongs there so intensely that he will
not wait to be dismissed, but will give notice himself.
And this will take place so rapidly that it will not cause
any great damage either to the shop or to the assistant.
Now, such a relationship is certainly not usual in the
world of business, but in our chief's case it obviously
proves its worth.

To preserve calm; to remain extremely aloof from whatever that passion wants; to know the way the current
flows and for that reason to swim against it; to swim
against the current out of a liking for being buoyed up.

It is a small shop, but it is full of life; there is no entrance to it from the street, one has to go through the
hall and across a small courtyard, and only then does one
come to the door of the shop, over which a little board
hangs with the shopkeeper's name on it. It is a lingerie
shop, ready-made underclothes are sold there, but even
more linen by the yard. Now, for anyone who is unini-
tiated, who comes into the shop for the first time, it is
entirely incredible how much underclothing and linen is
sold, or rather, since after all one does not get a general
view of what the turnover of the business is, on what a
scale and with what keenness trade is carried on. As has
been said, there is no direct entrance to the shop from
the street, but this is not all, one sees no customers coming even from the courtyard, and yet the shop is full of
people, and one continually sees new people, and the old
ones disappear, one does not know whither. Although

there are broad shelves on the walls, too, in the main the shelves are arranged round pillars, which support the vault, with its many small sections. As a consequence of this arrangement there is no spot from which one can tell exactly how many people there are in the shop, there are always new people appearing from behind the pillars, and the nodding of heads, the animated gestures, the tapping of footsteps as people crowd in, the rustling of the goods spread out for people to choose from, the endless negotiations and arguments, in which, even if they concern only one assistant and one customer, the whole shop always seems to join in—all this makes the bustle seem larger than life-size. In one corner there is a wooden enclosure, broad, but not higher than is necessary for people to be able to sit in it: this is the office. The wooden walls are obviously very strong, the door is tiny, care was taken not to put windows in, there is nothing but one spy-hole, but it is curtained inside and outside; but in spite of all this it is amazing that anyone should find peace to do clerical work in this office with all the noise going on outside. Sometimes the dark curtain that hangs on the inside of the door is pulled back, and then one sees standing there, filling the whole doorway, a small clerk with his pen behind his ear, his hand over his eyes, observing the tumult in the shop, either with curiosity or in fulfillment of an order. But it is not long before he slips back, letting the curtain fall so quickly that one does not get even the slightest glimpse of the interior of the office. There is a certain connection between the office and the cash desk in the shop. The desk is fixed close to the door of the shop and is in the charge of a young girl. She has not as much work as it might seem at first. Not everyone pays in cash, indeed very few do so, there are obviously yet other ways of settling accounts.

Festoon the dream through the twigs of the tree. The children's round dance. The admonition uttered by the father bending down. To break the log of wood over one's knee. Half swooning, pale, to lean against the wall of the shed, looking up to the sky as though for salvation. A puddle in the yard. Broken old agricultural tools beyond. A path winding hurriedly, and in many serpentine curves, along the hillside. It rained from time to time, but from time to time, too, the sun shone. A bulldog jumped out, making the coffin bearers start back.

For a long, long time now I have been wanting to go to that city. It is a large, lively city, many thousands of people live there, every stranger is allowed in.

The following military order was found in the avenue among stray autumn leaves; it is impossible to discover from whom it originates and to whom it is addressed:

Tonight the attack begins. Everything up to now, the defense, the withdrawal, the rout, the dispersal. . . .

Through the avenue an unfinished figure, the rag of a raincoat, one leg, the front brim of a hat, rain fleetingly shifting from place to place.

The friends were standing on the bank. The man who was to row me to the ship lifted my trunk in order to carry it into the boat. I had known the man for many years, he always walked very bent, some malady in this way twisted this man who was otherwise as strong as a giant.

What disturbs you? What tears at the moorings of your heart? What is groping round the handle of your door? What calls to you from the street and yet does not come through the open gate? Ah, it is the very one that you disturb, he at the moorings of whose heart you tear, round the handle of whose door you grope, whom you call to from the street and through whose open gate you will not come.

They came through the open gate, and we went towards them. We exchanged recent news. We looked into each other's eyes.

The carriage was completely useless. The right front wheel was missing, in consequence the right back wheel was overloaded and bent, the shaft was broken, a piece of it lay on the carriage roof.

A small old wall-cupboard was brought to us. Our neighbor had inherited it from a distant relative, as the sole legacy, had tried various ways of opening it and finally, since he had not succeeded in doing so, had brought it to my master. It was no easy task. Not only was there no key, there was no lock to be discovered either. Either there was a secret mechanism somewhere, the working of which could only be discovered by a man with a great deal of experience in such things, or the cupboard could not be opened at all, but only smashed open, which admittedly would have been an extremely easy thing to do.

Herr Ohmberg, a teacher at the higher elementary school in the little town, met us at the railway station. He was the chairman of the committee that had made it its task to explore the cave. He was a small, agile, plump gentleman with a pointed, as it were colorless, blond beard. Hardly had the train stopped when Ohmberg stood on the steps of our coach, and hardly had the first of us got out when he delivered a short speech. He was obviously keen to carry out all the usual formalities, but the importance of the matter entrusted to him by its sheer weight reduced all the formalities to the level of the ridiculous.

The jolly companions were sailing downstream. A Sunday fisherman. Unattainable abundance of life. Smash it up! Wood in the stagnant water. Nostalgically rippling waves. Arousing nostalgia.

Running, running. Glance from a side street. High buildings, a church even higher still.

The characteristic thing about the town is its emptiness. The great main square, for instance, is always empty. The trams that cross each other's tracks there are always empty. Loudly, shrilly, liberated from the necessity of the moment, their bells ring. The big Bazaar that begins on the main square and leads through many buildings into a far distant street is always empty. At the many small tables standing in the open air outside the café, which extends on both sides of the entrance to the Bazaar, there sits no customer. The big door of the old church in the middle of the square is wide open, but nobody goes in or out. The marble steps leading up to the door reflect the sunlight that falls on them with positively intractable force.[42]

It is my old home town, and slowly, hesitantly, I wander through its streets.

It is once again the old fight with the old giant. True, he does not fight, only I fight, he only sprawls over me as a laborer does on the tavern table, crosses his arms on the upper part of my chest and presses his chin on his arms. Shall I be able to endure this load? •

Through the mists of the town. In a narrow street one side of which is formed by a wall overgrown with ivy.

I am standing before my old teacher. He smiles at me and says: "How is it going? It's such a long time now since I dismissed you from my class. If I had not an inhumanly powerful memory for all my pupils, I would not have recognized you. But as it is I recognize you exactly, you are my pupil. But why have you come back again?"

It is my old home town, and I have returned to it; I am a wealthy citizen and have a house in the Old Town with the view over the river. It is an old two-storied house with two large courtyards. I have a coach-building business, and in both courtyards sawing and hammering goes on all day. But in the living-rooms, which are at the front of the house, nothing of that can be heard, there all is deep silence, and the little square before the house, which is enclosed all round and only open towards the river, is always empty. In these living-rooms, large rooms with parquet floors, always slightly darkened by curtains, the furniture is old; wrapped in a padded dressing gown I like to walk about among it.

Nothing of that, slanting through the words there come vestiges of light.

The body that has been steeled understands its tasks! I tend the animal with growing joy. The shining of the brown eyes thanks me. We are at one.

I here explain it clearly; everything that is said about me is false, if it is based on the statement that I was the first human being to be the soul mate of a horse. How strange it is that this monstrous assertion should be cir-

culated and believed; but it is yet far more strange that
people take the matter so lightly, circulating the story
and believing it, but letting it go at that, with scarcely
more than a shaking of the head. Here is a mystery that
would actually be much more fascinating to elucidate
than the trivial thing I really did. What I did was only
this: for a year I lived together with a horse in such a way
as, say, a man would live with a girl whom he respects,
but by whom he is rejected, if there were no external obstacle preventing him from doing everything that might
bring him to his goal. Well, so I locked the horse Eleonor
and myself into a stable and never left this shared dwelling
place except to give the lessons by means of which I
earned the fees for our own lessons. Unfortunately this
always took up five to six hours a day, and it is by no
means impossible that this amount of time lost was to
blame for the final failure of all my endeavors, and let the
gentlemen whom I so often asked, and in vain, for support for my undertaking and who would only have needed
to give a little money for something for which I was prepared to sacrifice myself in the same way as one sacrifices
a bundle of oats that one stuffs between a horse's molars
—let those gentlemen just take note of that.

A cat had caught a mouse. "What are you going to do
now?" the mouse asked. "You have terrible eyes." "Oh,"
the cat said, "my eyes are always like that. You'll get
used to it." "I think I'll go away, if you don't mind," the
mouse said, "my children are waiting for me." "Your
children are waiting?" the cat said. "Then go along as
quickly as you can. I was only just going to ask you something." "Then please ask, it's really very late indeed."

A coffin had been made, and the carpenter loaded it on
to the handcart in order to take it to the coffin-shop. It

was rainy weather, a dull day. Coming out of the side street, an old gentleman approached, stopped in front of the coffin, drew his stick over it, and began a little conversation with the carpenter about the coffin industry. A woman with a shopping bag, who came down the main street, jostled slightly against the gentleman, then recognized him as someone she knew quite well, and also stopped for a little while. The carpenter's mate came out of the workshop with some more questions for the master about the work he was now to go on with. At a window over the workshop the carpenter's wife appeared with her youngest child on her arm, the carpenter began teasing the baby a little from where he stood in the street, and the gentleman and the woman with the shopping bag also looked upwards, smiling. A sparrow, under the delusion that there was something eatable to be found there, had flown on to the coffin and was hopping up and down on it. A dog was sniffing at the wheels of the handcart.

Then suddenly there was a loud knocking on the coffin lid from inside. The bird flew up and circled timidly over the cart. The dog barked wildly, he was the most excited of them all, and it seemed as though he were in despair at having neglected his duty. The gentleman and the woman had jumped to one side and now stood waiting, with outspread hands. The carpenter's mate had made a sudden resolve and swung himself up on to the coffin, where he now sat, this seat being apparently less terrifying to him than the possibility that the coffin might open and the knocker emerge. Actually he was perhaps already sorry he had acted so rashly, but now that he was up there he did not dare to get down again and all the master's efforts to drive him down were unavailing. The woman up at the window, who had probably also heard the knocking but had not been able to judge where it came from and, in any case, had not been struck by the idea that it might come out of the coffin, could not make anything of what was going on down below and looked on in astonishment. A policeman, drawn to the scene by some vague desire but held back by some vague fear, strolled hesitantly towards them.

Then the lid was all at once flung upwards with such force that the carpenter's mate slipped to one side; there was a brief outcry from everyone standing round about, and the woman at the window disappeared, evidently rushing downstairs with the baby.

Seek him with pointed pen,[43] vigorously, firmly turning your head on your neck and looking around you calmly from where you sit. You are a faithful servant, respected within the limits of your position, a lord within the limits of your position, mighty are your thighs, broad is your chest, lightly bent is your neck when you begin the search. You are visible from a long way off, like the steeple of a village church, and along the paths through the fields, from a long way off, over hills and valleys, solitary persons come hastening towards you.

It is the food on which I thrive. Exquisite dishes, exquisitely cooked. From the windows of my house I see the porters carrying the provisions, a long cavalcade, which often halts, and then each one clutches his basket to him to protect it from damage. And they gaze up at me too, amiably, some of them in delight.

It is the food on which I thrive. It is the sweet juice that rises from my young root.

Leaping up from the table, the goblet still in my hand, I chase after the enemy who appeared opposite me, emerging from under the table.

When he broke out, went into the forest, and got lost, it was evening. Well, the house, of course, stood on the edge of the forest. It was a town house, built in the regular city style, one-storied, with an oriel, as was in keeping with urban or suburban taste, and with a small, railed front garden, with delicate lacy curtains across the windows, a town house, and yet it was isolated, with no other house far and wide. And it was a winter's evening, and it was very cold here in the open country. Yet it was not open country after all, but here was city traffic, for round the corner there came a tramcar, and yet it was not in town, for the tram was not moving, but had been standing there all the time, always in that position, as though it were just turning the corner. And it had always been empty and was not really a tramcar at all, it was a cart with four wheels, and in the vague moonlight glimmering through the mist it could remind one of anything. And the road was cobbled as in town, the ground was checkered as with cobbles, cobbles of exemplary smoothness, but it was only the twilight shadows of the trees that were cast on the snowbound highroad.

It is, according to how one looks at it, touching or frightening or revolting, the way young Borcher does his utmost to get into my house. He was always mad, of course, and unfit for any sort of work, his family had given him up, and, with only just enough food to keep body and soul together, he wandered around all day long, by preference in the marshes. Sometimes he spent days and nights at home, lying in a corner, and then again he would spend many nights out.

Recently I have been exposed to molestations by the village idiot. He has always been an idiot, only it did not affect me any more than anyone else.

Now again there's some mischief going on down there at the garden gate. I look out of the window. Of course, it is he again.

[44] If you want to be introduced into a strange family, you find someone who is a common acquaintance and ask him to do you the favor. If you cannot find one, you possess yourself in patience and wait for a favorable opportunity.

In the little place where we live there cannot be any lack of such. If the opportunity does not turn up today, it will certainly turn up tomorrow. And if it does not turn up, you will not on that account begin trying to move heaven and earth. If the family can endure having to get on without you, you will find it at least no harder to endure.

All this is quite obvious, only K. does not understand it. Recently he has got it into his head that he must penetrate into the family of our lord of the manor, and yet he does not attempt to do so by social means, but by going straight ahead. Perhaps the usual way seems to him to be too slow, and that is true, but the way he is trying to go is simply impossible. Not that I am exaggerating the importance of our lord of the manor. He is a sensible, hardworking, decent man, but nothing more than that. What does K. want of him? Does he want a job on the estate? No, that is not what he wants, he himself is well-off and leads a life without cares. Is he in love with the lord's daughter? No, no, he is quite free from that suspicion.

The housing department intervened, there were so many official regulations, and we had failed to comply with one of them, it turned out that one room in our apartment had to be given up to a subtenant; true, the case was not quite clear, and if we had notified the department of the room in question earlier and if at the same time we had recorded our objection to being obliged to let a room, our case would have been quite promising, but now we had incurred blame for failing to comply with official regulations and the penalty for this was that we could no longer appeal against the arrangements made by the department. It was a disagreeable matter. It was all the more disagreeable since the department now had the chance, furthermore, to allot us any tenant it chose. Yet we hoped we should still be able to do something at least about that. I have a nephew who is studying law at the university here; his parents, who are, it might be said, close, but in reality very distant, relatives, live in a little country town and I scarcely know them. When the boy came to the capital he came to pay his respects to us, a weakly, timid, shortsighted boy with a stoop and disagreeably awkward movements and ways of expressing himself. What is at the core of him may well be excellent, but we have neither the time nor the interest to penetrate so far, a boy like that, a long-stemmed, tremulous little plant like that, would require endless watching and tending, and we can't afford that, but then it is better not to do anything at all and to keep such a boy at bay. We can be of some help to him with money and introductions, and that we have done, but for the rest we have seen to it that there were no more futile visits. Now, however, in view of the letter from the housing department, we have remembered this boy. He lives somewhere in a northern district, I am sure in pretty miserable circumstances, and the food he gets is bound to be scarcely adequate to keep that frail, inefficient little body upright. How would it be if we were to get him over to our house? Not only out of pity—we could and perhaps should have done it out of pity long ago—not only out of pity, but neither shall it be accounted to us as one of our undoubtedly deserving acts, we should be richly rewarded by the mere fact that our little nephew would at the last moment save us from the housing department's ultimatum, from an intrusion on the part of some tenant or other, some utter stranger who would insist on his so-called rights. And so far as our inquiries have taken us, this would be quite possible. If one could present the housing department with the accomplished fact of a poor student as an occupant already in residence, if one could prove that by losing this room this student would not only lose a room but almost his whole means of existence, if, finally (our nephew will not refuse to lend us his assistance in this little maneuver, we shall take care of that), it could be made to seem credible that he had lodged in this room previously, even if only for a time, and had only been at his parents' house in the country during the—admittedly long—period while he was working for his examination—if we succeed in all this, then we scarcely have anything to fear. So now quickly by car to get our nephew. On the fourth floor, in a small cold back room, he is pacing up and down from one corner to the other, in his winter overcoat, learning. Everything about him and around him is so disgustingly dirty and neglected that one has to keep a tight hold on the order from the housing department in one's pocket in order to convince oneself all over again that it is absolutely necessary.

Fresh abundance. Gushing water. Tempestuous, peaceful, high, spreading growth. Blissful oasis. Morning after riotous night. Breast to breast with heaven. Peace, reconciliation. Submerging.

Creative. Stride forward! Come along the road! Render me account! Call me to account! Judge! Kill!

He sings in the choir.—We laughed a great deal. We were young, it was a fine day, the high windows in the passage overlooked a flowery garden stretching away farther than one could see. We leaned out of these open windows, which carried our gaze and ourselves away out into the distance. Sometimes the servant walking up and down behind us would say a word that was meant to admonish us to be quiet. We scarcely saw him, we scarcely understood him, all that I remember is his footsteps ringing on the stone flags, the warning sound from afar.

We did not quite know whether we felt the urge to see an occultist draughtsman. And just as it happens that an urge that has always been faintly and imperceptibly there may almost give one the slip under the pressure of increasing attention and is only held fast, in its appropriate place, by the reality that soon arrives on the scene, so it was that for a long time now we had been unobtrusively curious to see before us one of those ladies who, from some interior but alien resources, draw pictures for one of a flower from the lofty moon, then deep-sea plants, then twisted and distorted heads with the hair done in complicated styles, and helmets, and other things, as they simply can't help doing.

September 15, 1920. It begins with your having tried to stuff your mouth, much to its surprise, not with food but with a bundle of as many daggers as it could possibly hold.

Under every intention the disease lies curled up, as it does under every leaf on the tree. If you bend down to see it, and it feels itself discovered, it leaps up—the thin, dumb malignance—and instead of being squashed, it wants to be fertilized by you.

It is a mandate. In keeping with my nature I can only accept a mandate that nobody has given me. It is only in this contradiction, always only in a contradiction, that I can live. But this doubtless applies to everyone; for living, one dies, dying, one lives. It is just as, for instance, the circus has canvas stretched tight all over it, and so nobody who is not inside this canvas can see anything. Now, however, someone comes and finds a little hole in the canvas and can watch from outside after all. Of course, he has to be left in peace to do so. We are all left in peace in such a way for a moment. Of course—second "of course" —what one sees through such a hole is mostly nothing but the backs of the people who have only got standing room. Of course—third "of course"—one does, in any case, hear the music, and also the roaring of the animals. Until at last one collapses, senseless with terror, into the arms of the policeman whose job it is to patrol round the circus and who has only tapped you lightly on the shoulder in order to draw your attention to the impropriety of such tense watching, for which you have not paid anything.

Man's powers are not intended to be like an orchestra. Here, on the contrary, all the instruments must play, all the time, without stopping, and with all their might. After all, it is not intended for human ears, and the time a concert lasts, during which each instrument can hope to assert itself, is not available.

September 16, 1920. Sometimes it seems like this: you have the task, have the resources adequate to carry it out (not too much, not too little of them, you do have to keep them together, but you don't need to be nervous about it), there is sufficient time put at your disposal, and besides, you have the good will to do the work. Where

is the obstacle to success in the tremendous task? Do not
spend time in search of the obstacle; perhaps there is none.

September 17, 1920. There is only a goal, no way. What
we call the way is hesitation.

I have never been under the pressure of any responsibility but that imposed on me by the existence, the gaze,
the judgment of other people.

September 21, 1920.
> The remains preserved.
> The blissfully relaxed limbs
> under the balcony, in the moonlight.
> In the background a little foliage,
> blackish as hair.

Some object or other from a shipwreck, which was
new and beautiful when it went into the water, soaked
and made defenseless for years on end, finally moldering
away.

At the circus a great pantomime is being performed
today, a water pantomime, the whole ring will be filled
with water, Poseidon and all his followers will race
through the water, Ulysses' ship will appear and the Sirens will sing, then Venus will rise naked from the waves,
which will make the transition to the representation of
life in modern public baths. The manager, a white-haired
old gentleman, who is, however, still all the limber
circus-rider, expects a very great deal from the success
of this pantomime. And success is indeed extremely necessary, the last year was very bad, various failures on
tour caused great losses. Now they are here in this little town.

Some people came to me and asked me to build a city for them. I said there were far too few of them, there would be room enough for them in one house, I was not going to build any city for them. But they said there would be yet others coming along and that there were, after all, married people among them who were expecting children, nor need the city be built all at once, but only the ground plan established and the rest carried out bit by bit. I asked where they wanted to have the city built; they said they would show me the place in a moment. We went along the river until we came to a fairly high broad hill, steep on the side next to the river but otherwise sloping away gently. They said up there was where they wanted to have the city built. There was nothing there but thin-growing grass, and no trees, which suited me, but the drop to the river seemed too steep to me and I drew their attention to this. They said, however, that there was no harm in this, the city would, after all, extend along the other slopes and would have enough other means of access to the water, and besides, in the course of time ways would perhaps be found of somehow coping with the steep cliff; in any case, that was not to be any obstacle to founding a city on this spot. Besides, they said, they were young and strong and could easily climb up the cliff, which they said they would demonstrate to me at once. They did so; like lizards their bodies darted upwards among the crevices in the rock, and soon they were at the top. I went up too and asked them why they wanted the city to be built precisely here. The place did not seem to be particularly suitable for purposes of defense, its only natural protection was on the riverside, and precisely there, after all, protection was least necessary; on the contrary, here was where one would have wished to have the means of setting out easily and freely; but the plateau was easily accessible from all other sides, and for that reason, and also because of its greater expanse, difficult to defend. Apart from this, the ground up there had not yet been tested for its fertility, and to remain dependent on the lowlands and at the mercy of transport was always a dangerous thing for a city, especially in times of unrest. Further, it had not yet been established whether there was enough drinking water available up there; the little spring they showed me did not seem good enough to rely on.

"You're tired," one of them said, "you don't want to build the city." "Yes, I'm tired," I said and sat down on a boulder near the spring. They dipped a cloth in the water and freshened my face with it. I thanked them. Then I said that I wanted to walk round the plateau once by myself, and left them; it took a long time; when I came back it was dark; they were all lying round the spring, asleep; a light rain was falling.

In the morning I repeated my question. They did not immediately understand how I could repeat the evening's question in the morning. Then, however, they said they could not give me the exact reasons for which they had chosen this place, but there were ancient traditions that recommended the place. Even their forefathers had wanted to build the city here, but for some reasons, which tradition did not record exactly either, they had not begun after all. In any case, then, it was no wanton whim that had led them to this place; on the contrary they did not even much care for the place, and the counterarguments I had brought forward they had already thought of for themselves and acknowledged to be irrefutable, but there it was, they said, there was this tradition, and anyone who did not follow tradition would be annihilated. For this reason, they said, they could not understand why I was hesitating and had not, indeed, begun to build the day before.

I resolved to go away, and climbed down the cliff to
the river. But one of them had awakened and had waked
the others and now they stood on the edge of the cliff
and I was only halfway down and they pleaded and
called to me. So I turned back, they helped me and
pulled me up. I now promised them that I would build
the city. They were very grateful, made speeches to me,
kissed me.

[45]A peasant intercepted me on the highroad and asked
me to go home with him; perhaps I could help him, he
said; he had a quarrel with his wife which was embitter-
ing his life. Besides that he had good-for-nothing half-
witted children who only stood idling about or got up to
mischief. I said I would gladly go with him but that it
was, after all, very doubtful whether I, a stranger, would
be able to help him; I would perhaps be able to do
something with the children, but where his wife was
concerned I should probably be helpless, for a wife's
quarrelsomeness usually has its cause in the husband's nature, and since he did not want the quarrel he had probably endeavored already to change himself, but had not
been successful, and so how then could I succeed? The
most I could do would be to divert the wife's quarrelsomeness to myself. So I spoke, more to myself than to him,
but then I asked him frankly what he was going to pay
me for my trouble. He said we should easily come to
agreement on that point; if I should turn out to be of any
use, I could take away with me whatever I liked. At this
I stopped short and said such general promises could not
satisfy me, there must be a precise agreement as to what
he would give me by the month. He was amazed that I
asked for monthly payment. I was amazed at his amazement. But did he think—I asked—that I could put right
in two hours what two people had been doing wrong all

their lives, and did he think that after two hours I would take a little bag of peas in payment, gratefully kiss his hand, wrap myself in my rags and walk on along the icy highroad? No! The peasant listened in silence, with bowed head, but very attentively. On the contrary, I said, I should have to stay at his place for a long time in order to make myself acquainted with everything and, as it were, to work out methods by which to improve matters, then I should have to stay even longer in order really to put matters straight in so far as that was possible, and then I should be old and tired and should not go away again any more at all, but take my rest and enjoy the gratitude of them all.

"That will not be possible," the peasant said, "I see what you want, you want to settle down in my house and in the end you'll even turn me out. Then on top of all my burdens I should have the greatest of all." "Of course, without mutual trust we shall not come to any agreement," I said, "and don't I show that I trust you? All I want, after all, is your word, and you could perfectly well go and break it, couldn't you? After I have settled everything in accordance with your wishes, you could send me away in spite of all your promises, couldn't you?" The peasant looked at me and said: "You wouldn't let yourself be sent away." "Do as you like," I said, "think of me what you like, but don't forget—I say this simply in a friendly spirit, as man to man—that even if you don't take me along with you, you won't stand things at home for long. How are you to go on living with that wife and those children? If you won't risk taking me into your house, then it'll be better for you to give up your house at once, and with it the bother it will all be to you yet. Come with me, let us travel on together, I shan't bear you any grudge for your mistrust." "I'm not a free man," the peasant said, "I've been living together with my wife for over fifteen years now, it has been difficult, I simply don't understand how it was possible, but all the same, I can't go away from her without having tried everything that might make her bearable. And then I saw you on the highroad, and so I thought to myself, now I could make the last great attempt with you. Come along, I'll give you whatever you want. What do you want?" "Oh, I don't want much," I said, "I don't want to exploit your desperate situation, after all. You shall only take me on permanently as a laborer, I can do every sort of work and will be of great use to you. But I do not want to be a laborer like other laborers, you are not to give me orders, I must be allowed to work at my own will, now at this, now at that, and then again doing nothing, just as I feel inclined. You may ask me to do a job, but not in a pressing way; if you notice that I don't want to do that job, you must put up with that quietly. As for money, I need none, but the clothes, underclothes and boots I get, when it becomes necessary to replace them, must be exactly like those I have now. If you cannot get these things in the village, you must go to town to get them. But don't be afraid of that, what I am wearing will last for many years yet. The usual food laborers get is good enough for me, only I must have meat every day." "Every day?" he interpolated quickly, as though he agreed to all the other conditions. "Every day," I said. "You have queer teeth, haven't you," he said and tried to make this an excuse for my strange request, indeed he put his fingers into my mouth to feel the teeth." "How sharp they are," he said, "almost like a dog's teeth." "In short, I want meat every day," I said. "I want as much beer and gin as you take." "But that's a lot," he said, "I have to drink a lot." "All the better," I said, "but you can restrict yourself, then I shall restrict myself, too. Anyway, perhaps you only drink so much on account of your domestic misfortunes." "No," he said, "how could these things be connected? But you shall get as much as I do. We shall drink together." "No," I said, "I shan't eat and drink together with anyone else. I shall always eat and drink quite alone." "Alone?" the peasant asked in amazement. "My head's beginning to whirl from your wishes." "It isn't so much," I said, "and anyway that's almost the lot. The only other thing I want is oil for a little lamp that is to be kept alight beside me all night. I have this little lamp in my bag, quite a tiny little lamp, it needs very little oil. It isn't worth talking about, I only mention it for the sake of completeness, so that there won't be any arguments later on. For I can't stand any arguments in matters of wages. If I am refused what was agreed on, though I am usually the best-natured of men, I shall be a terror—take note of that. If I am not given what is due to me, and even though it might be a trifle, I am capable of setting fire to the house over your head while you're asleep. But you don't need to refuse me what is clearly agreed on, do you, and then, especially if now and then, too, you add a little present, just for love, and even though it may be quite without value, then I shall be faithful and hard-working and very useful in every way. And I don't ask for more than I have said, except that on August 24th, which is my name day, I want a little barrel with five liters of rum." "Five liters!" the peasant cried out, clasping his hands in dismay. "Well," I said, "five liters isn't so much, is it? I suppose you want to press me down. But I have re-stricted my needs so much already myself, out of con-sideration for you, that is to say, that I should be ashamed if a third person were listening to us. I couldn't possibly talk to you like this in front of a third person. And nobody must ever come to know of it. Still, nobody would believe it, anyway." But the peasant said: "You'd

better go on. I shall go home alone and try to conciliate
my wife myself. I have been beating her a lot recently,
I shall leave that off somewhat for a while now, perhaps
she will be grateful to me; I've been beating the children a lot too, I always fetch the whip from the stables
and beat them, I shall stop that for a while, and perhaps
things'll get better. Though I must say I've stopped often
enough before and it didn't do any good. But what you
demand is more than I could afford, and if I could perhaps afford it—but no, the farm won't stand it, no, it's
impossible—meat every day, five liters of rum—but even
if it were possible, my wife wouldn't allow it, and if she
doesn't allow it, I can't do it." "Why then all these long-
drawn negotiations?" I said. . . .

I was sitting in the box, and beside me was my wife.
The play being performed was an exciting one, it was
about jealousy; at that moment, in the midst of a brilliantly lit hall surrounded by pillars, a man was just raising his dagger against his wife, who was slowly retreating to the exit. Tense, we leaned forward over the
balustrade; I felt my wife's curls against my temple.
Then we started back, for something moved on the balustrade; what we had taken for the plush upholstery of
the balustrade was the back of a tall thin man, not an
inch broader than the balustrade, who had been lying flat
on his face there and was now slowly turning over as
though trying to find a more comfortable position. Trembling, my wife clung to me. His face was quite close to
me, narrower than my hand, meticulously clean as that
of a waxwork figure, and with a pointed black beard.
"Why do you come and frighten us?" I exclaimed. "What
are you up to here?" "Excuse me!" the man said, "I am
an admirer of your wife's. To feel her elbows on my body
makes me happy." "Emil, I implore you, protect me!" my

wife exclaimed. "I too am called Emil," the man said,
supporting his head on one hand and lying there as
though on a sofa. "Come to me, dear sweet little
woman." "You cad," I said, "another word and you'll find
yourself lying down there in the pit," and as though certain that this word was bound to come, I tried to push
him over, but it was not so easy, he seemed to be a
solid part of the balustrade, it was as though he were
built into it, I tried to roll him off, but I couldn't do it,
he only laughed and said: "Stop that, you silly little man,
don't wear your strength out prematurely, the struggle
is only beginning and it will end, as may well be said,
with your wife's granting my desire." "Never!" my wife
exclaimed, and then, turning to me: "Oh, please, do push
him down now." "I can't," I exclaimed, "you can see for
yourself how I'm straining, but there's some trickery in
it, it can't be done." "Oh dear, oh dear," my wife lamented, "what is to become of me?" "Keep calm," I said,
"I beg of you. By getting so worked up you're only making it worse, I have another plan now, I shall cut the
plush open here with my knife and then drop the
whole thing down and the fellow with it." But now I
could not find my knife. "Don't you know where I have
my knife?" I asked. "Can I have left it in my overcoat?"
I was almost going to dash along to the cloakroom when
my wife brought me to my senses. "Surely you're not
going to leave me alone now, Emil," she cried. "But if I
have no knife," I shouted back. "Take mine," she said and
began fumbling in her little bag, with trembling fingers,
but then of course all she produced was a tiny little mother-
of-pearl knife.

A delicate task, a tiptoeing over a rotten beam that
serves as a bridge, having nothing underfoot, first scraping together with one's feet the ground on which one

will walk, walking on nothing but one's reflection, which one sees in the water beneath one, holding the world together with one's feet, and only clenching one's hand in the air above one in order to be able to accomplish this labor.

On the steps outside the temple a priest kneels, transforming all the pleas and complaints of the faithful who come to him into prayers, or rather, he does not transform anything, but only repeats loudly and many times over what is said to him. There comes a merchant, for instance, and complains that he has had a great loss that day and that as a result of his business is on the verge of ruin. Hereupon the priest—he kneels on one step, keeps his hands laid flat on a higher step, and bobs up and down as he prays—"A. has had a great loss today, his business is on the verge of ruin. A. has had a great loss today, his business is on the verge of ruin, and so forth."

We are five friends, we once came out of a house one after the other, first one came and stood beside the gate, then the second came, or rather glided, as lightly as a globule of quicksilver glides, out of the gate and stood not far from the first, then the third, then the fourth, then the fifth. Finally we were all standing in a row. People began to notice us, pointed at us, and said: "These five have just come out of that house." Since then we have been living together, it would be a tranquil life if a sixth were not always interfering. He does not do anything to us, but he is a nuisance to us, and that is enough. Why does he push his way in where he is not wanted? We do not know him and do not want to take him into our midst. We five did not know each other previously either, and, if one wishes to put it so, we don't even know each other now, but what is possible and tolerated among the five of us is not possible and is not tolerated in the case of a sixth. Besides, we are five and do not wish to be six. And what is the sense of being continually together like this anyway? Even for the five of us there is no sense in it, but there it is, we are together and we remain so, but we want no new association, and this simply on the basis of our experience. But how is one to make the sixth understand all this? Long explanations would practically amount to taking him into our circle; we prefer to explain nothing and do not take him in. No matter how much he may pout his lips, we elbow him away, but no matter how much we may push him away, he keeps on coming back.

Just as sometimes, without even looking up first at the cloudy sky, one can feel, simply from the color of the landscape, that although the sunlight has not actually broken right through, the dullness *is* dissolving and making ready to pass away, in other words, that solely for this reason and without further proofs the sun will in a moment be shining everywhere.

Standing, I rowed the boat into the little harbor, which was almost empty, in one corner there were two sailing barges, but otherwise there were only little boats here and there. I soon found a place for my boat and stepped ashore. It was only a little harbor, but it had solid quay walls and was kept in good condition.

The boats were gliding past. I hailed one. The boatman was a tall white-bearded old man. I hesitated a little on the landing steps. He smiled, and, looking at him, I stepped in. He pointed to the farthest end of the boat, and there I sat down. But immediately I jumped up again and said: "What big bats you have here," for great wings had come rustling round my head. "Keep still," he

said, already busy with the pole, and we pushed off from
shore so that I almost collapsed on my little seat. Instead of telling the boatman where I wanted to go, I
only asked whether he knew, and judging by his nod, it
seemed he did know. That was an immense relief to me,
I stretched out my legs and leaned my head back, but I
kept my eye on the boatman all the time and said to myself: "He knows where you are going, behind that forehead he knows it. And he only drives his pole into the
sea in order to get you there. And by chance it was precisely he that you called out of the crowd, and you even
hesitated to step into the boat." I closed my eyes for a
moment in sheer contentment, but I wanted at least to
hear the man if I did not see him, and asked: "At your
age surely you would rather not work any more. Have
you no children?" "Only you," he said, "you are my only
child. It is only for you that I am making this last voyage, then I shall sell the boat, then I shall stop working."
"You call the passengers children here?" I said. "Yes," he
said, "that is the custom here. And the passengers say
'father' to us." "That is odd," I said. "And where is the
mother?" "Yonder," he said, "in the cabin." I sat up and
saw in the little porthole of the cabin that was built in
the middle of the boat a hand stretched out in greeting,
and there too a woman's strong-featured face appeared,
framed in a black lace kerchief. "Mother?" I asked, smiling. "If you like—" she said. "But you're much younger
than Father, aren't you?" I said. "Yes," she said, "much
younger, he might be my grandfather and you my husband." "You know," I said, "it's so astonishing to be sailing alone in a boat at night and suddenly there's a
woman there."

I was rowing on a lake. It was in a doomed cave where
there was no daylight, and yet it was bright, there was a

clear, steady light shining down from the bluish pallid stone. In spite of the fact that there was no breath of air to be felt, the waves beat high, but not to such an extent that there would have been any danger to my small but strongly made boat. I rowed calmly through the waves, but I was hardly thinking at all about the rowing, I was occupied only in bending all my powers to absorb the stillness that prevailed here, a stillness such as I had never come across before in my life. It was like a fruit that I had never eaten before and that was yet the most nourishing of all fruits; I had shut my eyes and was drinking it in. True, I was not undisturbed, the stillness was as perfect as ever, but there was the continual threat of a disturbance, there was still something holding the noise back, but it was already there outside the door, bursting with desire to break out at long last. I rolled my eyes at this noise that was not there, I pulled one oar out of the rowlock, stood up in the swaying boat, and made a threatening gesture into the void with the oar. All remained still for the time being and I rowed on.

We were running on smooth ground, sometimes one of us stumbled and fell headlong, sometimes one of us almost plunged over the edge, then the other always had to help him, but very cautiously, for, after all, even he had no firm foothold. At last we came to a hill that is called the Knee, but in spite of the fact that it is not at all high we could not climb across it, we kept on sliding down, we were desperate, and so now we had to make a detour round it since we could not climb across it; this was perhaps just as impossible, but much more dangerous, for here any failure of the attempt meant an instant plunge and the end of us. We decided that in order not to disturb each other each should try from a different side. I flung myself down and pushed myself slowly along the edge, I could see that here there was no trace of a path, no chance of holding on anywhere, without any transition there was everywhere a sheer drop into the depths. I was convinced that I should not get across; if it was not slightly better over there on the other side, which, of course, could only be discovered by making an attempt, then it was obviously all over with both of us. But we had to risk it, for we could not remain where we were, and behind us, formidably inaccessible, there towered up the five peaks that are called Toes. Once again I glanced over the situation, taking in the details, looking at the distance to be covered, which was in itself not at all long, but which was simply impossible to traverse, and then I closed my eyes—keeping my eyes open could only have been harmful to me here—firmly resolved not to open them again unless the incredible should happen and I should really get across after all. And then I let myself sink slowly to one side, almost as in sleep, then held on and began creeping forward. I held my arms stretched out wide to right and to left, for this covering and, as it were, embracing of as much ground as possible all round me seemed to give me a little equilibrium or, rather, a little comfort. But, in fact, I noticed to my astonishment that this ground was in some way positively of help to me, it was smooth and lent no support, but it was not cold ground, there was some sort of warmth radiating out of it to me and out of me to it, there was a connection that could not be established by means of hand and feet, but which existed and held firm.

Man's fundamental weakness lies by no means in the fact that he cannot achieve victory but in the fact that he cannot exploit his victory. Youth conquers everything, including the original deception, the concealed devilry, but there is no one there to catch hold of that victory and make it come alive, for by then youth is over. Old age is past daring to lay a finger on the victory, and the new generation of youth, tormented by the new attack that instantly begins, wants its own victory. So although the devil is constantly being overcome, he is never destroyed.

The perpetually mistrustful are people who assume that besides the great original deception there is in every case some extra little particular deception being arranged specially for them, in other words, that when a drama of love is being performed on the stage, the actress produces not only the hypocritical smile that is meant for her lover, but also a particularly deceitful smile for the quite particular spectator in the top balcony. Stupid arrogance.

Can you know anything but deception? For if deception is once annihilated, you must not look, of course, or you will turn into a pillar of salt.

I was fifteen years old when I went to town to become apprentice in a shop. It was *not* easy for me to get taken on anywhere; true, I had satisfactory references, but I was very small and weak. The shopkeeper, who was sitting in a narrow, windowless office, behind a glaring electric lamp, at his desk, one arm somehow linked into the back of his chair, his thumb firmly tucked into his waistcoat pocket, his head held as far back from me as possible, his chin on his chest, examined me and found me unsuitable. "You are," he said, shaking his head, "too weak to carry parcels, and I only need a boy who can carry heavy parcels." "I shall do my best," I said, "and besides, I shall get stronger." —At last, though actually only out of pity, I was taken on in an ironmonger's. It was a gloomy little shop in a courtyard and I had to carry loads that were much too heavy for my strength, but all the same I was very contented to have got a job.

"The great swimmer! The great swimmer!" the people shouted. I had come from the Olympic Games at Antwerp, where I had established a world record at swimming. I stood on the steps outside the railway station in my home town—where is it?—and looked at the crowd, indistinct in the dusk of evening. A girl, whose cheek I stroked in passing, nimbly put a sash over my shoulders, on which was written in some foreign language: To The Olympic Victor. A motorcar drew up, some gentlemen urged me to get in, two gentlemen came along too, the mayor and someone else. A moment later we were in a banqueting hall; from up in the gallery a choir began to sing as I came in; all the guests—there were hundreds—rose and called out, in unison, some slogan that I did not understand clearly. On my left there sat a minister, I don't know why the word startled me so much when we were introduced, I gazed at him wildly, but soon came to my senses; on my right there sat the mayor's wife, a voluptuous lady, everything about her, particularly about the bosom, seeming to me to be all roses and ostrich feathers. Opposite me there sat a fat man with a strikingly white face, I had not caught his name when we were introduced, he had put his elbows on the table—an especially large place had been left clear for him—gazed in front of himself and said nothing; to the right and to the left of him sat two pretty fair girls, very gay they were, they had something to say all the time, and I kept looking from one to the other. In spite of the splendid illumination I could not distinctly make out the faces of any of the guests sitting farther away, perhaps because everyone was moving about, the servants were dashing round, dishes were being offered, glasses were being raised, perhaps indeed everything was much too sharply illuminated. There was, besides, a certain disorder—it was, incidentally, the only one—consisting in the fact that some guests, especially ladies, sat with their backs to the table and indeed in such a way that the back of the chair did not come in between, but their backs almost touched the table. I drew the attention of the girls opposite me to this, but whereas they were otherwise so talkative, now they said nothing, but only smiled at me, gazing at me for a long time. On a signal being given by the ringing of a bell—the waiters froze between the rows of seats—the fat man opposite rose and delivered a speech. Oh, why was the man so sad? During his speech he kept on dabbing at his face with his handkerchief; that could have been passed over; considering his obesity, the heat of the room, the effort of making a speech, this was understandable, but I distinctly noticed that the whole thing was only a stratagem to hide the fact that he was wiping the tears from his eyes. At the same time he kept on glancing at me, but just as though he were seeing not me but my open grave. When he had concluded, naturally I rose and delivered a speech too. I felt positively impelled to speak, for there was much, here and probably elsewhere too, that seemed to me to require public and frank elucidation, and so I began:

Honored fellow guests! I have, it must be admitted, established a world record, but if you were to ask me how I achieved it I could not answer you satisfactorily. The fact is that I really can't swim at all. I have always wanted to learn, but there was never a chance to do so. How then did it come about that my country sent me to the Olympic Games? That is indeed the very question that exercises my mind too. First of all, I cannot but observe that here I am not in my native country and in spite of great efforts do not understand a word of what is being said here. The most obvious thing to do now would be to believe in a case of mistaken identity, but here is no mistaken identity, I have established the record, have traveled back home, my name is the one you call me by, up to that point everything fits, but from this point on nothing fits any more, I am not in my home country, I do not know you and do not understand you. But now something else that, though it does not do so exactly, yet somehow contradicts the possibility of mistaken identity: it does not disturb me very much that I do not understand you and it does not seem to disturb you very much, either, that you do not understand me. All that I believe I gather from the speech made by the honored gentleman who spoke before me is that it was dismally sad, but this knowledge is not only enough for me, it is indeed even too much for me. And it is the same with all the conversations that I have had since my arrival here. But let us return to my world record.

A partial narrative.

There are two men standing in front of the entrance to the house, they seem to be quite arbitrarily dressed, most of the things they have on are rags, dirty, torn, frayed, but individual bits, again, are in very good condition, one of them has a new high collar with a silk tie, the other has fine nankeen trousers, cut full but narrowing down to the ankles, delicately turned up over the boots. They are conversing together and blocking the door. There comes a man, seemingly a middle-aged country clergyman, tall, solidly built, thick-necked, upright, but swaying to and fro on his stiff legs. He wants to go in, it is an urgent matter that has brought him. But the two guard the entrance, one pulls out of his trousers a watch on a long gold chain—there seem to be several chains fastened to each other—it is not yet nine o'clock, and nobody may be let in before ten. This is very awkward for the clergymen, but the two men have already resumed their conversation. The clergyman looks at them for a little while, seems to recognize the futility of further pleading, and even goes on a few paces, but then he is struck by an idea and returns. Did the gentlemen actually know whom he wants to visit? It is his sister, Rebekka Zoufal, an old lady who lodges with her maid on the second floor. That, certainly, is something the watchers did not know; now they no longer have any objection to the clergyman's going in, they even make a kind of formal bow as he walks through between them. When the clergyman is in the passage, he cannot help smiling over the fact that it was so easy to trick the two men. Fleetingly he glances back once more, and to his amazement sees that the watchers are just going away, arm in arm. Were they perhaps only standing there on his account? So far as the clergyman can survey the situation, this is not quite impossible. He turns right round, the street has become a little more animated, often one of the passers-by glances into the passage, to the provocative it seems positively provocative how wide open both halves of the front door are, there is a tension in this openness, as though the door were in this way preparing for a final furious slam. Then he hears someone calling his name. "Arnold," the call rings out through the well of the stairs, a thin, strained voice, and an instant later a finger taps him lightly on the back. There stands a bent old woman, utterly enveloped in some dark-green, loose-woven fabric, looking at him positively not with her eyes, but with one long narrow tooth, which protrudes from her mouth, dismally and solitarily.

Away from it, away from it, we rode through the night. It was dark, moonless and starless, and even darker than moonless and starless nights usually are. We were on an important mission, our leader carrying orders with him in a sealed envelope. Anxious lest we might lose our leader, one of us would now and then ride forward and grope for our leader to make sure that he was still there. Once, just when I was doing this, our leader was no longer there. We were not all too frightened, for we had been fearing this all the time. We resolved to ride back.

The city resembles the sun; all the light is intensely concentrated in a central circle; it is dazzling; one loses one's way, one cannot find the streets, the houses, if once one has entered it one simply does not get out of it again; in a further, much larger circle the light is still very strong, but it is no longer an unbroken radiance, there are little dark alleys, hidden passages, even very small squares where all is twilight and coolness; then there is a yet larger circle, here the light is already so diffuse that one has to search for it, here large areas of the city lie only in a cold gray glimmer, and then finally there comes the open country, dull in color, late autumnal, bare, scarcely lit up by even a flash of something like sheet lightning.

In this city it is perpetually early morning, scarcely even dawn, the sky is of a smooth gray that scarcely grows any lighter at all, the streets are empty, clean and silent, somewhere a window casement that has not been fastened moves slowly to and fro, somewhere the ends of a cloth that has been hung over the balcony railing on a top story fly in the air, somewhere a curtain flutters faintly at an open window, otherwise nothing stirs.

Once a tiger was brought to the celebrated animal tamer Burson, for him to give his opinion as to the possibility of taming the animal. The small cage with the tiger in it was pushed into the training cage, which had the dimensions of a public hall; it was in a large hut-camp a long way outside the town. The attendants withdrew, Burson always wanted to be completely alone with an animal at his first encounter with it. The tiger lay quiet, having just been plentifully fed. It yawned a little, gazed wearily at its new surroundings, and immediately fell asleep.

In one of our ancient scriptures it is said:[46]
Those who curse life and therefore think not being born, or subjugating life, is the greatest or the sole non-deceptive happiness must be right, for the judgment concerning life. . . .

The ancient history of our people records terrible forms of punishment. This does not, however, imply anything in defense of the present penal code.

A man doubted that the emperor was descended from the gods; he asserted that the emperor was our rightful sovereign, he did not doubt the emperor's divine mission (that was evident to him), it was only the divine descent that he doubted. This, naturally, did not cause much of a stir; when the surf flings a drop of water on to the land, that does not interfere with the eternal rolling of the sea, on the contrary, it is caused by it.

There was brought before a judge of the imperial city a man who denied that the emperor was descended from the gods. He had been transported from his home by soldiers, the journey had taken weeks, he was so tired that he could scarcely sit, his cheeks were hollow, and. . . .

One is ashamed to say by what means the imperial colonel governs our little town in the mountains. His few soldiers could be disarmed immediately, if we so wished, and help for him, even supposing he could summon it— but how could he do that?—would not come for days, indeed for weeks. And so he is utterly dependent on our obedience, but he does not try either to enforce it by tyrannical means or to wheedle it out of us by cordiality. And so why do we tolerate his hated rule? There is no doubt about it: only because of his gaze. When one enters his study—a century ago it was the council chamber of our elders—there he sits at his desk, in uniform, pen in hand. Ceremonial is something he does not care for, and any form of play-acting far less, and so he does not go on writing, as he might, letting the visitor wait, but instantly interrupts his work and leans back, though he does keep his pen in his hand. And so, leaning back, his left hand in his trouser pocket, he gazes at the visitor. The petitioner has the impression that the colonel sees more than merely him, the unknown person who has emerged from the crowd for a little while, for why else should the colonel scrutinize him so closely, and long, and in silence? Nor is it a keen, probing, penetrating gaze, such as might be directed at an individual person; it is a nonchalant, roving, and yet steady gaze, a gaze with which one might, for instance, observe the movements of a crowd in the distance. And this long gaze is continuously accompanied by an indefinable smile, which seems to be now irony, now dreamy reminiscence.

A sudden change. On the lurk, timidly, hopefully, the answer prowls round the question, peering desperately into its impenetrable face, following it along paths that are utterly senseless (that is, leading as far as possible away from the answer).

An evening in autumn, clear and cool. Someone, whose movements, dress and outline are indistinct, comes out of the house and is about to turn immediately to the right. The caretaker's wife, in a lady's old white overcoat, stands leaning against a pillar of the porch and whispers something to him. He reflects for a moment, but then shakes his head and walks on. In crossing the road, through his own carelessness, he gets in the way of a tramcar and it runs through him. He draws his face together in pain until it is quite small, tightening all his muscles in such a way that when the tram has passed he is almost unable to relax the tension again. He stands still for a little while longer and sees a girl get out at the next stop, a girl who waves her hand in his direction, begins to run back a few paces, stops, and then gets into the tram again. When he walks past a church, there is a priest standing at the top of a flight of steps, who stretches out a hand to him and bends so far forward that he is almost in danger of falling over and tumbling down the steps. But he does not take the proffered hand, he is an opponent of missionaries, besides, he is irritated by the children who are roaming about on the steps as though it were a playground and shouting indecent expressions at each other, which, of course, they cannot understand and which they only suck at for lack of anything better—he buttons his coat up high and walks on.

On the steps outside the church the children roam about as though it were a playground and shout indecent expressions at each other which, of course, they cannot understand and which they only suck at as babies suck at dummies. The priest comes out, smooths his cassock down behind and seats himself on a step. He is anxious to quiet the children, for their shouting can be heard even inside the church. But he only now and then succeeds in pulling a child towards him, the crowd of children continually slips away from him and goes on playing without paying any heed to him. He cannot see the meaning of this game, nor can he perceive the remotest childlike meaning in it. Like balls being bounced on the ground, they hop about on all the steps, untiringly and seemingly without effort, and there is no link between them but their shouting; the effect is soporific. As though he were falling asleep, the priest reaches out for the nearest child, a little girl, undoes some of the top buttons at the front of her little dress—for this she slaps him on the cheek, lightly and jokingly—sees some sign there that he was not expecting or perhaps indeed was expecting, exclaims "Ah!", pushes the child away, exclaims "Fi!" and spits and makes a large sign of the Cross in the air and begins hastening back into the church. But in the doorway he collides with a gypsyish young woman, she is barefoot, is wearing a red skirt with a white pattern and a white, shirtlike blouse negligently left open in front, and has wildly tousled brown hair. "Who are you?" he exclaims, his voice still trembling with agitation about the children. "Your wife Emilie," she says in a low voice and slowly leans against his chest. He is silent, listening to the beating of her heart.

It was an ordinary day; it bared its teeth at me; I too was held by teeth and could not wriggle out of their grip; I did not know how they were holding me, for they were not clenched; nor did I see them in the form of the two rows of a set of teeth, but merely some here and some there. I wanted to hold on to them and vault over them, but I did not succeed in doing so.

You have come too late, he was here just now, in the autumn he does not stay long in one place, he feels something drawing him out into the dark unfenced fields, he has something of a crow's nature. If you want to see him, fly to the fields, he is sure to be there.

You say I should go down further still, but I am already very deep down, and yet, if it must be so, I will stay here. What a place! It is probably the deepest place there is. But I will stay here, only do not force me to climb down any deeper.

I was defenseless confronted with the figure, calmly it sat there at the table, gazing at the table-top. I walked round it in circles, feeling myself throttled by it. And around me there walked a third, feeling throttled by me. Around that third there walked a fourth, feeling throttled by him. And so it went on, right out to the circling of the constellations, and further still. Everything feels the grip at the throat.

In what district is it? I do not know the district. All things there correspond to one another, all things smoothly merging with one another. I know that this district exists somewhere, I can even see it, but I do not know where it is, and I cannot draw near to it.

By means of the strongest possible light one can dissolve the world. For weak eyes the world becomes solid, for eyes weaker still it grows fists, before those even weaker it becomes shamefaced and smashes anyone who dares to gaze upon it.

There was a little pool, and there we drank, belly and chest on the ground, our forelegs, weary with the bliss of drinking, dipping into the water. But we soon had to go back, the most prudent one among us tore himself away and called out: "Back, brothers!" Then we ran back. "Where have you been?" we were asked. "In the wood." "No, you have been at the pool." "No, we have not been there." "But the water is still dripping off you, you liars!" And the whips came into play. We ran through the long corridors that were filled with moonlight, now and then one of us was hit and leaped high into the air with pain. In the ancestral portrait gallery the chase was at an end, the door was slammed, we were left alone. We were all still thirsty, we licked the water off each other's fur and faces, sometimes instead of water what one got on one's tongue was blood, that was from the lashing of the whips.

Only one word. Only one plea. Only one stirring of the air. Only one proof that you are still alive and waiting. No, no plea, only a breathing, no breathing, only a readiness, no readiness, only a thought, no thought, only quiet sleep.

In the old confessional-box. I know how he will console, I know what he will confess. Those are little things, hole-and-corner traffickings, the daily din from morning to evening.

I was trying to collect my possessions. They were very few, but they were exactly defined, solid things, instantly convincing to anyone. There were six or seven articles, I say six or seven, because six of them undoubtedly belonged only to me, but the seventh had also belonged to a friend, though to be sure he had left our city many years earlier and had never been heard of since. And so it could doubtless be said that this seventh article also belonged to me.

In spite of the fact that these articles were really unique, they were not of great value.

The lament is senseless (to whom does he complain?), the jubilation is ridiculous (the kaleidoscope in the window).[47] Obviously all he wants is to lead the others in prayer, but then it is indecent to use the Jewish language, then it is quite sufficient for the lament if he spends his life repeating: "Dog-that-I-am, dog-that-I-am," and so forth, and we shall all understand him, but for happiness silence is not only sufficient, it is indeed the only thing possible.

"It is not a bleak wall, it is the very sweetest life that has been compressed into a wall, raisins upon raisins."— "I don't believe it."—"Taste it."—"I cannot raise my hand for unbelief."—"I shall put the grape into your mouth." —"I cannot taste it for unbelief."—"Then sink into the ground!"—"Did I not say that faced with the bleakness of this wall one must sink into the ground?"

I can swim like the others, only I have a better memory than the others, I have not forgotten my former inability to swim. But since I have not forgotten it, my ability to swim is of no avail and I cannot swim after all.

Yet a little more adornment to this grave. You say it is already adorned enough? Yes, but since it comes so easily to me to do. . . .

It is the animal with the big tail, a tail many yards long and like a fox's brush. How I should like to get my hand on this tail some time, but it is impossible, the ani-

mal is constantly moving about, the tail is constantly being flung this way and that. The animal resembles a kan-
garoo, but not as to the face, which is flat almost like a
human face, and small and oval; only its teeth have any
power of expression, whether they are concealed or
bared. Sometimes I have the feeling that the animal is
trying to tame me. What other purpose could it have in
withdrawing its tail when I snatch at it, and then again
waiting calmly until I am tempted again, and then leaping away once more?

In anticipation of what was to come I had crouched
down in a corner of the room and pushed the sofa across
at an angle. If anyone now came in he would really be
bound to think me mad, but he who came did not think
so. From one of his high thigh boots he drew out a dog
whip, flicked it in a circle around him, rose on his toes
and sank down again, straddling his legs, and called out:
"Come on out of that corner! How much longer is this
going on?"

A hearse was driving around the countryside, it had a
corpse aboard, but it did not deliver it to the cemetery,
the driver was drunk and believed he was driving a
coach, but where he was supposed to be driving this
coach was something he had forgotten too. So he drove
through the villages, stopping at the taverns, and, when
now and then his worry about his destination flashed
upon him in his drunkenness, hoping that sometime good
people would tell him all he needed to know. In this way
he once stopped outside the Golden Cockerel and had
roast pork. . . .

I see a town in the distance. Is that the one you
mean?

It is possible, yet I do not understand how you can make out a town there, I can only see something there since you have drawn my attention to it, and, even so, no more than some vague outlines in the mist.

Oh yes, I see it all right, it is a mountain with a castle on the top and houses, like those of a village, on the slopes.

Then it is that town, you are right, it is actually a large village.

Time and again I lose my way, it is a forest path, but clear and distinct, and only straight above it does one glimpse a strip of sky, everywhere else the forest is dense and dark. And yet there is this continual, desperate going astray, and besides: if I move one step off the path, I am at once a thousand steps deep in the forest, and so forlorn that I should like to drop down and lie there forever.

"You keep on talking about death, and yet you do not die." "And yet I shall die. I am just saying my swan song. One man's song is longer, another man's song is shorter. But the difference can never be more than a matter of a few words."

A watchman! A watchman! What are you watching over? Who has appointed me? Only by one thing, by your disgust with yourself, are you richer than the wood louse that lies under that old stone, watching and waiting.

Just contrive to make yourself intelligible to the woodlouse. Once you have taught it to ask what is the purpose of its work, you will have exterminated the nation of the wood lice.

Life is a constant distraction that does not even allow for reflection as to what it distracts from.

To think that even the most conservative of men is capable of the radicalism of dying!

The most insatiable people are certain ascetics, who go on hunger-strike in all spheres of life, thinking that in this way they will simultaneously achieve the following:

1) a voice will say: Enough, you have fasted enough, now you may eat like the others and it will not be accounted unto you as eating.

2) the same voice will at the same time say: You have fasted for so long under compulsion, from now on you will fast with joy, it will be sweeter than food (at the same time, however, you will also really eat).

3) the same voice will at the same time say: You have conquered the world, I release you from it, as from eating and from fasting (at the same time, however, you will both fast and eat).

In addition to this there also comes a voice that has been speaking to them ceaselessly all the time: Though you do not fast completely, you have the good will, and that suffices.

You say you do not understand it. Try to understand it by calling it illness. It is one of the many manifestations of illness that psychoanalysis believes it has revealed.[48] I do not call it illness, and I regard the therapeutic claims of psychoanalysis as an impotent error. All these so-called illnesses, however sad they may look, are facts of belief, the distressed human being's anchorages in some maternal ground or other; thus, it is not surprising that psychoanalysis finds the primal ground of all religions to be precisely the same thing as what causes the individual's "illnesses"; true, nowadays there is no sense of religious fellowship, there are innumerable sects, most of them confined to individuals, yet perhaps this only appears so to one who is biased by his awareness of the present. Such anchorages, which do grip real ground, are, however, not an individual possession of each man's; they are something that is pre-established in man's nature and which afterwards goes on transforming his nature (and his body too) in the same direction. And does anyone really think this is a subject for treatment?

In my case one can imagine three circles, an innermost one, A, then B, then C. The core A explains to B why this man must torment and mistrust himself, why he must renounce, why he must not live. (Was not Diogenes, for instance, gravely ill in this sense? Which of us would not have been happy under Alexander's radiant gaze? But Diogenes frantically begged him to move out of the way of the sun. That tub was full of ghosts.) To C, the active man, no explanations are given, he is merely terribly ordered about by B; C acts under the most severe pressure, but more in fear than in understanding, he trusts, he believes, that A explains everything to B and that B has understood everything rightly.

I was sitting at a little table outside the door of a sailors' tavern, a few paces in front of me there lay the little harbor, evening was approaching. A cumbersome fishing smack sailed past, quite close, in the single cabin window there was a gleam of light, on deck a man was working at the sails, then he stopped and glanced over at me. "Can you take me along?" I shouted. He distinctly nodded. I had already leaped up, in such a way that the little table rocked and the coffee cup fell to the ground and was smashed, and once again I asked: "Answer! Can you take me along?" "Yes," he said drawlingly, his head held high.

"Lie alongside!" I called, "I am ready." "Shall I bring

you your trunk?" asked the innkeeper, who had come
over to me. "No," I said, seized with loathing and looking at the innkeeper as though he had insulted me. "You
don't really want to bring me my trunk. . . ."

"Why haven't you mechanized the work yet?" I asked.
"It is too delicate," the overseer said. He was sitting at a
little table in a corner of a large, barnlike wooden building; hanging from a wire that came from the dark height
above him, and so low over the table that he almost
knocked his head against it, was an electric lamp that
gave out a glaring light. On the table lay wage lists,
which the overseer was checking.

"I dare say I'm disturbing you," I said. "No," the overseer said absent-mindedly, "but I still have some work to
do, as you see." "Why then was I called?" I said. "What
am I to do here, in the middle of the forest?" "Save yourself the trouble of asking questions," said the overseer,
who had scarcely listened; but then he became aware of
the incivility, looked up at me, laughed, and said: "The
fact is, that's an expression we are in the habit of using
here. We are overrun with questions. But one can't work
and answer questions at the same time. Anyone who can
see for himself doesn't have to ask. Besides, if you take
an interest in technical matters, you will have plenty of
entertainment here. Horace!" he then shouted into the
darkness of the room, from which nothing could be heard
but the squeaking of one or two saws.

A young man came forward, a little reluctantly, as
it seemed to me. "This gentleman," the overseer said,
pointing at me with his pen, "is staying with us over
night. He wants to look over the works tomorrow. Give
him something to eat and then take him to where he is
to sleep. Have you understood me?" Horace nodded, he

was probably a little hard of hearing, at any rate he
held his head bent down to the overseer.

"Never will you draw the water out of the depths of
this well."
"What water? What well?"
"Who is it asking?"
Silence.
"What silence?"

My longing was for the ancient times,
my longing was for the present,
my longing was for the future,
and with all this I am dying in a watchman's hut
    at the edge of the street,
an upright coffin that has always been
a piece of State property.
I have spent my life
restraining myself from smashing it to pieces.

I have spent my life resisting the desire to end it.

You must push your head through the wall. It is not
difficult to penetrate it, for it is made of thin paper. But
what is difficult is not to let yourself be deceived by the
fact that there is already an extremely deceptive paint-
ing on the wall showing you pushing your head through.
It tempts you to say: "Am I not pushing through it all
the time?"

I am fighting; nobody knows this; some have an inkling of it, that cannot be avoided; but nobody knows it. I
carry out my daily duties, I can be criticized for a little
absent-mindedness, but not for much. Of course, every-

one fights, but I fight more than others, most people fight as though they were asleep, just as one moves one's hand in a dream in order to drive off an apparition, but I have stepped forward and am fighting with the most carefully considered deployment of all my forces. Why have I stepped forward out of the crowd, which, noisy as it is, in this respect is frighteningly quiet? Why have I drawn attention to myself? Why am I now on the enemy's top list? I don't know. Another life did not seem worth living. "Born soldiers" is what military history calls such people. And yet this is not so, I am not hoping for victory and I do not like fighting for its own sake, I like it solely because it is the only thing to do. As such I have, I must admit, more liking for it than I can actually enjoy, more than I can give away, perhaps I shall not die of fighting, but of this joy.

They are strangers and yet my own people. Having been set free, they talk, with the unconsciousness of those who have been set free, in a slightly intoxicated way, they have not a moment to spare for any recognition. As one master talks to another, so they talk among themselves, each one presupposing freedom and the right of independent action in the other. But fundamentally they have not changed, their opinions have remained the same, so have their gestures, their gaze. Something, it is true, is different, but I cannot grasp the difference, and if I speak of having been set free it is only for want of any better way of explaining. Why *should* they feel they have been set free? All the circles and all the forms of subordination have been preserved, the tension between each individual and all the others unimpaired, each one is in his place and so primed for the fighting that is allotted him that he cannot even speak of anything but that, no matter what one may ask him. Wherein then does the difference lie? I sniff round them like a dog and cannot detect the difference.

Farm laborers returning home at evening found an old man quite collapsed at the bottom of the embankment beside the road. He was dozing with half-open eyes. At first he made the impression of being very drunk, but he was not drunk. Nor did he seem to be ill, nor weak with hunger, nor faint from wounds; at least he shook his head in answer to all such questions. "But who are you?" he was asked at last. "I am a great general," he said without looking up. "Oh, so that's it," they said, "so that's your trouble." "No," he said, "I really am." "Of course," they said, "how else should you be that but really?" "Laugh according to your lights," he said. "I shall not punish you." "But we are not laughing," they said, "be whatever you like, be top general if you like." "That's just what I am," he said, "I am top general." "There you are. you see how we recognized that. But that doesn't concern us, we only wanted to draw your attention to the fact that it will freeze hard tonight and so you should go away from here." "I can't go away, and besides, I don't know where I could go." "But why can't you go?" "I can't go, I don't know why. If I could go, then I should instantly be the general in the midst of my army again." "They threw you out, did they?" "A general? No, I fell down." "Where from?" "From the sky." "From up there?" "Yes." "So your army's up there?" "No. But you ask too many questions. Go away and leave me."

Consolidation. We were employees in the shop; the bookeeper, a shortsighted melancholy man who lay sprawled over the ledger like a frog, motionless, just faintly rising and falling with his laborious breathing; then the salesman, a little man with the broad chest of a gymnast, who only needed to support himself on the counter with one hand in order to vault over it lightly and beautifully, only as he did so his face remained solemn and he gazed around with a severe look. Then we had a saleswoman, an elderly spinster, slender and frail, in a tight-fitting dress; most of the time she held her head on one side and smiled with the thin lips of her large mouth. I, the apprentice, who had not much more to do than to hang about the counter with a duster, often felt an urge to take our saleswoman's hand, a long, weak, dried-up hand the color of wood, when it lay on the counter, negligent and self-forgetful, and to stroke it or even to kiss it or—this would have been the acme—to lay my face on it, letting my face rest in that good place, and only now and then to change my position so that each cheek should get its fair share in the enjoyment of that hand. But this never happened; on the contrary, just as I drew near the saleswoman would stretch out her hand and point to some new job for me to do somewhere in a distant corner or at the top of the ladder. This second sort of job was particularly unpleasant, it was oppressively hot up there from the open gas jets by which the shop was lighted, and besides, I was inclined to get dizzy, I often felt sick up there, sometimes, on the pretext of cleaning out in a particularly thorough way up there I would put my head into a shelf and weep for a little while, or if no one happened to be looking up, I would make a short, mute speech to the saleswoman down below, reproaching her bitterly; true, I knew that she was very far from having decisive power here or anywhere else, but somehow I believed she could have that power if she wanted to and then use it in my favor. But she did not want to, she did not even use the power she had. For instance, she was the only person on the staff whom the shop messenger to some extent obeyed, who

was the most stubborn person imaginable; to be sure, he
was the oldest in the firm and had served under the old
proprietor, he had been through so much here of which
the rest of us had no notion, but from all this he drew
the mistaken conclusion that he knew better about
everything than the others, that, for instance, he would
not only keep the books just as well as the bookkeeper,
but much better, would serve the customers much better
than the salesman, and so on, and that he had only
taken on the job of shop messenger of his own free will
because nobody else, not even a quite incapable person,
had been found to do it. And so he, who had probably
never been very strong and was now a mere wreck,
toiled and moiled with the handcart, the crates and parcels, as he had been doing for forty years. He had taken
it on voluntarily, but that had been forgotten, new times
had come, he was no longer recognized and respected,
and while all around him in the business the most frightful mistakes were being made, he, who was not allowed
to intervene, had to swallow his despair about it and remain fettered to his heavy work, into the bargain.

He has inclined his head to one side, and where his
neck is thus exposed, there is a wound, boiling in burning
blood and flesh, having been struck by a flash of lightning that still continues.

In bed, the knee slightly raised, lying there amid the
folds of the blanket draped around it, gigantic as a stone
figure at the side of the steps outside a public building,
rigid among the living crowd drifting by, and yet in a
remote relationship to it that is scarcely definable in its
remoteness.

In a certain country they pray only to a single group
of divinities, which are called: the clenched teeth. Yester-

day I was in their temple. A priest received me on the steps outside. A certain initiation is necessary before one is allowed to enter. It consists of the visitor's bowing his head and the priest's briefly stroking the back of his neck downwards with his hard fingertips. Then one enters the antechamber, which is chock-full of sacrificial gifts. The forecourt and the sanctuary are open to all, but the innermost chamber may be entered only by the priests and unbelievers. "You will not see a great deal," the priest said, smiling, "but you can come along."

One can see how great the circle of life is from the fact that, on the one hand, for as far back as it can think, mankind has been overflowing with speech and, on the other hand, speech is possible only where one wants to lie.

Confession and the lie are one and the same. In order to be able to confess, one tells lies. One cannot express what one is, for that *is* precisely what one is; one can communicate only what one is not, that is, the lie. Only in the chorus there may be a certain truth.

It was a night school for shop apprentices, they had been given some little sums to do, which they were now supposed to be working out on paper. But there was such a tremendous noise from the whole class that nobody could do a sum even with the best will in the world. The quietest person was the teacher up on the dais, a thin young student who was still somehow clinging desperately to the conviction that the pupils were doing their work and that he was therefore at liberty to get on with his own studies, which he did, pressing his thumbs over his ears. Then there was a knock at the door, it was the inspector of night schools. The boys became quiet as quickly as they could after being in such a wild state of uproar, and the teacher laid the gradebook on top of his own notebooks. The inspector, still a young man, not much older than the student, surveyed the class with weary eyes, which were obviously rather shortsighted. Then he went up on to the dais, took the gradebook, not in order to open it but in order to expose the teacher's own notebooks, then made a sign to the teacher to sit down and seated himself, half beside him, half opposite him, on the second chair. The following conversation then took place, to which the whole class—and those sitting at the back had stood up in order to see better—listened attentively:

INSPECTOR: So nothing at all is being learnt here. I could hear the noise all the way down on the story below.

TEACHER: There are some very badly behaved boys in the class, but the others are working out a sum.

INSPECTOR: No, nobody is working, nor can it possibly be otherwise if you sit up here, studying Roman law.

TEACHER: It is true, I have been using the time during which the class does written work for study, I wanted to cut down my night's work a little for once, I have no time to study by day.

INSPECTOR: All right, that sounds quite innocent, but let us look a little closer. What school is this we are in here?

TEACHER: The night school for apprentices of the Honorable Company of Shopkeepers.

INSPECTOR: Is this school a high one or a low one?

TEACHER: A low one.

INSPECTOR: Perhaps one of the lowest?

TEACHER: Yes, one of the lowest.

INSPECTOR: That is correct, it is one of the lowest. It is lower than the elementary schools, for apart from what is merely a repetition of what is taught at the elemen-

tary schools, that is to say, something that is still quite
respectable, it is the veriest rudiments that are taught
here. And so all of us—pupils, teacher, and myself, the
inspector—work, or rather, are supposed to work, as our
duty bids us, at one of the lowest schools. Is that by any
chance dishonorable?

TEACHER: No, learning is never dishonorable. Besides,
the school is only a transition period for the boys.

INSPECTOR: And for you?

TEACHER: For me too, really.

It was not a prison cell, for the fourth side was completely open. To be sure, the notion that this side too
might have been or might yet be walled up was horrible,
for then, in a room of those dimensions, three feet across
and only a little higher than my head, I would be in an
upright stone coffin. Still, for the present it was not
walled up, I could stretch my hands out into the open,
freely, and if I held on to an iron hook that was fixed in
the ceiling, I could also stretch my head out cautiously—
very cautiously for I did not know how high my cell
was from the ground. It seemed to be very high up, at
least I could see nothing in the depths but a gray haze,
and the same to right and to left and in the distance too,
and it was only above me that it seemed to clear
slightly. It was a view such as one might have from a
tower on a dull day.

I was tired and sat down on the edge in front, letting
my feet dangle. It was annoying that I was quite naked,
otherwise I should have knotted my clothes and underclothes together, fastened them to the hook, and let myself down outside a long way below my cell and perhaps
been able to spy out a good deal. On the other hand it
was just as well that I could not do so, in my restlessness
I should probably have done it, but it might have turned

out very badly. Better to have nothing and to do nothing.

At the back of the cell, which was otherwise quite empty, its walls bare, there were two holes in the floor. The hole in the one corner seemed intended for the prisoner's natural needs, and in front of the hole in the other corner there lay a piece of bread and a little wooden barrel with a lid screwed on, which contained water, and so it seemed that this was where my food was pushed inside for me.

I have no inherent dislike of snakes, and even less fear of them. It is only now, retrospectively, that the fear sets in. But in my situation this is perhaps quite understandable. First of all, there are no snakes at all in the whole of the town, except in collections or one or two shops, yet my room is full of them. It began with my sitting at my table one evening, writing a letter. I have no inkwell and was using a large ink-bottle. I was just about to dip my pen in again when I saw a snake raising its small, delicate, flat head out of the neck of the bottle. Its body hung down inside the bottle and vanished below in the up-churned ink. This was certainly very queer, but I at once stopped staring at it when it struck me that it might be a poisonous snake, which was very probable, for it was darting its tongue out in a suspicious way, and a menacing three-colored star. . . .

It is not that you are buried in the mine, the masses of rock separating you, one weak individual, from the world and its light; you are outside and are trying to make your way in to him who is buried, and you are helpless, confronted with the rocks, and the world and its light make you still more helpless. And at every moment he whom you are trying to save is suffocating, so that you must work like a madman, and he will never quite suffocate, so that you will never be free to cease from work.

It was a small party on the terrace, under the roof supported by pillars. Three steps led down into the garden. There was a full moon, and it was a warm night in June. We were all very gay, laughing about everything; when a dog barked in the distance, we laughed about that.

"Are we on the right road?" I asked our guide, a Greek Jew. In the light of the torch he turned his gentle, sad, wan face to me. It seemed to be a matter of indifference to him whether we were on the right road or not. And how, anyway, did we come to have this guide, who, instead of taking us through the catacombs of Rome, had so far done nothing but walk along with us, in silence, wherever we went? I stopped and waited until our whole party was close together. I asked if nobody was missing; nobody seemed to be missing. I had to be content with that, for I myself knew nobody among them; in the crowd, strangers as we were, we had descended into the catacombs here behind the guide, and it was only now that I tried to strike up some sort of acquaintance with them.

I have a heavy hammer, but I cannot use it, for the handle is red-hot.

Many people prowl round Mount Sinai. Their speech is blurred, either they are garrulous or they shout or they are taciturn. But none of them comes straight down a broad, newly made, smooth road that does its own part in making one's strides long and swifter.

Writing as a form of prayer.

Difference between Zürau and Prague. Did I not fight hard enough at that time?

Did he not fight hard enough? When he was working, he was already lost; he knew that, he said to himself frankly: if I stop working, I am lost. And so was it a mistake for him to begin working? Scarcely.

He believed he had made a statue, but he had only been hitting away at the same dent all the time out of stupid obstinacy, and yet still more out of helplessness.

The spiritual desert. The corpses from the caravans of your earlier and your later days.

Nothing, only an image, nothing else, utter oblivion.

In the caravansary there was never any sleep, there no one slept. But if one did not sleep there, why did one go at all? In order to let the beasts of burden rest. It was only a small place, a tiny oasis, but it was entirely occupied by the caravansary and that, to be sure, was immense. It was impossible, or at least so it seemed to me, for a stranger to find his way about there. The manner in which it was built was partly to blame for this. For instance, one went into the first courtyard, out of which two round arches, about thirty feet distant from each other, led into a second court; one went through one arch and then, instead of coming into another large court, as one had expected, found oneself in a small gloomy square between walls that were sky-high, and only at a great height above one did one see loggias with light burning. And so now one thought one had lost one's way and tried to go back through the archway, but, as it happened, one did not go through the archway

one had come through but through the other one next to
it. But now one was not in the first courtyard after all,
but in another and much larger court, full of noise,
music, and the bellowing of animals. So one had lost
one's way, went back into the dark square and through
the first arch. It was of no avail, once again one was in
the second court and had to ask one's way through several courtyards before arriving back in the first courtyard, from which one had, however, actually gone only a
few paces away. What was unpleasant, now, was that
the first courtyard was always crowded, one could
scarcely find any lodging there. It looked almost as
though the quarters in the first courtyard were occupied
by permanent guests, yet it could not be so in reality, for
only caravans stopped here, who else would have wanted
or been able to live in this dirt and uproar; after all, the
little oasis provided nothing but water and was many
miles away from larger oases. And so nobody could want
to lodge, to live, here permanently, unless it was the
owner of the caravansary and his employees, but these
people I never saw, in spite of having been there several
times, nor did I ever hear anything about them. And it
would have been difficult to imagine that if an owner
had been present he would have permitted such disorder,
indeed such acts of violence, as were usual there by day
and night. On the contrary, I had the impression that
whichever happened to be the strongest caravan domi-
nated everything there, and then came the others, according to their strength. True, that does not explain
everything. The great main gate, for instance, was usually locked and barred; to open it for caravans coming or
going was always a positively ceremonial act, and to
bring this about was a very complicated matter. Caravans would often wait outside in the glaring sunshine for
hours before they were let in. This, of course, was obvi-

ously wanton behavior, but one could never discover the reason for it. And so one waited outside and had time to contemplate the framework of the ancient gateway. Round the gate there were two or three ranks of angels in high relief, blowing trumpets; one of these instruments, right at the apex of the arch, extended fairly far down into the gateway itself. The animals always had to be carefully led round it, so that they should not bump against it; it was strange, particularly in view of the ruinous condition of the whole building, that this work, beautiful as it was, was not damaged at all, not even by those who had been waiting so long in impotent anger outside the gate. Perhaps this is connected with the fact that. . . .

This is a life between stage scenery. It is light, that is a morning in the open air, then an instant later darkness falls and now it is evening. This is not a very complicated deception, but one must come to terms with it so long as one is standing on the stage. The only direction in which one may break out, if one has the strength, is towards the background, cutting through the canvas and, dashing between the tatters of the painted sky, away across bits of junk lying about, to escape into the real, narrow, dark, damp street, which, though it is called Theater Street, from being still close to the theater, is nevertheless true and has all the depths of truth itself.

"This piece of twisted root is what you now propose playing the flute on?"

"I shouldn't have thought of it, it is only because you expect it that I am going to do it."

"I expect it?"

"Yes, for at the sight of my hands you say to yourself

that no wood can help resounding in accordance with my will."

"You are right."

In a side current a fish is drifting, gazing down, as anxiously as joyfully, into the depths where there is a small stirring in the deep mud, and then up, as anxiously as joyfully, to where there is a huge preparation being made in the upper waters.

In the evening he slammed the door of his shop and ran up as into a music hall.

If you keep on running forwards, if you go on splashing in the warm air, your hands at your sides like fins, looking fleetingly, in the half-sleep of haste, at everything you pass, you will sometime let the carriage bowl past you too. But if you remain firm, letting the roots grow deep and broad with the strength of your gaze—nothing can shift you, and yet they are not roots at all, but only the strength of your gaze, always focused on its goal—then you will also see the immutable dark distance out of which there can come nothing but, sometime, that very carriage, bowling nearer, growing ever larger, filling the whole world in the instant when it draws level with you, and you will sink into it like a child among the cushions of a traveling coach driving through the storm and the night.

Thou shalt not make any graven image. . . .

They were a small party in the narrow room, at tea, in the evening. A bird was flying round them, a raven, tugging at the girls' hair and dipping its beak into the cups. They took no notice of it, singing and laughing, and so it became bolder. . . .

"Teach the children," I was told. The small room was overcrowded. Many were so squeezed up against the wall that it looked alarming; on the other hand, they resisted, pushing the others back, and so the whole mass of them was in constant movement. Only some older children, who stood head and shoulders above the others and had nothing to fear from them, stood quietly along the back wall, gazing across at me.

The whipmasters were assembled, sturdy but slender gentlemen, always in readiness; they were called whip-masters, but they held birches in their hands; they stood out from the back wall of the state room and between the mirrors. I entered with my bride, it was the wedding. Through a narrow door facing us the relatives came forth, spinning out of the doorway, voluminous women; on their left, beside them, smaller men in high-buttoned morning coats who walked with short steps. Many of the relatives flung their arms up in amazement at the sight of my bride, but all was still quiet.

Having taken a walk one Sunday, I had gone farther beyond the town than I had really meant to. And when I had gone so far, something drove me yet farther. On a lit-tle hill there was an old oak, very twisted but not very big. It somehow reminded me that now at long last it was really time to turn back. By now it was well into the evening. I stood before it, stroking its hard bark, and read two names carved there. I read them, but without taking them in; it was something like childish defiance that now, if I was really not to go any farther, at least held me fast here, preventing me from going back. One is sometimes spellbound by such forces, it is a spell one can easily break, since it is merely something like a gentle joke made by a stranger, but it was Sunday, there was nothing that had to be attended to, I was now tired, and so I resigned myself to everything. Now I realized that one of the names was Josef and remembered a school-friend who had had that name. In my recollection he was a small boy, perhaps the smallest in the class; for some years he had sat next to me, at the same desk. He had been ugly; even to us, who at that time did, after all, understand more about strength and skill—and he had both—than about beauty, he seemed very ugly.

We ran out in front of the house. There was a beggar standing there with a concertina. The hem of his garment, a sort of long gown, was so ragged that it looked as if the material had originally not been cut off a length of cloth but brutally torn off, by force. And the beggar's bewildered air seemed to be somehow in keeping with this, he seemed to have been roused out of deep sleep and to be unable to discover where he was, no matter how much he tried. It was as though he were falling asleep again all the time and always being roused again.

We children did not dare to speak to him and ask him for a song as we always asked beggar musicians. Besides, he kept on running his eyes over us all the time as if, in spite of being aware of our presence, he could not see us quite so distinctly as he wanted to.

And so we waited until father came. He was in the workshop at the back, and it was a little while before he came striding down the long passage. "Who are you?" he asked loudly and sternly in the next room, his gaze was sullen, perhaps he was dissatisfied with our behavior to the beggar, but still, we hadn't done anything, or at any rate we had not yet done any damage. We became, if possible, even quieter. Everything, indeed, was very still, only the lime tree outside our house rustled in the breeze.

"I have come from Italy," the beggar said, yet not as though it were an answer, but as though it were a confession of guilt. It was as though he recognized our father as his master. He hugged the concertina to his chest as though it were a protection to him. . . .

He had fastened his upper teeth on his lower lip, and he gazed ahead of him, not stirring. "Your behavior is quite senseless. What has happened to you anyway? Your business isn't going too brilliantly, but it's not going badly either; even if it were to go to wrack and ruin— but there is no question of that—you will, after all, very easily get a foothold somewhere, you're young, healthy, strong, an experienced and efficient businessman, you've only yourself and your mother to look after, well then, for heaven's sake, man, pull yourself together and tell me why you've sent for me right in the middle of the day and why you're sitting there like that." Now there was a little pause, I was sitting on the window sill, he was sitting in a chair in the middle of the room. At last he said: "All right, I'll explain everything to you. All you have said is true, but think of this: since yesterday it has been raining ceaselessly, it was about five o'clock in the afternoon"—he looked at his watch—"yesterday when it began raining and at four o'clock today it's still raining. That's enough to start anyone thinking. But whereas at other times it only rains in the street and not indoors, this time it seems to be the other way round. Look out of the window, if you please, it's dry down in the street, isn't it? Well then. But here the water is rising incessantly. Let it, let it rise. It's bad, but I can stand it. A little good will and one can stand it; one simply floats a little higher together with one's chair; after all, it doesn't change conditions so very much. Everything is floating, that's all there is to it, and one floats a little higher. But the raindrops beating on my head is something I can't stand. It seems to be a trifle, but this very trifle is what I can't stand, or perhaps I would stand even that, only I can't stand being defenseless against it. And I am defenseless; I put a hat on, I put my umbrella up, I hold a board over my head; it's all no good, either the rain penetrates through everything, or under the hat, the umbrella, the board, a new rain begins to fall with the same intensity."

I was standing in front of the mining engineer, in his office. It was a weatherboard shack, on barren clay ground that had been only roughly leveled off. An unshaded electric bulb was burning over the middle of the table. "So you want to be taken on?" the engineer said, resting his forehead on his left hand and with his right holding the pen poised over a sheet of paper. It was not a question, he said it just to himself; he was a weakly young man of less than middle height, it was obvious that he was very tired, his eyes were doubtless naturally so small and narrow, but it looked as though he had not the strength to open them any wider. "Sit down," he said then. But all there was to sit on was a crate with one side torn off it, out of which small machine-parts had tumbled forth. He had now detached himself entirely from his desk, only his right hand still lay there, its position unchanged, but for the rest he had leaned back in his chair, put his left hand in his trouser-pocket, and was gazing at me. "Who sent you here?" he asked. "I read an announcement in a technical journal saying that people were being taken on here," I said. "I see," he said, smiling, "and so you read that. But you set about it in a very rough-and-ready way." "What does that mean?" I asked. "I don't understand you." "It means," he said, "that nobody is being taken on here. And if nobody is being taken on, you can't be taken on either." "That's true, that's true," I said and stood up, annoyed, "there was no need for me to sit down in order to be told that." But then I thought better of it and asked: "Couldn't I spend the night here? It's raining outside and the village is over an hour's journey away." "I have no guest room here," the engineer said. "Couldn't I stay here in the office?" "No, this is where I work and there"—he pointed to a corner—"is where I sleep." Sure enough, there were blankets there and also a little heap of straw, but there was also such a jumble of unidentifiable things, mainly tools, that I had not taken it for a place where anyone would sleep.

. . . me to pick it up. I did so and he said: "I am on a journey, don't disturb me, open your shirt and bring me close to your body." I did so, he took a long stride and disappeared into me as into a house. I stretched as though constricted, I was overcome by something that was almost a swoon, I dropped the spade and went home. There were men sitting at table there, all eating out of the one common dish, and the two women were at the stove and the washtub. I at once recounted what had happened to me and, while doing so, fell down on the bench by the door; they all stood around me. An old man of proven skill was fetched from a farm nearby. While we were waiting for him, children came to me, we took each other's hands, linked fingers. . . .

It was a great river, with muddy waters, tossing along in tremendous but somehow sleepy, all-too-regular haste, with low, soundless ripples. Perhaps nothing else was possible, because it was overbrimming. . . .

A horseman was riding along a forest path, a dog running ahead of him. Behind him came a few geese, a small girl driving them in front of her with an osier twig. In spite of the fact that all of them, from the dog in front to the little girl at the rear, were all hastening on as fast as possible, it all nevertheless did not go very fast, and each easily kept pace with the others. Besides, the forest trees on both sides were also running along with them, somehow reluctantly, wearily, old trees as they were. The girl was joined by a young athlete, a swimmer; he swam along with powerful strokes, his head deep in the water, for water was rippling all around him, and as he swam, so did the water flow with him; then there came a carpenter who had a table to deliver, which he was carrying on his back, holding its two front legs firmly in his hands; he was followed by the courier of the Czar, and he was unhappy on account of all the people he had met with here in the forest, he kept on craning his neck and peering ahead to see what the situation was up in front and why everything was going so tiresomely slowly, but he had to put up with it—for though he might have been able to overtake the carpenter in front of him, how would he have got through the water surrounding the swimmer? Behind the courier, oddly enough, there came the Czar himself, a man still young, with a pointed fair beard and a delicate but chubby face radiant with enjoyment of life. Here it was apparent what were the disadvantages of such great empires: the Czar did not know his courier, the courier did not know his Czar, the Czar was out for a little constitutional and progressed no less rapidly than his courier, and so he might as well have carried the mail himself.

⁴⁹ I ran past the first watchman. Then I was horrified, ran back again and said to the watchman: "I ran through here while you were looking the other way." The watchman gazed ahead of him and said nothing. "I suppose I

really oughtn't to have done it," I said. The watchman still said nothing. "Does your silence indicate permission to pass?" . . .

Two threshers had been sent for and were standing in the dark barn with their flails. "Come," they said, and I was laid on the threshing floor. The farmer stood leaning against the door, half outside, half in.

The animal wrests the whip from its master and whips itself in order to become master, not knowing that this is only a fantasy produced by a new knot in the master's whiplash.

Man is an immense swamp. If he is seized with enthusiasm, the effect in the general picture is as though somewhere in a corner of this swamp a little frog had flopped into the green water.

If only one person were capable of leaving off one word before the truth! Everyone (I too in this dictum) overruns truth by hundreds of words.

To tell the truth, the whole affair does not concern me very much. I lie in the corner, looking on in so far as one can look on while lying down, and listening in so far as I understand him, and for the rest I have for months now been living in a sort of twilight, waiting for the night. It is otherwise with my cell mate, an unyielding man, a former army captain. I can imagine what his state of mind is. He is of the opinion that his situation is rather like that of a Polar explorer who has been frozen in somewhere, in utter misery, but who is certain of being saved, or rather, who is already saved, as one can discover by reading the history of Polar expeditions.

And now the following dilemma comes about: his being saved is, for him, undoubtedly independent of his will, it is simply through the victorious weight of his personality that he will be saved—but should he wish for it? His wishing or not wishing will not alter anything, he is going to be saved anyway, but the question whether he should also wish for it remains. It is with this seemingly so irrelevant question that he is preoccupied, he keeps on thinking it out and putting it before me, and we keep on discussing it. He does not understand that this posing of the question seals his fate. Of rescue itself we do not speak. All that he needs for rescue seems to be the little hammer that he has somehow got hold of, a tiny hammer for knocking tacks into a drawing board, it could not be used for anything more, but he does not demand anything of it, the mere possession of it delights him. Sometimes he kneels beside me and holds this hammer, which I have seen a thousand times, under my nose, or he takes my hand, splays it out on the floor and hammers all the fingers, one after the other. He knows he cannot knock so much as a splinter out of the wall with this hammer, nor does he want to, only sometimes he passes the hammer lightly over the walls as though in this way he could give the signal that would set the vast waiting apparatus of rescue into motion. It will not be exactly like this, the rescue will begin in its own time, independently of the hammer, but still, the hammer is something, it is something tangible, a surety, something that one can kiss as one will never be able to kiss the rescue itself.

Well, my answer to all his questions is simply: "No, rescue is not to be wished for." I do not want to set up any general laws, that is the jailer's affair. I speak only of myself. And so far as I am concerned, I was scarcely able to endure living in freedom, in the same freedom that is now to be our salvation, or perhaps I was really quite unable to endure it, for, after all, here I am in this cell. To be sure, it was not actually the cell I was striving to reach, I was only trying to get away somehow in general, perhaps to some other planet—to some other planet for a start. But would the atmosphere there have been such that I could breathe it, or would I not suffocate there as I do here in this cell? And so I might just as well have been striving to reach the cell.

Sometimes two jailers come into our cell to play cards. I don't know why they do this, it is actually a certain alleviation of our punishment. They usually come towards evening, I am always slightly feverish then and cannot quite keep my eyes open, and I only see them indistinctly in the light of the big lantern they bring with them. Is it then really still a cell if it suffices the jailers themselves? But this reflection does not always gladden me, for a convict's class-consciousness awakens in me—what do they want here among the convicts? I *am* glad that they are here, I feel reassured by the presence of these mighty men, I also feel myself elevated beyond myself by them, but I do not really want this, I want to open my mouth and blow them out of the cell, as it were by the force of my breath.

Certainly, it can be said that the captain has gone mad as a result of being imprisoned. His orbit of ideas is so limited that he scarcely has any room left for any idea at all. He has simply thought the idea of rescue to a finish, there is nothing left of it but a little vestige, exactly as much as is necessary to keep him slightly buoyed up, in a convuslive way, but even this expedient he sometimes lets go of now, though then, of course, he grabs at it again and then positively snorts with pride and delight. Yet I am not superior to him on that account, in method perhaps, in something inessential perhaps, but not otherwise.

A rainy day. You are standing before the radiance of a puddle. You are not tired, not sad, not thoughtful, you merely stand there in all the weight of your earthliness, waiting for someone. Then you hear a voice, and the mere sound of it, even without words, makes you smile. "Come along," the voice says. But there is no one there round about for you to go with. "I would go all right," you say, "but I don't see you." And then you hear no more. But here comes the man you have been waiting for, a big strong man with little eyes, bushy eyebrows, fat, rather sagging cheeks, and an imperial. You have a feeling that you must have seen him once before. Of course, you have seen him before, for he is your old business friend, you had made an appointment with him to meet here and to talk over a matter of business that has been undecided for a long time. But in spite of the fact that he is standing there in front of you and the rain is slowly dripping from the brim of his hat, which you have known so long, it is only with an effort that you recognize him. There is something that prevents you, you try to drive it away, you want to get into immediate contact with the man, and for this reason you take him by the arm. But you have to let go of him again instantly, shuddering—what have you touched? You look at your hand, but in spite of seeing nothing, you feel disgusted to the point of nausea. You make up an excuse, which is probably not an excuse at all, for while you are uttering it you have forgotten it, and you walk away, walk straight into the wall of a house—the man shouts after you, perhaps a warning, you wave him off —the wall opens up in front of you, a servant carries a

candelabrum on high, you follow him. However, he con-
ducts you not into an apartment, but into a chemist's
shop.

It is a large chemist's shop with a high semicircular
wall containing hundreds of identical drawers. There are
many customers there too, most of them have long thin
poles with which they immediately tap on the drawer
out of which they want something. Thereupon the assistants go climbing up with very rapid but tiny climbing
movements—one does not see what they are climbing on,
one rubs one's eyes and still one does not see it—and
fetch down what is asked for. It is done only for amuse-
ment or is it innate in the assistants? In any case, they
have bushy tails sticking out of the seats of the trousers,
rather like squirrels' but much longer, and as they climb
the tails quiver with all the many little movements. Because of the crowd of customers pouring this way and
that in the shop, one simply cannot see how the shop is
connected with the street; on the other hand, one sees a
small shut window overlooking the street, on the right of
what is probably the main entrance. Through this window one sees three people outside, blocking the view so
completely that one cannot say whether the street beyond is full of people or perhaps empty. What one
mainly sees is a man who attracts the gaze entirely to
himself, on each side of him stands a woman, but one
scarcely notices them, they are bowed or sunken or just
sinking into the depths, slanting towards the man, they
are utterly irrelevant; on the other hand, the man himself has something feminine about him too. He is power-
fully built, is wearing a workman's blue blouse; his face
is broad and open, the nose squashed, it looks as though
it were just being squashed and the nostrils were struggling, writhing in the attempt to survive; the cheeks are
very ruddy with life. He gazes steadily into the chem-

ist's shop, moving his lips, bending to right and to left, as
though he were looking for something inside. In the shop
a man is noticeable who is neither asking for anything
nor serving, but walking about, very straight, trying to
survey everything, holding his restless lower lip with two
fingers, sometimes glancing at his fob-watch. He is obviously the proprietor, the customers point him out to
each other, he is easily recognizable by numerous thin,
round, long leather straps tied, not too loosely and not
too tightly, round the upper part of his body, lengthwise
and crosswise. A fair boy of about ten is clinging to his
jacket, and sometimes grabs at the straps too, he is asking for something that the chemist is not going to allow
him. Then the doorbell rings. Why does it ring? So many
customers came and went without its ringing, but now
it rings. The crowd surges back from the door; it is as
though this ringing had been expected; it is, indeed, as
though the crowd knew more than it confesses to knowing. And now, too, one sees the big double glass door.
Outside there is a narrow empty street, neatly paved with
bricks, it is an overcast, rainy day, but it is not raining yet. A gentleman has just opened the door from outside in the street, thus setting the bell in motion, but
now he is in doubt, he steps back again, reads the name
of the shop once more, yet, it is right, and now he comes
in. It is the doctor, Herodias; everyone in the crowd
knows this. His left hand in his trouser pocket, he walks
over to the chemist, who is now standing alone with a
clear space all round him; even the boy, though he is
still in the front row, has hung back and gazes across out
of his wide-open blue eyes. Herodias has a smiling, superior manner of talking, he carries his head thrown
back, and even when he himself is speaking, it looks as
though he were listening. At the same time he is very
absent-minded, he has to be told some things twice, it is

difficult to get through to him, and this, too, is something he seems to be smiling about. How should it be that a doctor does not know the chemist's shop? And yet he looks around him as though he were here for the first time, and he shakes his head over the assistants with their tails. Then he goes up to the chemist, lays his right arm round his shoulders, and turns him round, and now the two of them, keeping close together, walk on through the crowd, which falls back to make room for them, and go into the back of the shop, the boy in front of them, time and again glancing back shyly. Behind the counters they come to a curtain that the boy in front of them lifts, then they go on through some little laboratories, and finally they come to a small door, which, since the boy does not dare to open it, the doctor must open. There is a certain danger that the crowd, which has hitherto pushed on after them, will follow them right into this room. But the assistants, who have meanwhile made their way to the front of the crowd, without waiting for any command from their master, turn towards the crowd, they are young men, and strong, but sensible too; slowly and quietly they press back the crowd, which has, indeed, come rolling forward simply as a result of its own weight and not with any intention of being a nuisance. In any case, a countermovement is established. It is caused by the man with the two women, he has left his place at the window, has come into the shop and now wants to get further forward than everyone else. Precisely as a result of the yieldingness of the crowd, which is visibly full of respect for this place, he succeeds in doing so. Forcing his way through between the assistants, whom he thrusts aside more by means of two swift glances than by using his elbows, in an instant he, with his two women, has reached the gentlemen and, being taller than either of them, gazes between their heads into the darkness of the room beyond. "Who's that coming?" a woman's faint voice asks from inside the room. "Keep calm, it's the doctor," the chemist answers, and now they enter the room. Nobody thinks of turning on a light. The doctor has left the chemist and goes up to the bed alone. The man and the women lean on the bedposts at the sick woman's feet, as though against a railing. The chemist does not dare to do anything about it, and the boy is clinging to him again. The doctor feels impeded by the three strangers. "Who are you people?" he asks, speaking in a low voice out of consideration for the sick woman. "Neighbors," the man says. "What do you want?" "We want," the man says, speaking much more loudly than the doctor. . . .

50 [A fragment of *The Assistant Public Prosecutor*.]

. . . grown tired of organizing hunts after freaks, then, to be sure, the district judge would be the first object. But there is no sense in getting annoyed about him. And so the Assistant Public Prosecutor does not get annoyed about him, he is only annoyed at the stupidity that puts such a person in the position of district judge. And so stupidity sets up to dispense justice. As regards the Assistant Attorney's private affairs, it is actually very much to be deplored that he only holds such a low rank, but his real aspirations would perhaps not be satisfied even with being Chief Public Prosecutor. He would have to become a yet much higher Public Prosecutor in order to bring an effective case against even all the stupidity that he sees before his eyes. Yet he would not dream of condescending to bring a case against the district judge, he would not even acknowledge him from the lofty height of his prosecutor's seat. But he certainly would create such a splendid order of things all round about that the district judge would not be able to continue existing in it and, without his being touched, his knees would begin to shake and he would in the end be bound to perish. Then perhaps it would also be time to bring the case of the Assistant Public Prosecutor himself out of the disciplinary courts, where proceedings are conducted *in camera*, into the public law court. Then the Assistant Public Prosecutor would no longer be personally involved; by virtue of higher authority he would have broken the chains in which he had been fettered and would now be able to sit in judgment over them himself. He imagines that a powerful personage whispers into his ear before the proceedings: "Now you will receive satisfaction." And now the proceedings begin. The accused members of the disciplinary board lie, of course; they lie with clenched teeth; they lie in the way that only men of the law can lie when for once it is they who are charged. But everything has been prepared in such a way that the facts themselves shake off all lies and reveal themselves freely and in accordance with the truth, in the presence of the audience. There is a large audience there, on three sides of the courtroom, only the judges' bench is empty, no judges have been found, the judges are crowded together in the narrow space where the accused usually stands, and try to give an account of themselves before the empty bench. Only the Public Attorney, the former Assistant Public Prosecutor, is of course present and in his usual place. He is much calmer than at other times, he only nods now and then; everything is taking its proper course, like clockwork. Only now, after the case has been disentangled from all written statements, witnesses' depositions, minutes of proceedings, conferrings as to the verdict, and references to precedent, does its overwhelming simplicity become immediately apparent. The affair itself dates back some fifteen years. The Assistant Public Prosecutor was at that time in the capital,

he was recognized as an able lawyer, was very popular
with his superiors, and even then had hopes of soon out-
distancing many rivals and becoming tenth Public Prosecutor. The second Public Prosecutor showed a particular
liking for him and let him deputize for him, even in cases
that were not entirely unimportant. This also happened
in a small case of lese majeste. A shop assistant, a man not
without education, who was very active politically, had
uttered a remark insulting to His Majesty, glass in hand,
while in a state of semi-drunkenness, in a wine room. Another guest at the next table, who was probably even
drunker, had denounced him, probably believing, in his
befuddlement, that he was doing something meritorious,
had instantly rushed to get a policeman and had returned
with him, smiling blissfully, in order to give the man in
charge. Later, admittedly, he struck to his statement,
even if not completely, yet at least as regards the most
important part, and besides the insult to His Majesty must
have been quite unmistakable, for none of the witnesses
could deny it completely. The wording of it, however,
could not be established beyond doubt; the greatest probability lay in the assumption that the accused had waved
his wineglass at a picture of the King hanging on the wall,
saying: "You low scamp up there!" The gravity of this insult was modified only by the accused's condition at the
time, which was one of partial irresponsibility, as also
by the fact that he had uttered the insult in some sort of
connection with a line from a song, which went: "so long
as glows the lamp," in this way obscuring the meaning of
the exclamation. Almost every witness was of a different
opinion regarding the nature of the connection between
the exclamation and the song, and the denunciator even
maintained that it was someone else, and not the accused,
who had been singing. What gravely militated against the
accused was his political activity, which made it seem

at any rate very credible that he was capable of uttering the same exclamation in a state of complete sobriety and with entire conviction. The Assistant Public Prosecutor remembers distinctly—these are, after all, things he has gone over in his mind very often—how it was almost with ecstasy that he took up that prosecution, not only because it would bring him honor to appear for the prosecution in a case of lese majeste, but also because he sincerely hated the accused and his cause. Without having any systematic political views, he was, however, out-and-out conservative, he was almost childlike about it; there are sure to be other assistant attorneys, too, who are like that; if everyone were calmly and trustfully loyal to the King and the Government, it must be possible to remove all difficulties; whether the attitude one adopted was one of standing or of kneeling before the King seemed to him something that did not in itself matter; the more trustful one was, the better it was, and the more trustful one was, the more deeply must one bow in a natural expression of one's attitude, without sycophancy. These desirable conditions, however, were prevented from coming into existence by people of the accused's sort, people who, making their way up from some underworld or other, split up the solid mass of the reliable nation with their shouting.—There now stood a political careerist, who was not content with the honest mètier of shop assistant, probably because it could not provide him with the means for winebibbing, a man with a gigantic jaw that was gigantically moved, too, by strong muscles, a born demagogue, who shouted even at the judge presiding over the preliminary hearing, in this case, unfortunately, a man of a nervous and excitable disposition. This hearing, which the Assistant Public Prosecutor had several times attended out of interest in the case, had been a continual wrangle. Now the judge leapt up, another time it was the accused, and one would thunder at the other. This, of course, had an unfavorable influence on the results of the proceedings, and when it became the Assistant Public Prosecutor's task to build up the case for the prosecution on these results, he had to expend a great deal of work and perspicacity in order to make his case fairly watertight. He worked for nights on end, but with delight. Those were beautiful spring nights; the house on the ground floor of which the Assistant Public Prosecutor lived had a small garden in front, about two paces across; whenever the Assistant Public Prosecutor was fatigued from his work or when his surging thoughts made it imperative that he should restore his calm and composure, then he would climb out of the window into the garden and walk up and down there, or lean against the garden railings, with his eyes closed. He did not spare himself at that time, he revised the whole indictment several times, and some parts ten or twenty times. Apart from this, the material prepared for the main hearing of the case was accumulating to an almost unmanageable extent. "Heaven grant that I shall be able to comprehend and make use of all this," was his constant plea in those nights. With the completion of the case for the prosecution itself he considered only the very least part of his work to be finished, and this was why he did not regard the second Public Prosecutor's praise, with which the latter returned the act of indictment to him, as a reward, but only as encouragement, and this praise was great, and it came, moreover, from a severe, taciturn man. It was worded, as the Assistant Public Prosecutor often repeated in his subsequent applications, without, to be sure, being able to induce the second Public Prosecutor to recollect it, as follows: "This file, my dear colleague, not only contains the indictment, so far as can be humanly foreseen it also contains your appointment to the position of tenth Public Prosecutor." And when the Assistant Public Prosecu-

tor modestly remained silent, the second Public Prosecutor added: "Rely on me." The Assistant Public Prosecutor set forth to the main hearing steadily and calmly.
Nobody in the courtroom knew all the subtleties and ram-
ifications of the case he did. The counsel for the defense
was not dangerous, a mannikin well known to the Assistant Public Prosecutor, who was always shouting, but who
lacked acuity. On that day he was certainly not even in
very good fighting spirit, he conducted the defense because he had to, because the accused was a member of
his own political party, because there might be opportu-
nities to deliver tirades, and because the party press was
paying some little attention to the case, but as for hope
of getting his client acquitted, he had none. The Assistant
Public Prosecutor still remembers watching this counsel
for the defense, shortly before the beginning of the trial,
with a smile he could hardly suppress; incapable of con-
trolling himself as this counsel was in every respect, he
jumbled up all the things on his table, tore sheets out of
his papers and covered them with notes at whirl-
wind speed; under the table his little feet kept on tapping,
and at every moment, without knowing it, he passed his
hand over his bald head, with an anxious gesture, as
though he were feeling for some injury or other. To the
Assistant Public Prosecutor he seemed an unworthy opponent. When he hopped to his feet right at the beginning
of the proceedings and, in an ugly, piping voice, proposed
that the case should be tried in public session, the Assistant Public Prosecutor rose from his seat almost clum-
sily. Everything was so clear and so well thought out,
it was as though all the people round about were interfering in a matter that belonged to him alone, a matter
that he himself could carry through to its conclusion in a
way that was in accord with its nature, without any judge,
without any counsel, without any accused. And he sup-

ported the proposal made by counsel for the defense; his action was exactly as unexpected as the defending counsel's had been a matter of course. But he explained his action, and during his explanation the courtroom was so quiet that if there had not been all those eyes fixed on him from all sides, as though they were trying to draw him to them, one would have thought he was talking to himself in an empty courtroom. He noticed at once that he was convincing them. The judges craned their necks and gazed at each other in astonishment; defending counsel leaned back stiffly in his chair, as though the Assistant Public Prosecutor were an apparition that had just this minute come up through the floor; the accused grated his huge teeth in suspense, and people in the packed audience clutched each other by the hand. They realized that here one man was wresting the entire matter, with which they had this or that faint connection, from them and making it his own inalienable property. Each of them had thought he was going to be present at a small case of lese majeste, and now he heard the Assistant Public Prosecutor, in his very first speech, in a few words dispose of the insult itself as though it were something irrelevant.

[End of the fragment of *The Assistant Public Prosecutor*.]

I went in through a side entrance, timidly, not knowing what things were like, I was small and weak, I looked down anxiously at my suit, here it was fairly dark, one could not see beyond a certain empty space all round, the ground was covered with grass, I began to doubt whether I had come to the right place; if I had come in through the main entrance there would have been no possibility of doubt, but I had come through a side entrance; perhaps it would be well to go back and look at the inscription over the door, but I seemed to remember that there had not been any inscription there at all. Then in the distance I saw a dim silvery gleam, which gave me confidence, and I went in that direction. There was a table, in the middle of it a candle, and round it there sat three cardplayers. "Have I come to the right place?" I said, "I have been trying to get to the three cardplayers." "That is what we are," one of them said, without glancing up from the cards.

How the forest breathes in the moonlight, now drawing itself together until it is small and compact, the trees towering up high, now spreading itself out, gliding down all the slopes, is low-growing scrub, is even less, is a hazy, distant glimmer.

A: "Be frank! After all, when are you ever likely to be sitting together like this again, over a glass of beer, in confidential chat with someone who will listen to you? Be frank! In what does your power consist?"

B: "*Have* I any power? What sort of power are you thinking of?"

A: "You are trying to dodge the issue. You insincere soul! Perhaps your power consists in your insincerity."

B: "My power! So I am powerful, am I, because I am sitting in this little inn and have come across an old schoolmate who will sit down with me."

A: "Well then, I shall approach it from another direction. Do you consider yourself powerful? But now answer frankly, or else I'll get up and go home. Do you consider yourself powerful?"

B: "Yes, I consider myself powerful."

A: "Very well then."

B: "But that is exclusively my own business. Nobody sees any trace of that power, not a grain of it, not even I."

A: "But you consider yourself powerful. And why, then, do you consider yourself powerful?"

B: "It is not quite correct to say: I consider myself powerful. That is overweeningness. I myself, sitting here, old, decrepit, and dirty as I am, do not consider myself powerful. The power in which I believe is not exercised by myself, but by others, and these others submit to me. This, of course, can only make me very much ashamed, and not proud at all. Either I am their servant, whom they, out of a whim such as great masters have, have made into a master over themselves, and that would still be all right, then it would all be mere appearance—or, on the other hand, I am really appointed master over them, and what am I to do then, poor helpless old man that I am? I cannot lift the glass from the table to my mouth without trembling, and now I am supposed to rule the storm or the ocean."

A: "There you are, you see how powerful you are, and you were trying to hush all that up. But you have been found out. Even if you always sit alone in the corner, all the regulars here know who you are."

B: "Well, yes, the regulars know a great deal, I only hear little scraps of their conversation, but what I do hear is the one thing from which I derive instruction and confidence."

A: "What? Surely you don't rule according to what you hear in this place?"

B: "Of course not. And so you too are one of those who believe that I rule?"

A: "You yourself said so just now."

B: "I said something of that sort? No, I only said that I consider myself powerful but I do not exercise that power.

I cannot exercise it, for although my assistants are already there, they are not yet at their posts and never will be. They are fickle, they are always roving about where they have no business to be, their eyes are bent on me from everywhere, I approve everything and nod to them. And so was I not right in saying that I am not powerful? And do not again consider me lacking in frankness."

"On what is your power based?"

"So you consider me powerful?"

"I consider you very powerful and what I admire almost as much as your power is the restraint, the unselfishness, with which you exercise it, or rather, the resolution and conviction with which you exercise this power against yourself. Not only do you restrain yourself, you even combat yourself. I do not ask for the reasons why you do that, they are your most private property, I ask only about the origin of your power. I believe myself entitled to do so by the fact of having recognized this power, as not many people have hitherto succeeded in doing, and that I feel even its menace—for as yet, in consequence of your self-control, it is no more than that—as something irresistible."

"I can answer your question easily: my power is based on my two wives."

"On your wives?"

"Yes. You know them, don't you?"

"Do you mean the women I saw in your kitchen yesterday?"

"Yes."

"Those two fat women?"

"Yes."

"Those women. I took scarcely any notice of them. Forgive my saying so, they looked like two cooks. But they weren't very clean, and they were sloppily dressed."

"Yes, that they are."

"Well, whatever you say I always instantly believe, only now you are being even more incomprehensible than previously, before I knew of those women."

"But there is no enigma, it is all quite plain, I shall try to tell you about it. Now, I live with these women, you have seen them in the kitchen, but it's seldom that they cook, most of the time meals are fetched from the restaurant opposite, Resi going one time, and one time Alba. Actually no one is against the cooking being done at home, but it is too difficult, because the two of them don't get on together, that is to say, they get on excellently, but only when they live quietly alongside each other. For instance, they are capable of lying side by side on the narrow sofa for hours, quite peacefully, without sleeping, which is no small matter if only because they are so fat. But at work they don't get on together, in less than no time they begin quarreling, and from quarreling they go to beating each other. For this reason we have agreed —they are very ready to listen to reasoned argument —that as little work as possible should be done. This, incidentally, is in accord with their disposition. For instance, they think they clean the apartment particularly well, and yet it is so dirty that it disgusts me to step over the threshold, but once I have taken that step, I get used to it quite easily.

"Once work is out of the way, every occasion for quarreling is removed, and jealousy, in particular, is utterly unknown to them. Whence should jealousy arise, anyway? After all, I can scarcely distinguish one from the other. Perhaps Alba's nose and lips are even somewhat more Negroid than Resi's, but sometimes, again, the opposite seems to be the case. Perhaps Resi has somewhat less hair than Alba—really, it is almost beyond what is permissible how little hair she has—but, after all, do I pay any attention to that? I stick to what I said, I can scarcely distinguish one from the other.

"Besides, I don't come home from work until evening, it's only on Sundays that I see them for any length of time by day. Well then, since I like to roam about alone for as long as possible after work, I come home late. For reasons of economy we do not turn on the light in the evening. I really can't afford that; keeping the women, who are capable of eating quite incessantly, swallows up my wages. So in the evening I ring the bell of the dark apartment. I hear the two women panting as they come to the door. Resi or Alba says: 'It's him,' and both of them begin panting even more heavily. If it were not I, but a stranger standing there, it might well frighten him.

"Then they open the door, and my usual joke, when they have scarcely opened a chink, is to squeeze through and embrace them both at the same time. 'You,' one of them will say, which means: 'How incredible you are,' and both of them burst into deep, gurgling laughter. Now they are entirely busied about me, and if I did not snatch one hand away from them and shut the door, it would remain open all night.

"Then there is always the crossing of the hall, a journey of only a few steps, which takes from a quarter of an hour to a whole hour, with them almost carrying me. I am indeed really tired after an anything but easy day, and one time I lay my head on Resi's soft shoulder, and one time on Alba's. Both are almost naked, only in their shifts, they go about like that most of the day; only when a visitor is expected, as you were recently, do they put on a few dirty rags.

"Then we arrive at my room, and usually they push me in, but they themselves remain outside and shut the door. It is a game, for now they begin fighting for the privilege of being the first to come in. It is not jealousy, by no means, it is not a real fight, only a game. I hear the light, loud slaps that they give each other, the panting that is now really the result of being short of breath, and now and then a few words. Finally I myself open the door and they tumble in, hot, with torn shifts and the acrid smell of their breath. Then we collapse on the carpet, and then everything gradually quietens down."

"Well, why do you say no more?"

"I have forgotten the connection. How was it? You were asking me about the origin of my alleged power and I spoke of the women. Well, yes, that is how it is, it is from the women that my power comes."

"From the mere cohabitation with them?"

"From the cohabitation."

"You have grown so silent."

"You see, my power has limitations. Something commands me to be silent. Goodbye."

The horse stumbled, fell down on its forelegs, the rider was thrown. Two men, who had been lounging about in the shadow of the trees, each by himself, came forward and looked at the fallen horseman. All this seemed somehow suspicious to each of them, the sunlight, the horse, which had got up again, the rider, the other man opposite, who had suddenly emerged, attracted to the spot by the accident. They approached slowly, with sullenly pursed lips, each irresolutely fidgeting at his chest and neck with the hand that he had pushed under his shirt, which was open in front.

It is a city among cities, its past was greater than its present is, but even this present amounts to something quite considerable.

The mayor had signed several documents, then he leaned back, picked up a scissors and began to toy with it, listening to the midday chiming of the bells in the old square outside, and he said to the secretary, who stood beside the desk, stiff with reverence, almost arrogant with reverence: "Have you too noticed that there is something special under way in the town? You are young, you surely must have an eye for such things."

In a night when there was a new moon I was walking home from a neighboring village, it was a short distance, along a straight highroad completely exposed to the moon, every detail on the ground could be seen more clearly than by day. I was no longer far from the little avenue of poplars, the end of which leads on to our village bridge, when I saw a few paces ahead of me—I must have been dreaming not to have seen it sooner—a little shed built of wood and cloth, a small but very low tent, in which human beings could not have sat upright. It was completely closed; even when I walked round it, quite close to it, and ran my hand over it, I found no gap. One sees all sorts of things in the country and from this one learns to arrive at a quick judgment even of strange things, but how this tent had got here and what it was supposed to be was more than I could understand.

A gypsy-like young woman is making a soft bed out of eiderdowns and blankets, in front of the altar. She is barefoot, is wearing a red skirt with a white pattern, a shirtlike white blouse, carelessly open in front, and has wildly tousled brown hair. On the altar is a washbowl.

On the table there lay a large loaf of bread. Father came with a knife and tried to cut it into two halves. But in spite of the fact that the knife was strong and sharp, the bread not too soft and not to hard, the knife would not penetrate. We children gazed up at father in amazement. He said: "Why are you amazed? Is it not more remarkable that something should succeed than that it should not succeed? Go to bed, perhaps I shall manage it yet."

We went to bed, but now and then, at various hours of the night, one or the other of us would sit up in bed and crane his neck in order to look at father, that tall man in the long coat, who was still standing, one leg well forward, trying to drive the knife into the bread. When we woke up early in the morning, father was just laying the knife down, and he said: "You see, I have not yet succeeded, it is so difficult." We wanted to show our prowess and try it ourselves, and he allowed us to do so, but we could scarcely lift the knife, and besides the handle was almost red-hot from father's grip, it positively reared up in our hands. Father laughed and said: "Leave it, I am going to town now, in the evening I shall again try to cut it. I am not going to let myself be made a fool of by a loaf of bread. It must let itself be cut through in the end, all it may do is resist, and so let it resist." But as he said this the loaf tightened up, like the mouth of a person who is resolute and ready for anything, and now it had become a very small loaf.

I sharpened the scythe and began to mow. Much fell down before me, dark masses, I walked through between them, I did not know what it was. Warning voices called from the village, but I took them to be encouraging voices and walked on. I came to a little wooden bridge, now the work was finished, and I handed the scythe over to a man who was waiting there, holding out one hand for it and with the other stroked my cheek as if I were a child. In the middle of the bridge I began to feel doubt whether I was on the right road, and I shouted into the darkness, but nobody answered. So I went back again on to firm ground, in order to ask the man, but he was no longer there.

"All that is quite useless," he said, "you can't even recognize me, and here I am standing breast to breast with you. How do you expect to get along, since here I am standing right in front of you and you do not even recognize me?"

"You are right," I said, "and that's the way I talk to myself too, but since I get no answer, I stay where I am."

"And so do I," he said.

"And I no less than you," I said, "and therefore it applies just as much to you that it is all quite useless."

I had posted a sentry in the midst of the swampy forests. But now everything was empty, nobody answered the calls, the sentry had run away, I had to post a new sentry. I looked into the man's fresh, big-boned face. "The last sentry ran away," I said, "I don't know why, but it sometimes happens that this bleak countryside lures the sentry from his post. So be on your guard!" He stood very straight before me, as though on parade. I then added: "But if you should let yourself be lured away, you are the only person who will suffer. You will sink into the swamp, but I shall instantly post a new sentry here, and if he should prove faithless, yet another, and so on without an end. So if I do not win, at least I shall not lose either."

My father took me to the headmaster. It seemed to be a big school, we walked through several rooms as large as halls, though they were all empty. We did not find a servant, and so we walked on regardless, and in any case, all the doors were open. Suddenly we started back, the room that we had entered as hastily as all the others, though it had very little furniture in it, was nevertheless furnished as a study and there was a man lying on a sofa. It was—I recognized him from photographs—the headmaster; without getting up, he told us to come right in. To my father's apologies for our uncivil intrusion into the headmaster's sanctum he listened with closed eyes, then he asked what we wanted. I was myself eager to hear that, and so the two of us, the headmaster and I, looked at my father. My father said he was anxious that his son, now eighteen years of age. . . .

He looks out of the window. A dull day. It is November. It seems to him that although every month has its peculiar significance, November has some peculiar added touch of peculiarity. For the time being, to be sure, there is nothing of it to be seen, only sleet is falling. But that is perhaps merely the external appearance, which is always deceptive; for since human beings in the mass instantly adapt themselves to everything and since one does, after all, first judge things by the appearance of human beings, one should actually never be able to perceive any alteration in the state of the world. Yet since one is, after all, a human being oneself, knowing one's power of adaptation and judging on the basis of it, one does discover some things and knows what to make of the fact that the traffic down below has not come to a standstill, but keeps moving, up-street and down-street, with stubborn, untiring, impenetrable superiority.

The sick man had been lying alone for many hours, the fever had fallen a little, now and then he had been able to drop off into a light doze, and for the rest, since he was too weak to move, he had been gazing up at the ceiling and had had to fight off many thoughts. All his thinking seemed to consist solely of warding something off, everything he began to think about bored or tormented him, and he wore out his strength in the attempt to suffocate his thoughts.

It was certainly evening by now, at any rate—since it was November—it had been dark for a long time when the door to the adjoining room opened, the landlady slipped in in order to switch on the electric light, and the doctor followed her. The sick man was amazed at how little ill he really was or at how little the illness affected him, for he recognized the people who had come in perfectly clearly, none of the familiar details of their appearance was missing; not even those that usually aroused feelings of desolation or disgust in him seemed in any way exaggerated, everything was as it always was.

. . . to shake it off, in normal times endured calmly, but in drunkenness, on the other hand, rebelled against it. And even if, of course, I had no intention of revealing to the newspaper the intimate facts that I learned in such circumstances, still, I already had the outlines of an article ready in my head, one in which I meant to show that everywhere where human greatness can stand revealed, that is to say, above all in sport, riffraff immediately comes pushing in too, ruthlessly seeking its own advantage, without any serious attempt at all to look up to the hero, only bent over its own interests, and at best excusing its behavior by saying that it is all done for the public good.

. . . Then the plain lay before K. and far away, remote in the blue distance, on a little hill, scarcely distinguishable, the house that he was striving to reach. But it still took him until evening, and many times during the day he had lost sight of his goal, until on a darkening field-path he suddenly found himself standing at the foot of that hill. "And so that is my house," he said to himself, "a house that is small and old and miserable, but it is mine, and in a few months it shall look differently." And he climbed up the hill between meadows. The door was open, indeed it could not be shut at all, for one side of it was missing. A cat that had been sitting on the doorstep vanished with loud screams, as cats do not otherwise scream. Two rooms to right and left of the stairs, with their doors open, were furnished with a few half-broken old pieces of furniture; they were otherwise empty. But from above, from the top of the staircase, which vanished into the darkness, a tremulous, almost rattling voice asked who had come. K. took a great stride over the first three stairs, which were broken in the middle—oddly enough the broken places looked as fresh as if it had happened only today or the day before—and went up. Upstairs too the door of the room was open. . . .

I escaped from her. I ran down the slope. The tall grass hindered me in running. She stood up there by a tree and watched me go.

It is unbearable here. Yesterday I had a talk with Jericho. He was sitting huddled up in a corner, reading the newspaper. I said: "Jericho, are you going to vote for me?" He only shook his head and went on reading. I said: "I don't want your vote simply as I want any ordinary vote. I shall not get enough votes in any case, my failure is a certainty. But. . . .

Once too I was in the midst of the election campaign. But that is many years ago now. A candidate had engaged me to do clerical work for him during the election period. Of course, I only have a very vague memory of the whole thing now.

What are you building?—I want to dig a subterranean passage. Some progress must be made. My station up there is much too high.

We are digging the pit of Babel.

All that was left of him was three zigzag lines. How buried he had been in his work. And how in reality he had not been buried at all.

A straw? Many a one keeps himself above water by holding on to a pencil mark. Holding on? A drowned man dreaming of being saved.

Death has to lift him out of life as a cripple is lifted out of a bath chair. He sat in his life as solidly and heavily as the cripple does in the bath chair.

Those prepared to die—they lay on the ground, they leaned against the furniture, their teeth chattered, without stirring from where they were they groped over the wall.

One evening in January, at the time when people give big parties, a young student wanted to call on his best friend, the son of a high civil servant. He wanted to show him a book that he was just reading and of which he had already told him a great deal. It was a difficult book on the elements of the history of economics, one could follow it only with difficulty, the author hugged his subject to him—as it had been well put in a review—as a father might hug the child with which he was riding through the night. In spite of all its difficulty, however, it was very alluring to the student; when he got through a section of it he felt he had greatly profited; not only the opinion that had just been conveyed to him, but everything around him, seemed to him more evident, better proved, and more resistant. Several times on the way to his friend he stopped by a lamppost and read some sentences in the light, which was dimmed by the snow-laden fog. He was oppressed by great cares surpassing his power of comprehension, the present was intelligible, but the task lying ahead of him seemed vague and endless, comparable only to his own powers, which he felt within him in the same way and as something not yet roused.

Writing denies itself to me. Hence plan for autobiographical investigations. Not biography but investigation and detection of the smallest possible component parts. Out of these I will then construct myself, as one whose house is unsafe wants to build a safe one next to it, if possible out of the material of the old one. What is bad, admittedly, is if in the midst of building his strength gives out and now, instead of one house, unsafe but yet complete, he has one half-destroyed and one half-finished house, that is to say, nothing. What follows is madness, that is to say, something like a Cossack dance between the two houses, whereby the Cossack goes on scraping and throwing aside the earth with the heels of his boots until his grave is dug out under him.

The unthinkingness of children is incomprehensible. From the window of my room I can see down into a small public garden. It is a small urban garden, not much more than a dusty open space separated from the street by withering shrubs. There the children were playing this afternoon too, just as they always do.

"How did I get here?" I exclaimed. It was a moderately large hall, lit by soft electric light, and I was walking

along close to the walls. Although there were several doors,
if one opened them one only found oneself standing in
front of a dark, smooth rock-face, scarcely a handbreadth
beyond the threshold and extending vertically upwards
and horizontally on both sides, seemingly without any
end. Here was no way out. Only one door led into an adjoining room, the prospect there was more hopeful, but
no less startling than that behind the other doors. One
looked into a royal apartment, the prevailing colors were
red and gold, there were several mirrors as high as the
ceiling, and a large glass chandelier. But that was not all.

I do not have to go back again, the cell is burst open,
I move, I feel my body.

I gave orders for my horse to be brought round from
the stable. The servant did not understand me. I myself
went to the stable, saddled my horse and mounted. In the
distance I heard a bugle call, I asked him what this meant.
He knew nothing and had heard nothing. At the gate he
stopped me, asking: "Where are you riding to, master?"
"I don't know," I said, "only away from here, away from
here. Always away from here, only by doing so can I reach
my destination." "And so you know your destination?" he
asked. "Yes," I answered, "didn't I say so? Away-From-
Here, that is my destination." "You have no provisions
with you," he said. "I need none," I said, "the journey is so
long that I must die of hunger if I don't get anything on
the way. No provisions can save me. For it is, fortunately,
a truly immense journey."

I arrived breathless. A pole had been rammed into the
ground, slightly crooked, and on it was a board bearing
the inscription: "Trap door." I seem to have reached my
goal, I said to myself and gazed around. Only a few
paces away there was an unobtrusive arbor, densely over-

grown with greenery, from which I heard some slight clatter of plates. I went across, stuck my head in through the low opening, could scarcely see anything in the dark interior, but said good day and asked: "Do you happen to know who works the trap door?" "I myself, at your service," a friendly voice said, "I'll come at once." Now I was able slowly to distinguish the little group, it was a young couple, three small children whose heads were scarcely on a level with the table, and a baby still in its mother's arms. The man, who was sitting at the back of the arbor, wanted to raise immediately and make his way out, but the woman urged him to finish his meal first; he, however, pointed at me; she then said I would be kind enough to wait a little and do them the honor of sharing their humble midday meal, and finally I, being extremely annoyed with myself for disturbing the Sunday peace in such a horrid way, had to say: "Alas, alas, good woman, I cannot accept your invitation, for I must be lowered through the trap instantly, yes really, it must be instantly." "Oh, dear," the woman said, "on Sunday of all days and at dinnertime too. Oh dear, the fancies people have. The everlasting slavery." "Don't go on scolding like that," I said, "if I ask your husband to do it, it is no mere whim, and if I knew how it is done I would have done it on my own long ago." "Don't listen to the wife," said the man, who was already at my side and drawing me away. "Don't go expecting any sense from women."

It was a narrow, low, vaulted, whitewashed passage, I stood at the entrance to it, it slanted away into the depths. I did not know whether I ought to go in, with my feet I irresolutely scuffed the thin grass that grew outside the entrance. Then a gentleman came past, doubtless by chance, he stooped a little, but intentionally, because he wanted to speak to me. "Where are you off to, little fellow?" he asked. "Nowhere yet," I said, looking into his jovial but arrogant face—it would have been arrogant even without the monocle that he wore—"nowhere yet. I am only just thinking it over."

"Queer!" the dog said, passing his hand over his forehead. "How I have been running around, first across the market place, then along the narrow path up the hill, then many times this way and that across the great plateau, then down the cliff, then some distance along the highroad, then left to the brook, then along by the poplars, then past the church, and now I am here. Why all that? And I was desperate too. Lucky to be back again. I am afraid of all that senseless running about, of those great bleak spaces, what a poor, helpless, little dog that can't ever be found again I am when I am there! Nor is there anything to tempt me to run away from here, here in the yard is my place, here is my kennel, here is my chain for the occasional spells when I want to bite, everything is here, and ample food. Well then. Nor would I ever run away from here of my own free will, I feel at home here, am proud of my position, I quiver with agreeable but justifiable arrogance at the sight of the other animals. But does any of the other animals run away as senselessly as I do? Not a single one, except the cat, that soft thing with claws, which nobody wants and nobody misses, she has her secrets, which don't concern me, and runs around on her errands, but even she only does so in the vicinity of the house. And so I am the only one who now and then deserts, I am sure it may cost me my pre-eminent position some day. Fortunately nobody seems to have noticed anything today, but only recently Richard, the master's son, made a remark about it. It was Sunday, Richard was sitting on the seat, smoking, I was lying at his feet, my cheek pressed to the ground. 'Caesar,' he said, 'you bad, faithless dog, where were you this morning? At five o'clock this morning, that is to say, at a time when you should still be keeping guard, I was looking for you and couldn't find you anywhere in the yard, and you didn't come back till a quarter to seven. That is an unparalleled dereliction of duty—do you know that?' And so I had been found out yet once again. I got up, sat down beside him, put my arm around him, and said: 'Dear Richard, overlook it just this once and don't mention the matter to anyone. As far as I can help it, it shan't happen again.' And I wept so much, for all possible reasons, out of despair about myself, out of fear of punishment, because I was so touched by Richard's friendly expression, for joy because there was at the moment no instrument of punishment handy, I wept so much that I made Richard's jacket wet with my tears, he shook me off and ordered me to lie down. And so at that time I promised to reform, and today the same thing has happened, and I was out even longer than that time. To be sure, I only promised to reform in so far as I could help it. And it is not my fault. . . ."

The fight with the wall of the cell.
A draw.

It is a beautiful and effective performance, this ride that we call the Ride of the Dreams. We have been showing it for years now; the man who invented it died long ago, of consumption, but this, his legacy to us, has remained, and we still have no cause to take the Ride out of the programs, all the less since it cannot be imitated by our competitors; in spite of the fact that this cannot be appreciated at a first glance, it is inimitable. We are in the habit of putting it at the end of the first part of the show, it would not be suitable at the close of the evening, there is nothing dazzling, nothing costly, about it, nothing to talk about on the way home, the show must finish with something that is unforgettable even for the crudest mind, something that saves the whole evening from oblivion, this Ride is nothing of that sort, but it is doubtless suitable. . . .[51]

A friend whom I had not seen for many, for more than twenty, years and from whom I had received news only very irregularly, sometimes not for years on end, was now expected to return to our town, his home town. Since he no longer had any relatives here and I was far and away the most intimate of his friends, I had offered him a room in my apartment and had the pleasure of receiving his acceptance of this invitation. I went to great trouble to get the room ready for my friend in a way he would like, I tried to recollect his particular tastes, special wishes that he had sometimes expressed, particularly on our holiday trips together, tried to recollect what he had liked to have in his immediate surroundings and what he had abhorred, tried to imagine the details of his room as a boy, and in all these ways found nothing I could have done about my apartment to make it more homelike for him. He came from a poor family with many children, want and noise and quarreling had been the characteristics of his home. In my memory I could still clearly see the room next to the kitchen, where sometimes, though seldom enough, we were able to huddle together on our own, while next door in the kitchen the rest of the family were carrying on their quarrels, of which there was never any lack. It was a small dark room with an ineradicable smell of coffee in it, for the door to the kitchen, which was even darker, was open day and night. There we would sit by the window, which opened on to a covered balcony running all round the courtyard, and played chess. Two of the chessmen were missing and we had to substitute trouser buttons for them, and although this caused trouble when we made mistakes about what the buttons represented, we were used to these substitutes and kept to them. Adjacent, in the same passage, there lived a dealer in canonical vestments, a jolly but restless man with long-drawn-out mustachios, which he fingered like a flute. When this man came home in the evening, he had to pass our window, and then he would usually stop, lean in through the window, and watch us. He was almost always dissatisfied with the way we played, with me as well as with my friend, gave him and me advice, then himself picked up the men and made moves that we had to accept, for if we tried to change them, he pushed our hands away; for a long time we put up with it, for he was a better player than we were, not much better, but still, enough for us to be able to learn from him; but when once, when it was already dark, he leaned in and took the whole board away from us and put it on the window sill in front of him in order to be able to see better how the game stood, I, who had just been in a particularly advantageous position in the game and who thought this endangered by his rough intervention, got up, in the unreflecting rage of a boy to whom a flagrant wrong is being done, and said that he was disturbing our game. He glanced at us briefly, picked the board up again, put it back in its old place with ironically exaggerated obligingness, went away, and from then on ceased to know us. Only, whenever he came past the window, always, without looking in at us, he made a disdainful gesture with his hand. At first we hailed the whole thing as a great victory, but then we began to miss him and his instruction, his jolliness, and all his interest, and without then knowing exactly what the reason was, we began to neglect the game and soon diverted our attention entirely to other things. We began to collect stamps, and, as I only came to understand later, it was the sign of an almost incomprehensibly close friendship that we had a stamp album in common. It was always kept one night at my house, and the next at his. The difficulties arising out of the mere fact of this common ownership were further increased by the fact that my friend was not allowed to come to see me at all, my parents did not permit it. This prohibition was not actually directed against him, whom my parents hardly knew, but against his parents, against his family. From this point of view, too, it was probably not unjustified, but the way it was handled was not very sensible, for nothing was achieved by it except that I went to see my friend every day and so got much deeper into the atmosphere of that family than I would have if my friend had been allowed to come to our house. The thing was that my parents's decisions were often the product less of common sense than of a despotic attitude, not only towards me, but towards the whole world. In this case it was enough for them—and this was more my mother's doing than my father's—that my friend's family was punished and humiliated by this prohibition. That I also was affected by this, indeed that my friend's parents in natural self-defense treated me scornfully and contemptuously, was something, of course, that my parents did not know, but in this direction they did not concern themselves about me at all, and if they had come to know of it, it would not have made much impression on them, either. This is naturally only the way I regard the whole thing now, in retrospect; at that time we were two friends, contented enough with the situation, and suffering on account of the imperfection of earthly things was something that had not yet come our way. It was a complicated matter carrying the album to and fro every day, but. . . .

The sound of singing came from a tavern, a window was open, it was not latched, and swayed to and fro. It

was a little cabin, one-storied, and round about was
emptiness, it was a long way out of town. There came a
late guest, creeping on tiptoe, in a tight-fitting garment,
groping his way along as though in the dark, and yet it
was a moonlit night, he listened at the window, shook his
head, not understanding how this beautiful singing could
come from such a tavern, swung himself up backwards on
to the window sill, and must have done so carelessly, for
he could not keep his balance up there and instantly fell
into the room, but not far, for there was a table at the window. The wineglasses flew on to the floor, two men who
had been sitting at the table rose and resolutely flung the
newcomer, whose feet were, in any case, still outside, back
through the window again, he fell on soft grass, instantly
got up again and listened, but the singing had stopped.

The place was called Thamühl. It was very damp there.

In the synagogue at Thamühl lives an animal about the
size and shape of a marten.

The synagogue in Thamühl is a simple, bare, low building dating from the end of the last century. Small as this
synagogue is, it is entirely adequate, for the congregation is small too and is becoming smaller every year. Even
now it is difficult for the congregation to raise the money
for the upkeep of the synagogue, and there are some people who openly say a small prayer-room would utterly suffice for divine service.

In our synagogue there lives an animal about the size of
a marten. One can often get a very good view of it, for it
allows people to approach to a distance of about six feet
from it. It is pale blue-green in color. Nobody has ever yet
touched its fur, and so nothing can be said about that, and

one might almost go so far as to assert that the real color of its coat is unknown, perhaps the color one sees is only caused by the dust and mortar with which its fur is matted, and indeed the color does resemble that of the paint inside the synagogue, only it is a little brighter. Apart from its timidity, it is an uncommonly quiet animal of settled habits; if it were not so often disturbed, it would doubtless scarcely be in this place at all, its favorite haunt being the latticework in front of the women's compartment, with visible delight it sinks its claws into the lattice, stretching itself and gazing down into the main chamber, this audacious attitude seems to please it, but the beadle has instructions never to tolerate the animal's being on the lattice, for it would get used to the place, and that cannot be permitted on account of the women, who are afraid of the animal. Why they are afraid is not clear. True, at a first glance it looks frightening, particularly the long neck, the triangular face, the upper teeth, which jut out almost horizontally, and on the upper lip a row of long, obviously hard, pale bristles, which extend even farther than the teeth—all that may be frightening, but it does not take one long to realize how harmless this whole apparent horror is. Above all, it keeps away from human beings, it is more shy than a denizen of the forest, and seems to be attached only to the building, and it is doubtless its personal misfortune that this building is a synagogue, that is a place that is at times full of people. If only one could communicate with the animal, one could, of course, comfort it by telling it that the congregation in this little town of ours in the mountains is becoming smaller every year and that it is already having trouble in raising the money for the upkeep of the synagogue. It is not impossible that before long the synagogue will have become a granary or something of the sort and the animal will then have the peace it now so sorely lacks.

To be sure, it is only the women who are afraid of the animal, the men have long ceased to bother about it, one generation has pointed it out to the next, it has been seen over and over again, and by this time nobody any longer wastes a glance on it, until now even the children, seeing it for the first time, do not show any amazement. It has become that animal which belongs to the synagogue—why should not the synagogue have a special domestic animal not found anywhere else? If it were not for the women, one would hardly be aware of the animal's existence any more now at all. But even the women are not really afriad of the animal, indeed it would be more than odd to go on being afraid of such an animal, day in, day out, for years, for decades. Their excuse is that the animal is usually much nearer to them than to the men, and this is true. The animal does not dare to go down below where the men are, it has never yet been seen on the floor. If it is stopped from getting on the lattice of the women's compartment, then at least it wants to be at the same height on the opposite wall. There, on a very narrow ledge scarcely two inches wide, which extends round three sides of the synagogue, the animal will sometimes flit to and fro, but mostly it sits quietly curled up on a certain spot opposite the women. It is almost incomprehensible how it so easily contrives to use this narrow path, and it is remarkable to see the way it turns round up there when it gets to the end, for after all, it is by now a very old animal, but it does not shrink from taking a most daring leap into the air, nor does it ever miss its foothold, and having turned in mid-air it runs straight back again the way it came. Of course, when one has seen this several times one has had enough of it, and there is no reason why one should go on staring. Nor is it either fear or curiosity that keeps the women fidgeting about; if they were to pay more attention to their prayers, they might be able to forget all about the animal; the devout women would certainly do so if the others, who are in the great majority, would let them, but these others always like attracting attention to themselves, and the animal provides them with a welcome pretext. If they could and if they dared, they would long ago have enticed the animal to come yet closer to them, so that they might be more frightened than ever. But in reality the animal is not at all eager to approach them, so long as it is left alone it takes just as little notice of them as of the men, and probably what it would like best would be to remain in the hiding place where it lives in the periods between the services, evidently some hole in the wall that we have not yet discovered. It is only when prayers begin that it appears, startled by the noise. Does it want to see what has happened? Does it want to remain on the alert? Does it want to be in the open, ready to take flight? It is in terror that it comes running out, it is in terror that it performs its capers, and it does not dare to withdraw until divine service is at an end. It naturally prefers being high up because that is where it is safest, and the places where it can run best are the lattice and the ledge, but it does not always stay there, sometimes too it climbs down farther towards the men, the curtain of the Ark of the Covenant hangs from a shining brass rod, and this seems to attract the animal, it quite often creeps towards it, but when it is there it is always quiet, not even when it is right up close to the Ark can it be said to be causing a disturbance, it seems to be gazing at the congregation with its bright, unwinking, and perhaps lidless eyes, but it is certainly not looking at anybody, it is only facing the dangers by which it feels itself threatened.

In this respect it seemed, at least until recently, to be not much more intelligent than our women. What dangers has it to fear, anyway? Who intends it any harm? Has it not been left entirely to itself for many years? The men take no notice of its presence, and the majority of the women would probably be miserable if it were to disappear. And since it is the only animal in the building, it has no enemy of any kind. This is something it really ought to have come to realize in the course of the years. And though divine service, with all its noise, may be very frightening for the animal, still, it does recur, on a modest scale daily and on a grander scale during the festivals, always regularly and without ever a break; and so even the most timid of animals could by now have got used to it, particularly when it sees that this is not the noise of pursuers, but some noise that it cannot understand at all. And yet there is this terror. Is it the memory of times long past or the premonition of times to come? Does this old animal perhaps know more than the three generations of those who are gathered together in the synagogue?

Many years ago, so it is recounted, attempts were really made to drive the animal away. It is possible, of course, that this is true, but it is more likely that such stories are mere inventions. There is evidence, however, that at that time the question whether the presence of such an animal might be tolerated in the house of God was investigated from the point of view of the Law and the Commandments. Opinions were sought from various celebrated rabbis, views were divided, the majority were for the expulsion of the animal and a reconsecration of the house of God. But it was easy to issue decrees from afar, in reality it was simply impossible to catch the animal, and hence it was also impossible to drive it out for good. For only if one could have caught it and taken it a long distance away could one have had anything approximating to a certainty of being rid of it.

Many years ago, so it is recounted, attempts were really still made to drive the animal away. The beadle of the synagogue says he remembers how his grandfather, who was also beadle, liked to tell the story. As a small boy his grandfather had frequently heard talk about the impossibility of getting rid of the animal, and so, fired by ambition and being an excellent climber, one bright morning when the whole synagogue, with all its nooks and crannies, lay open in the sunlight, he had sneaked in, armed with a rope, a catapult, and a crookhandled stick.

I had got into the midst of an impenetrable bramble thicket and shouted for the park attendant. He came at once, but could not get through to where I was. "How did you get there into the middle of the brambles, anyway?" he shouted, "Can't you get back again the same way?" "No, I can't," I called back, "I can't find the way any more. I was walking along quietly, thinking to myself, and suddenly I found myself here; it's as though the thicket had only grown after I got here. I can't get out again, I am doomed." "You're like a child," the attendant said, "first you go pushing along a forbidden path through the wildest of brambles, and then you start moaning. You're not in a jungle, you know, this is the public park and you will be got out." "But a park is no place for a thicket like this," I said, "and how is anyone to rescue me, when nobody can get in here? But if an attempt is going to be made, it must be done at once, it's almost evening, I can't last out overnight, I'm all scratched to bits from the thorns even now, and I've dropped my spectacles, and I can't find them, and I'm half-blind without my spectacles." "That's all very well," the attendant said, "but you'll have to possess yourself in patience for a little while longer, first of all I have to fetch workmen to cut a way through, and before that I have to get permission from the park superintendent. So just a little patience and manliness, if you please."

[52]A gentleman came to our house whom I had frequently seen before, but without attaching any importance to him. He went into the bedroom with my parents, they were quite fascinated by what he was saying and absent mindedly shut the door behind them; when I tried to follow them, Frieda, the cook, held me back, and of course, I lashed around me and cried, but Frieda was the strongest cook I can remember, she had a way of squeezing my hands in an irresistible grip, at the same time holding me at arm's length, so that I could not get at her with my feet. Then I was helpless and could only scold. "You're like a dragoon," I screamed, "shame on you, a girl, and being like a dragoon." But nothing I could say would rouse her; she was a quiet, almost melancholy girl. She let me go only when Mother came out of the bedroom to fetch something from the kitchen. I clung to Mother's skirt. "What does the gentleman want?" I asked. "Oh, nothing," she said, kissing me, "it's nothing, he only wants us to go on a journey." At this I was delighted, for it was much nicer in the village where we always went in the holidays than in town. But Mother explained that I could not go with them, I had to go to school, it was not the holidays now, and winter was coming, besides, they were not going to the village, but to a city, much farther away, but then she corrected herself, when she saw how horrified I was, and said no, the city was not farther away, but much nearer than the village. And when I could not quite believe it, she led me over to the window and said the city was so near that it could almost be seen from the window, but that was not so, at least not on this cloudy day, for one could not see anything more than what one always saw, the narrow street below and the church opposite. Then she left me, hurried into the kitchen, came back with a glass of water, waved away Frieda, who was about to take hold of me again, and pushed me ahead of her, into

the bedroom. There Father was sitting in the armchair, looking tired, and holding his hand out for the water. When he saw me, he smiled and asked what I had to say about their going away on a journey. I said I should very much like to go too. But he said I was still too small and it was a very strenuous journey. I asked why they had to go. Father pointed to the gentleman. The gentleman had gold buttons on his jacket and was just polishing one of them with his handkerchief. I begged him to let my parents stay at home, for if they went away, I should have to stay behind alone with Frieda, and that was impossible.

The wheels of the golden coach come rolling along, with a crunching sound they stop in the gravel, a girl begins to get out, the tip of her foot is already touching the step, when she sees me and slips back into the coach.

Once there was a Chinese puzzle, a cheap simple toy, not much bigger than a pocket watch and without any sort of surprising contrivances. Cut into the flat wood, which was painted reddish-brown, there were some blue labyrinthine paths, which all led into a little hole. The ball, which was also blue, had to be got into one of the paths by means of tilting and shaking the box, and then into the hole. Once the ball was in the hole, the game was over, and if one wanted to start all over again, one had first to shake the ball out of the hole. The whole thing was covered over with a strong, convex glass, one could put the puzzle in one's pocket and carry it about with one, and wherever one was, one could take it out and play with it.

If the ball was unemployed, it spent most of the time strolling to and fro, its hands clasped behind its back, on the plateau, avoiding the paths. It held the view that it was quite enough bothered with the paths during the game and that it had every right to recuperate on the open plain when no game was going on. Sometimes it would look up at the vaulted glass, but merely out of habit and quite without any intention of trying to make out anything up there. It had a rather straddling gait and maintained that it was not made for those narrow paths. That was partly true, for indeed the paths could hardly contain it, but it was also untrue, for the fact was that it was very carefully made to fit the width of the paths exactly, but the paths were certainly not meant to be comfortable for it, or else it would not have been a puzzle at all.

I was given permission to go into a strange garden. There were some difficulties to be overcome at the entrance, but at last a man sitting at a little table half rose and pushed a dark-green paper badge, with a pin run through it, into my buttonhole. "I suppose this is an order," I said jokingly, but the man only patted me briefly on the shoulder, as if to reassure me—but should I be reassured? We exchanged a glance that made it clear between us that now I could go in. But after I had gone a few steps I remembered that I had not paid. I was about to go back, but at that moment I saw a tall lady in a traveling coat of yellowish-gray, rough material standing at that little table and counting out a number of tiny coins onto the table. "This is for me," the man, who had probably noticed my uneasiness, called out to me over the head of the lady, who was bending very low. "For me?" I asked incredulously, and glanced behind me to see whether he did not mean somebody else. "It's always the same, these pettifogging little things," said a gentleman who came over from the lawn, slowly crossed the path in front of me, and walked on over the lawn on the other side. "For you. Whom else should it be for? Here one pays for the other." I thanked the gentleman for this information, although he had given it in a disobliging manner, but also drew his attention to the fact that I had not paid for anyone. "Whom should you pay for, anyway?" the gentleman said as he walked away. However that might be, I meant to wait for the lady and try to come to an understanding with her, but she turned down another path, rustling along in her coat, and a bluish veil fluttered delicately in the air behind her majestic figure. "You are admiring Isabella," said a man beside me who was always taking a stroll, and he too followed the lady with his gaze. After a while he said: "That is Isabella."

It is Isabella, the dapple-gray, the old horse, I should never have recognized her in the crowd, she has become a lady, we met only recently in a garden, at a charity fete. There is a little copse there, standing somewhat apart and enclosing a cool, shaded lawn, which is crossed this way and that by several narrow paths, and at times it is a very pleasant place to be. I used to know the garden in the old days, and when I was tired of the fete, I turned aside into this copse. Scarcely had I stepped among the trees when I saw a tall lady coming towards me from the other side; I was almost dismayed at her tallness, there was nobody else nearby whom I could have compared her with, but I was sure I knew no woman whom this one would not have overtopped by several heads—in my first amazement I even thought by innumerable heads. But as I drew nearer, I was quickly reassured. My old friend Isabella! "Well, and how did you get out of your stable?" "Oh, that wasn't difficult, the fact is I am really kept on only for old times' sake, my day is over. When I explain to my master that instead of standing in the stable, being no use to anyone, I want to see a little of the world now too while I can, as long as I have the strength for it—when I explain this to my master, he understands me, he looks up some of the late mistress's clothes, helps me to dress and then sends me off out with his best wishes." "How beautiful you are!" I said, not quite sincerely, but also not altogether dishonestly.

The synagogue animal—Seligmann and Graubart—Has this reached the point of being serious?—The bricklayer.

Very careful preparations were made for Lisbeth Seligmann's marriage to Franz Graubart.

Pray forgive me for suddenly having become so absent-minded. You are informing me of your engagement, the most delightful news one could hope to hear, and suddenly I cease to take any interest and seem to be wholly preoccupied with other things. But it is, I assure you, only a seeming lack of interest, the fact is I have just remembered a story, an old story, something that I myself was closely involved in, though without any risk at all to myself, without any risk at all, and yet I was more interested in it than in things directly affecting myself. It is in the nature of the matter, at that time it was impossible to remain unaffected, even if one only caught a glimpse of the very fringe of the affair.

The jailer came to unlock the iron gate, but the lock was rusty, the old man had not the strength for it, his assistant had to come, but he looked very doubtful, though not on account of the rusty lock.

The heroes were let out of the jail, they lined up, shuffling rather awkwardly, having lost much of their ability through being imprisoned. My friend, the chief warder of the prison, took the list of heroes out of his dispatch-case, it was the only document in it, as I remarked without any malicious intention—after all, it was not a clerical job—

and set about calling out the heroes' names one by one
and then striking them off the list. I sat beside his desk
and surveyed the row of heroes together with him.

Don Quixote had to emigrate, all Spain was laughing at
him, he had made himself impossible there. He traveled
through Southern France, here and there encountering
kind people with whom he struck up a friendship, crossed
the Alps in midwinter, with the greatest of exertions and
hardships, and then journeyed on through the North Italian plain, where, however, he did not feel very happy,
and finally came to Milan.

On the estates in the principality of M. the introduction
of what is called a whipper-up has proved very effective.
If this innovation is adopted elsewhere, however, it can
only turn out a success if one can be sure of engaging a
person who is as outstandingly suited to the job as the
whipper-up in M. is. It was the prince himself who discovered him; shortly before the work of harvesting really
gets under way the prince walks through the main street
in the village, leaning on his crutch-stick, he is not an old
man, but for some years now he has had to resort to the
crutch-stick on account of some trouble with his leg,
which is not yet bad, but which the doctors fear may yet
take a dangerous course. Well, as the prince is slowly
walking along, and now and then stopping and leaning on
his stick, reflecting on the best way of organizing the har-
vest work—he is a very up-and-doing sort of farmer, going
about it with real professional pleasure—and, in these reflections, ever and again coming up against the fact that in
spite of the constant alarming rise in wages there is always a shortage of labor, or rather, that there would actually be plenty of labor and to spare if only the peasants
would really work as they should and as indeed they do in

their own fields, but as, alas, they are far from doing in their overlord's fields—as he is once again, in anger, thinking over all these things that he has thought over so many times before—and his bad foot is causing him more trouble than usual, too—in the doorway of a tumble-down cabin he notices a young fellow who attracts his attention by the fact that, although he must be quite twenty years of age, he is barefoot, dirty, and ragged, and looks like a good-for-nothing little schoolboy.

The very lowest place of all in this ocean-going steamer, a chamber extending the entire length of the ship, is completely empty; to be sure, it is scarcely three feet high. The construction of the ship makes this empty chamber necessary. Actually it is not quite empty, it belongs to the rats.

I have always had a certain suspicion about myself. But it only occurred now and then, at intervals, there were long gaps in between, quite enough to let me forget about it. Besides, it was a matter of mere trifles, which are certainly to be found in other people's case too, where they do not signify anything very serious, things like astonishment at the sight of one's own face in the looking glass, or at the reflection of the back of one's head, or indeed of the whole figure, when, walking along the street, one suddenly passes a mirror.

I have always had a certain suspicion about myself, a suspicion rather like that which an adopted child [feels] in relation to its foster parents, even if it is carefully left secure in the belief that the foster parents are its real parents. There is some kind of suspicion there, however much the foster parents may love the child as their own and see that it lacks for nothing they can give it in the way of affection and patience, it is a suspicion that may manifest itself only at times and at long intervals, in little random instances, but it is nevertheless there and alive, and even when it is quiescent, it has not disappeared, it is only gathering its strength, waiting for the favorable opportunity when, at a single bound, it will grow from a minute discomfort into a big, wild, malevolent suspicion that breaks free of its fetters and ruthlessly destroys everything that there is in common between him who has the suspicion and him who is suspect. I feel it stirring, as a pregnant woman feels the child moving within her, and I know too that I shall not survive its actual birth. Live, you beautiful suspicion, great and mighty god, and let me die, I who have given birth to you, you who have let yourself be born of me.

My name is Kalmus, it is not an unusual name and yet it is meaningless enough. It has always given me food for thought. "What?" I said to myself, "you are called Kalmus? Is that in fact so?" Even if you do not go beyond the large number of your own relatives, there are many people who are called Kalmus and by their existence endow this name, meaningless in itself, with a quite adequate meaning. They are born Kalmus and will die peacefully as such, at least in so far as being at peace with the name is concerned.[53]

An ambitious young student who took a great interest in the case of the horses of Elberfeld, and who had carefully read and reflected on everything that had appeared in print concerning this subject, resolved to make experiments along those lines all on his own and to set about the matter from the very beginning quite differently from his predecessors and, in his opinion, in an infinitely better way. His financial resources, to be sure, were in themselves not sufficient to enable him to conduct experiments on a large scale, and if the first horse he meant to buy for his experiments turned out to be stubborn, something that can only be ascertained after weeks even of the hardest work, he would have no prospect of beginning any new experiments for a long time. Yet he was not excessively worried about this, because by his method every sort of stubbornness would probably turn out to be manageable. Be that as it might, as was in keeping with his cautious disposition he set to work quite systematically and began by working out the expenses he would incur and the means he could provide. The sum he required for his bare existence during his studies had hitherto been sent to him regularly every month by his parents, poor shopkeepers in the provinces, and he had no thought of renouncing this support, in spite of the fact that he would, of course, have no alternative but to abandon his studies, which his parents followed from afar and set great hopes on, if he wanted to achieve the great successes he expected in the new sphere he was now about to enter. There was not the slightest chance that his parents would have any appreciation of this work or be at all inclined to subsidize it, and so, distressing though he found it to do so, he had to keep his intentions a secret from them and let them continue to believe that he was making steady progress in the studies in which he had hitherto been engaged. This deception of his parents was only one of the sacrifices he was going to impose on himself for the sake of the cause. The money from his parents could not possibly cover the expenses, great as he expected them to be, in which his work would involve him. Hence the student decided that from now on he would spend the greatest part of the day, which had hitherto been devoted to his studies, giving private lessons. The greatest part of the night, however, was to be devoted to the real work. It was not only because he was compelled to do so as a result of his unfavorable material circumstances that the student chose the night as the time for training the horse; the new principles that he intended to introduce into the training of horses made it essential to work by night, for several reasons. Even the very briefest distraction of the horse's attention, in his opinion, meant an irreparable setback to the training, and he was best safeguarded against this at night. The irritability with which human beings and animals are seized when they stay up working at night was something that his plan expressly demanded. Unlike other experts, he was not afraid of the horse's wildness; on the contrary, he required it, indeed he meant to induce it, though not by the whip, but through the stimulus of his uninterrupted presence and uninterrupted training. He maintained that the proper training of horses excluded any piecemeal progress; progress that was made piecemeal, of which various equestrians had recently been boasting so excessively, was nothing, he said, but either the product of the trainer's imagination or, what was still worse, the most glaring sign that no general progress would ever be made. There was nothing against which he himself meant to be so much on his guard as achieving piecemeal advances, he simply could not understand the modesty of his predecessors' demands, which accounted it an achievement to have succeeded in teaching the horses to do little sums, it was as if people had tried to begin educating children by cramming the child with the multiplication table regardless of whether it was blind, deaf, or insensitive to the rest of mankind. This was all so foolish, and the errors made by other horse trainers sometimes struck him as so alarmingly glaring that he would then become suspicious about himself as well, for it was, of course, almost impossible that one lone individual —and, what was more, an individual without experience, who was driven forward solely by a conviction that, profound and impassioned as it was, had not yet been put to the test—should turn out to be right in defiance of all the experts.

The facts, as they were first established with regard to the sudden death of the advocate Monderry, were as follows: about half-past four one morning, it was a fine June morning and already daylight, Frau Monderry ran out of her apartment on the third floor, leaned over the banisters and, flinging her arms wide, evidently with the intention of summoning everyone in the building to her aid, yelled: "My husband has been murdered! Mercy! Mercy! My good husband has been murdered!" The first person to see and hear Frau Monderry was a baker's boy, who happened to be climbing the last of the stairs to the third floor just at this time, carrying in both hands a large basket full of rolls. It was he too who at the inquest asserted that he remembered the exact words uttered by Frau Monderry. Later, however, when he was confronted with Frau Monderry, he withdrew this statement and declared he might have been mistaken after all, since in the very first moment he had been extremely startled by the woman's appearance. Now, this was very probable, since even weeks later, whenever he gave an account of the episode, he was always so agitated that he accompanied his description with exaggerated movements of his hands and feet, in order to produce in the listener an impression at least faintly approximating to that in his own memory. According to his story, Frau Monderry had come flying out of the door with a scream—he had not noticed the door opening and was therefore inclined to believe it had been open even before that—had wrenched her hands apart, which she had been holding convulsively clasped above her head, and had rushed to the banisters. She had been wearing nothing but a nightdress and a little gray shawl, which, however, did not entirely conceal even the upper part of her body. Her hair was loose and some of it hung down over her face, which also contributed to making her outcry indistinct. As soon as she set eyes on the baker's boy, she ran to the staircase, with trembling hands drew him up to her, stepped behind him and pushed him along in front of her by way of a shield, clutching him round the shoulders. It all happened so fast that the boy did not think of putting his basket of rolls down anywhere, and he did not let go of it all the time. So they walked— the woman clutching the boy ever more tightly in her rising terror—with swift but very short steps to the door of the apartment, crossed the threshold, and advanced into the dark, narrow passage. All the time the woman's face kept moving forward to right or to left of the boy, she seemed to be in suspense, waiting for something to appear at any moment, sometimes she snatched the boy back as though it were impossible to go any farther, and then again she would push him forward with her whole body. The woman opened the first door they came to with one hand, with the other holding on to the back of the boy's neck. She surveyed the floor, walls, and ceiling of the room, found nothing, left the door open, and went on, now more resolutely, but still with the boy, to the next door. This one was wide open. On entering the room one saw little more than two beds arranged side by side. The room was in darkness, for the heavy curtains, which were still drawn right across the window, only let in a glimmer of daylight through some narrow chinks. On the table by the bed nearest to the door there was a little stub of candle burning. There was nothing at all unusual to be seen about this bed, but something must have happened in the other one. Now it was the boy who did not want to go any farther, but the woman drove him forward with her fists and knees. In the course of the investigation he was asked why he had hesitated, and whether it was by any chance for fear of something he expected to see in the bed. To this he replied that he was not frightened of anything and had not been frightened then either, but he had had the feeling at the time that there was something hiding somewhere in the room, which might suddenly leap out. This "something," which he could not define more exactly, was what he had wanted to wait for before going any farther. But since the woman seemed to attach such importance to reaching the second bed, he finally gave way.

There was a large flag spread out over me, I worked my way out with difficulty. I found myself on a little hill, with meadowland and bare rock alternating all round. Similar little hills extended, undulatingly, in all directions, there was a wide view, only in the west the shapes of things were all dissolved in haze and in the radiance of the setting sun. The first person I saw was my commanding officer, he was sitting on a boulder, his legs crossed, one elbow on his knee, head in hand, asleep.

PARALIPOMENA

Paralipomena

To the series of aphorisms called "He" [54]

HE HAS FOUND Archimedes' fulcrum, but he has turned it to account against himself, clearly he was permitted to find it only on this condition.

January 14, 1920. Himself he knows, the others he believes, everything is sawn apart for him by this antithesis.

He is neither bold nor frivolous. But he is not timid, either. A free life would not cause him anxiety. Now, such a life has not been his lot, but even this does not worry him, and for that matter he does not worry about himself at all. But there is a certain Someone, utterly unknown to him, who worries about him a great deal and continuously, and only about him. This Someone's worries concerning him, especially the continuity of these worries, are what sometimes, in a quiet hour, gives him a racking headache.

He lives in the Diaspora. His elements, a horde that lives in freedom, roam about the world. And it is only because his room is, after all, part of the world that he sometimes sees them in the distance. How is he to shoulder the responsibility for them? Can that still be called responsibility.

He has a peculiar door to his apartment, once it has slammed, it cannot be opened again, but has to be taken

378

off its hinges. Consequently he never shuts it, on the contrary, he keeps the door permanently ajar by putting a wooden trestle in the doorway. As a result he is, of course, deprived of all the comfort of home life. Though his neighbors are trustworthy, he has nevertheless to carry his valuables about in a briefcase all day long, and when he is lying on the sofa in his room, it is actually as though he were lying out in the passage, and the air from the passage blows in, stuffy in the summer, icy cold in the winter.

Everything, even what is most commonplace, such as being waited on in a restaurant, he can only get by enforcing it with the assistance of the police. This robs life of all comfort.

He has many judges, they are like a host of birds perching in a tree. Their voices intermingle, questions of precedence and competence cannot be disentangled, and there is also a continual changing of places. But one can nevertheless single out individuals among them, for instance, one who is of the opinion that one has only once to cross over to the side of the good and one is saved, without reference to the past and even without reference to the future. This is an opinion that holds an obvious temptation to evil, unless the definition of this crossing over to the good is a very strict one. And this it admittedly is, this judge has never yet acknowledged a single case as coming within his competence. On the other hand, however, he has a crowd of candidates around him, an everlastingly chattering mob that apes him. These people always hear him. . . .

February 2, 1920. He remembers a picture of a summer Sunday on the Thames. The whole breadth of the river was packed with boats, waiting for a lock-gate to be opened. In all the boats were gay young people in light, bright clothes, half reclining, abandoned to the warm air and the coolness of the water. As a result of all there was in common, their sociability was not confined to the individual boats, and joking and laughter passed from boat to boat.

He now imagined that in a meadow on the bank—the banks were only faintly suggested in the picture, what predominated was the assemblage of boats—he himself was standing. He contemplated the gala, which was not really a gala at all, but still, one could call it so. He naturally had a great desire to join in, indeed he longed to do so, but he could not conceal from himself that he was excluded from it, it was impossible for him to fit in there, it would have required such a great deal of preparation that not only this Sunday, but many years and he himself would have passed away in making it, and even if time could have come to a standstill here, it still would have been impossible to arrive at any other result: his whole origin, upbringing, and physique would have had to be different.

And so that was how far removed he was from these holidaymakers, and yet through the very fact of being so he was, again, very near to them, and this was the more difficult thing to understand. For they were, after all, human beings like himself, nothing human could be utterly alien to them, and so if one were to probe into them, one would surely find that the emotion dominating him and excluding him from the river-party was alive in them too, only with the difference that it was, of course, very far from dominating them, and merely flickered spectrally somewhere in dark recesses of their being.

My prison cell—my fortress.

"He is prevented from rising by a certain heaviness, a sense of being secure against any event, the awareness of a resting place that is ready waiting for him and meant only for him; but he is prevented from lying still by an uneasiness that drives him from his resting place, what prevents him is his conscience, the ceaseless beating of his heart, the fear of death and the desire to refute it—all this will not let him lie, and he rises again. This alternation of up and down, and some random, fleeting, odd observations made on the way, make up his life."

"Your representation of it is dismal, but only as regards the analysis, the fundamental error of which it reveals. It is indeed so that man rises, falls back, rises again, and so forth, but at the same time it is also—and with yet much greater truth—utterly otherwise, for man is One, and hence in flight there is also repose, in repose there is flight, and both unite again in each individual being, and the union in each, and the union of the union in each, and so forth, until, well, until what is attained is real life, and yet this representation of it is just as wrong as yours and perhaps even more deceptive than yours. The fact is, out of this realm there is no road leading to life, whereas there surely must have been a road leading hither from life. You see how lost we are."

An Introductory Talk on the Yiddish Language [55]

BEFORE we come to the first poems by our Eastern Jewish poets, I should like, ladies and gentlemen, just to say something about how much more Yiddish you understand than you think.

I am not really worried about the experience this evening holds in store for each of you, but I should like it to be universally comprehensible, if it merits it. Yet this cannot be the case so long as many of you are so frightened of Yiddish that one can almost see it in your faces. Of those who take an arrogant attitude to Yiddish I do not even speak. But dread of Yiddish, dread mingled with a certain fundamental distaste, is, after all, understandable, if one has the good will to understand it.

Our Western European conditions, if we glance at them only in a deliberately superficial way, appear so well ordered; everything takes its quiet course. We live in positively cheerful concord, understanding each other whenever necessary, getting along without each other whenever it suits us, and understanding each other even then. From within such an order of things who could possibly understand the tangle of Yiddish—indeed, who would even care to do so?

Yiddish is the youngest European language, only four hundred years old and actually a good deal younger even than that. It has not yet developed any linguistic forms of a lucidity such as we need. Its idiom is brief and rapid.

No grammars of the language exist. Devotees of the language try to write grammars, but Yiddish remains a spoken language that is in continuous flux. The people will not leave it to the grammarians.

It consists solely of foreign words. But these words are not firmly rooted in it, they retain the speed and liveliness with which they were adopted. Great migrations move through Yiddish, from one end to the other. All this German, Hebrew, French, English, Slavonic, Dutch, Rumanian, and even Latin, is seized with curiosity and frivolity once it is contained within Yiddish, and it takes a good deal of strength to hold all these languages together in this state. And this, too, is why no sensible person thinks of making Yiddish into an international language, obvious though the idea might seem. It is only thieves' cant that is in the habit of borrowing from it, because it needs linguistic complexes less than single words, and then too, because Yiddish was, after all, for a long time a despised language.

In this whirl of language there are, however, certain fragments of recognized linguistic laws which dominate it. For instance, Yiddish originated in the period when Middle High German was undergoing transition into Modern High German. At that time there was a choice of forms, and Middle High German took one course and Yiddish the other. Or Yiddish developed Middle High German forms more logically than even Modern High German did. For instance, the Yiddish *mir seien* (we are) is a more natural development from the Middle High German *sîn* than is the modern German *wir sind*. Or Yiddish keeps to Middle High German forms in spite of Modern High German. Whatever once entered the ghetto had come to stay. And so we still find forms like *kerzlach, blümlach, liedlach*.

And now the dialects enter into this linguistic medley of whim and law. Indeed, Yiddish as a whole consists only of dialect, even the written language; though agreement has been largely reached as to its spelling.

With all this I think I have for the present convinced most of you, ladies and gentlemen, that you will not understand a word of Yiddish.

Do not expect any help from the explanation of the poems. If you happen to be unable to understand Yiddish, no explanation on the spur of the moment can be of any help to you. At best you will understand the explanation and become aware that something difficult is about to follow. That will be all. I can, for instance, tell you:

Herr Löwy will now—and this is indeed the case—recite three poems. First *Die Grine* by Rosenfeld. *Grine* are the green ones, the greenhorns, the new arrivals in America.

In this poem a little group of such Jewish immigrants are walking along a street in New York, carrying their seedy luggage. A crowd, of course, gathers, stares at them, follows them, and laughs. The poet, his emotion at this sight transcending the limits of his own personality, speaks across these street scenes to Jewry and to mankind. One has the feeling that the group of immigrants comes to a stop while the poet is speaking, in spite of the fact that they are far away and cannot hear him.

The second poem is by Frug and is called "Sand and Stars."

It is a bitter commentary on a promise in the Bible that we shall be as the sand which is upon the seashore and as the stars of the heaven. Well, we are trodden down like the sand. When will it come true that we are as the stars?

The third poem is by Frischmann and is called "The Night is Still."

In the night two lovers meet with a devout and learned man who is going to the synagogue. They are startled, afraid of having given themselves away, but later they reassure each other.

Now you see, such explanations are quite useless.

Strait-jacketed in these explanations, when you hear the poems you will try to make out what you know already, and you will miss what is really there. Fortunately, however, everyone who speaks the German language is also capable of understanding Yiddish. For, seen from a distance, though of course only from a great distance, the superficial comprehensibility of Yiddish is a product of the German language; this is an advantage it has over all the other languages in the world. To make up for that, it is only fair that it should also have a disadvantage in comparison with all others. The fact is, Yiddish cannot be translated into German. The links between Yiddish and German are too delicate and significant not to be torn to shreds the instant Yiddish is transformed back into German, that is to say, it is no longer Yiddish that is transformed, but something that has utterly lost its essential character. If it is translated into French, for instance, Yiddish can be conveyed to the French, but if it is translated into German it is destroyed. *Toit*, for instance, is not the same thing as *tot* (dead), and *blüt* is far from being *blut* (blood).

But it is not only at this distance from the German language that you yourselves speak, ladies and gentlemen, that you can understand Yiddish; you are even allowed to come a step closer. It is, to say the least of it, not so very long ago that the familiar colloquial language of German Jews, according to whether they lived in town or in the country, more in the East or in the West, seemed to be a remoter or a closer approximation to Yiddish, and many nuances remain to this day. For this reason the historical development of Yiddish could have been followed just as well on the surface of the present day as in the depths of history.

You begin to come quite close to Yiddish if you bear in mind that apart from what you know there are active in yourselves forces and associations with forces that enable you to understand Yiddish intuitively. It is only here that the interpreter can help, reassuring you, so that you no longer feel shut out from something and also that you may realize that you must cease to complain that you do not understand Yiddish. This is the most important point, for with every complaint understanding diminishes. But if you relax, you suddenly find yourselves in the midst of Yiddish. But once Yiddish has taken hold of you and moved you—and Yiddish is everything, the words, the Chasidic melody, and the essential character of this East European Jewish actor himself—you will have forgotten your former reserve. Then you will come to feel the true unity of Yiddish, and so strongly that it will frighten you, yet it will no longer be fear of Yiddish but of yourselves. You would not be capable of bearing this fear on its own, but Yiddish instantly gives you, besides, a self-confidence that can stand up to this fear and is even stronger than it is. Enjoy this self-confidence as much as you can! But then, when it fades out, tomorrow and later—for how could it last, fed only on the memory of a single evening's recitations!—then my wish for you is that you may also have forgotten the fear. For we did not set out to punish you.

An Inaugural Address [56]

THIS APPOINTMENT is very much to be welcomed. With this appointment a man takes up in reality a position that is also in an ideal sense his due, and the position is filled by the man it needs.

Dr. Marschner's untiring energy and devotion to his work has made him capable of such far-reaching and so widely ramified activity that it is not easy for one person to do him justice, since any one person cannot ever see more than one aspect of this activity. Having been Secretary to the Association for many years, Dr. Marschner knows its whole machinery all the better for having himself taken a part in reorganizing it, in so far as his influence has hitherto extended; he places his comprehensive legal knowledge and abilities at the disposal of the Association; as a thorough and conscientious writer he is known and respected by the experts of his own profession; his influence on the schemes for social legislation in recent years (particularly those relating to liability) must not be underestimated; he has appeared as a speaker at the great international assurance congresses, and in

Prague lecture halls, too, we have heard his always welcome, concise and informative expositions of insurance problems of general importance and topical interest; as a lecturer at the Technical College he uses his mutually complementary knowledge and experience to prepare students for the problems of social insurance, which are now becoming of ever more urgent importance; at the Technical College he organized the course in the study of actuarial problems, being particularly fitted to do so since he is also an expert in actuarial mathematics; his talents as a teacher, which a larger public was given the opportunity of appreciating last year in connection with the course in insurance problems at the Prague College of Commerce, received public recognition when he was appointed a member of a State Board of Examiners. To sum up: he is a man who has done and is still doing very useful and untiring work in all the fields of his profession and who lives in active professional contact with all the generations of our time.

Now, all this is, of course, very important and places Dr. Marschner, as a specialist, in such a light that doubtless no one in Bohemia would presume to put himself on an equal level—or, let us add, at any rate not without some measure of audacity.

Yet when we consider the highly responsible position, right in the public eye and at the head of such a highly complicated organization, to which Dr. Marschner has now been appointed, we may say that the human side of his professional and social activity is even more important.

Hitherto he has taken no step that was not actuated by honest objectivity; to act openly and frankly is second nature to him; sure of himself as he is, he has never—and in this he is, I dare say, especially unique—sought any reward other than what he found in his work; his sole ambition has lain in striving to reach that sphere of activity in which he was needed; his impartiality, his fairness, are unswerving, and we can confidently expect that the Association staff will value their good fortune in having him, of all people, as their chief; those who are acquainted with his writings, his professional work, and his personality, are always impressed by his strong and lively sympathy for the working class, which has a zealous friend in him, but one who will always respect the limits set to his endeavors in this direction by the law and the present-day economic situation; he has never been one to make promises, that he leaves to others (in whose nature it is, who need that, and who, finally, have the time for it), but the real work is something he has always done himself, quietly, without ever intentionally making a public stir, and ruthless only towards himself; and this, too, is doubtless why, apart, perhaps, from the field of his special knowledge, he has no opponents; if he had any, it would be a sorry kind of opposition.

That the Board of the Association, in the midst of very various currents of opinion, was guided solely by objective considerations and thus arrived at this fortunate decision, is something for which it deserves the gratitude of all concerned: the government, the employers, the workers, and the Association staff.

Complaints about the Association, just and unjust, have accumulated in the course of the years. One thing is now certain: good work will be done, and whatever is possible in the way of desirable and useful reforms, within the framework of our present laws, will be done.

Draft for Richard and Samuel [57]

SAMUEL knows at least all Richard's superficial intentions and capacities through and through, but since he is accustomed to thinking precisely and unerringly, he lets himself be surprised by quite small, at least not completely expected irregularities in Richard's utterances, and they give him food for thought. The distressing thing about his friendship, so far as Richard is concerned, lies in the fact that Samuel never needs any support that is not stated in public and hence, if only out of a sense of fairness, will never let any support be felt from his side, either, and as a consequence will not tolerate any subordination in matters of friendship. His unconscious principle is that what one admires, for instance, in one's friend is actually being admired not in the friend but in one's fellow man and that the friendship must therefore begin at a level deep down below all differences. Now this hurts Richard's feelings; he would often like to subordinate himself to Samuel and often wishes to make him realize what a splendid person he is, but he could only begin to do so if he could foresee being allowed to go on doing so forever. Be that as it may, from this relationship, forced upon him by Samuel, he gains the questionable advantage of rising above Samuel in the consciousness of the independence he has hitherto preserved outwardly, of seeing him become small and of making demands on him, though only inwardly, whereas he would otherwise have liked to ask Samuel to make demands on him. Thus, for instance, Samuel's need of Richard's money has, at least so far as his consciousness goes, nothing to do with their friendship; while for Richard even this point of view is something admirable, since this need of money on Samuel's part makes him, on the one hand, embarrassed, but on the other hand, valuable as well, and both within the core of his friendship. Hence, too, it comes about that in spite of his slower way of thinking, embedded in the abundance of his uncertainty, Richard actually judges Samuel more accurately than Samuel judges him, since

Samuel, even though by means of well-developed reasoning power, believes he can arrive at the surest judgment of him by direct means and does not wait for him to settle down and take on his true form. And this, too, is why Samuel so often says things that are beside the point and that he is the one, in this relationship, who withdraws. He seemingly takes more and more out of the friendship; Richard, for his part, brings more and more into it; and so the friendship progresses ever further, and, what is more, moves, oddly and yet understandably, in Samuel's direction, until it comes to a standstill in Stresa, where Richard is exhausted from sheer well-being and Samuel, on the other hand, is so strong that he can do anything and even surrounds Richard, until then in Paris there comes the last blow, which brings the friendship to its final rest—the blow that was foreseen by Samuel, no longer expected by Richard, and hence experienced in a state of death-wish. In spite of this position, which would exclude this externally, Richard is the more conscious one in their friendship, at least as far as Stresa, for he set out on the journey with a complete but false friendship, whereas Samuel did so with one that was only in its beginnings (though it had been so for a long time), but which was a true friendship. Hence, on the journey Richard gets deeper and deeper into himself, becoming almost more casual, with half-glances but with a stronger sense of relationship, whereas Samuel, from the nature of his true inner being—his disposition, and likewise his friendship, demanding it—that is to say, with a double impulse, can and must see quickly and accurately, and often, as it were, carry Richard. Conscious (as far as Stresa) as Richard is in his friendship, ever and anew under compulsion from every little incident, and in this being capable of always giving explanations that nobody asks for, he himself least of all, for he has enough to do coping with the mere manifestations of his changing friendship; where everything else that has to do with the journey is concerned he is cool and collected, finds it difficult to endure the changes from hotel to hotel, does not understand simple connections that might cause him no difficulty at home, is often very serious, but this by no means out of boredom, indeed not even out of the desire to be patted on the cheek by Samuel for once, has a great yearning for music and for women. Samuel can only speak French, Richard French and Italian, and in this way, without either of them having intended it and in spite of the fact that Richard knows the opposite would be more likely, in Italy, wherever it is a matter of getting information he finds himself in a sort of servant relationship to Samuel. Besides, Samuel speaks French very well, Richard speaks both his languages imperfectly.

Application to a Government Department [58]

YOUR INQUIRY of the—has already been answered by me, not verbally, because I am seriously ill, but on a postcard and immediately. This card was certainly delivered, for sometime later I received from your Department an inquiry as to what I was referring to on that card, there being no record at your office of any summons dated September 25, 1922 Rp 38/21. In order to avoid complicating this matter, as completely unimportant to the Revenue Department as to myself, I did not answer this second inquiry, incidentally wishing to save postage; if the original letter, of the ——, was no longer on your files, I was quite justified in letting it go at that. But since the matter has now been revived by your communication of November 3 and I am now, in spite of having long ago answered in a correct manner, even being threatened with a fine, I should like to inform you once again that since

Paul Hermann's entry into the firm of Erste Prager
Asbestwerke (First Prague Asbestos Works) no further
investments have been made by the partners and that the
firm ceased to exist in March 1917. I hope that this time
my answer will reach the department concerned.

On Suspended Animation [59]

ANYONE who has once been in a state of suspended animation can tell terrible stories about it, but he cannot say
what it is like after death, he has actually been no nearer
to death than anyone else, fundamentally he has only
"lived" through an extraordinary experience, and not-
extraordinary, everyday life has become more valuable to
him as a result. It is similar with everyone who has experienced something extraordinary. For instance, Moses certainly experienced something extraordinary on Mount
Sinai, but instead of submitting to this extraordinary experience, like someone in a state of suspended animation,
not answering and remaining quiet in his coffin, he fled
down the mountain and, of course, had valuable things to
tell and loved, even more than before, the people to
whom he had fled and then sacrificed his life for them,
one might say: in gratitude. From both, however, from
those who have returned from a state of suspended animation and from Moses, who returned, one can learn a
great deal, but the decisive thing cannot be discovered
from them, for they themselves have not discovered [it].
If they had discovered it, they would not have come back
at all. But we do not even want to discover it. This can be
shown by the fact that we may occasionally, for instance,
have the wish to experience the experience of the man
in a state of suspended animation, or Moses' experience,
so long as the return is guaranteed, to undergo it as it

were with a "safe-conduct," indeed, we may even wish death for ourselves, but not even in our thoughts should we wish to be alive and in the coffin without any chance of return, or to remain on Mount Sinai. . . .

(This actually has nothing to do with the fear of death. . . .)

NOTES

Notes

[1] "Wedding Preparations in the Country." These fragments of a novel are certainly among Kafka's earliest works. In my diary excerpt of 1909 I find an entry recording that Kafka read some of it to me. Then, under the date March 14, 1910, there is a note that Kafka read the story *Beschreibung eines Kampfes* (Description of a Struggle) to me. Hence the fragment of a novel called *Hochzeitsvorbereitungen* (Wedding Preparations) would seem to be the older work. I should indeed—since the quarto notebooks begin only in May 1910—describe it as Kafka's oldest extant work if it were not certain that as early as February 1907 I knew works of Kafka's, to which reference is made in a note on Kafka published by me in the journal *Die Gegenwart* and in his jesting letter of February 12, 1907. These works were probably short pieces of prose that Kafka had read to me before 1907 and then included in his first book in 1912. Since the majority of my diaries for the years 1914 to 1939 were lost as a result of Hitler's occupation of Prague, in order to establish all these facts I have to resort to the small number of my diaries that I still have, above all to the excerpt from my then still complete diaries that I fortunately made in 1937, when I was writing the biography of Kafka, in order to have all data relating to Kafka collected in one place.

A clue to the dating of "Wedding Preparations" is provided also by Kafka's handwriting. The letters and postcards from Kafka that are still in my possession are up to and including 1907 written in Gothic script, Roman letters appearing only in the addresses; from 1908 onwards the handwriting is exclusively Roman. Now the first manuscript of "Wedding Preparations" (in the following note referred to as Manuscript A) is in Gothic script, the second (B) and third (C) in Roman. The handwriting of B and C has a marked resemblance to that of the letters written in 1908. I therefore believe I am not mistaken in dating the Fragment 1907 and the beginnings of fair copies 1908. In my postscript to the New York edition (*Beschreibung eines Kampfes*, published as *Band V*, Schocken Books, and referred to as such throughout these Notes). I have accordingly dated the story "Description of a Struggle" too early. This story (first fair copy in Gothic script, second fair copy in

Roman) also presumably dates from the years 1907 and 1908.

All three manuscripts of the "Wedding Preparations" are written on loose octavo pages, numbered by Kafka himself. In many places single pages are missing. The lacunae are indicated in the present text.

Manuscript A, in Gothic script, appears here on pp. 2-25. It is written in pencil and in places the writing is blurred and often difficult to read. None of the manuscript has a title; but I have a clear memory of Kafka's having been in the habit of referring to the novel by the title that it is given in this volume. Manuscript A begins with pages numbered 1 to 58. At the end half a page is left empty, evidently because this was the end of the first chapter. Then the pagination begins afresh, 1 to 16. This section, the contents of which are a direct continuation of the first 58 pages, I have therefore called Chapter II; the Roman I at the beginning is also inserted by me. Page 16 is covered with writing right down to the bottom and breaks off in the middle of a sentence; it is therefore evident that there were further pages.

Manuscript B is the beginning of a fair copy, begun in beautiful clear Roman letters. Up to and including page 12 it is written in ink, and from there to the end (page 22) in pencil. Even this section written in pencil is very legible, but it breaks off at the top of page 22, after the second line, in the middle of a sentence. In other words, the copying out was not continued.

Manuscript C is short, containing only 6 pages. But the sixth page breaks off at the bottom in the middle of a sentence; in other words, as with A, the continuation has been lost. Since C is substantially the same as B, I have not published it. I quote only the following variant of the beginning; it follows directly on the first two sentences, which are more or less the same in all three manuscripts.

"Raban looked at the clock on a fairly high tower, which seemed to be quite close, in a street farther down the hill: just for an instant a little flag fastened up there was waved across the clockface. A swarm of little birds flew down, forming an unstable but always level plane. It was past five o'clock. Raban set down his suitcase, which was covered in black cloth, leaned his umbrella against a doorstone, and set his pocket watch, a lady's watch, which he wore on a narrow black ribbon round his neck, by the clock on the tower, several times glancing from one to the other. For a while he was utterly immersed in this operation and, his face now lowered, now lifted, was thinking of nothing else in the world. Finally he put the watch back in his pocket and licked his lips for joy at having plenty of time and therefore not having to go out into the rain."

I should mention that at that time in Old Prague a sign was given with a flag at noon every day from the gallery of the Dientzenhofer Observatory (a beautiful Baroque tower in the courtyard of the University), whereupon the midday cannon shot was fired from the Marienschanze. Startled by this shot, countless swarms of pigeons rose fluttering over the town. This towards the understanding of the genesis of this scene. The end of Manuscript C reads as follows:

"Tugged along by its governess, a child ran past, taking short steps, its free arm stretched out, its hat, as everyone could see, made of red plaited straw, a little green wreath on the wavy brim. Raising both hands, Raban pointed it out to an old gentleman standing beside him, sheltering from the rain, which, driven by fitful gusts of wind, sometimes poured straight down and then at other times floated forlornly and fell in wavering showers. Raban laughed. Everything suited children, he said. He was fond of children. Well, if one rarely had anything to do with them, it was no wonder. He rarely had anything to do with children. The old gentleman laughed too. The governess would not have found it so amusing. When one was older, he remarked, one was not so quick to be enthusiastic. In one's youth one was enthusiastic and, as one could see in old age, it had not brought one any profit, and that was why one was even" . . . . Here Manuscript C breaks off.

[2] A fair copy of these *Betrachtungen* (Reflections) was made by the author himself, who also numbered them and arranged them in the manner in which they here appear. It is not possible to establish exactly when this arrangement was made; the first drafts of the aphorisms (some of them in slight variations) are contained in the blue octavo notebooks in which Kafka recorded his thoughts in the years 1917 and 1918. These octavo notebooks contain much else, besides the first draft of the aphorisms (cf. the Note following). The text here given follows the fair copy made by the author himself and the variants, in so far as they contain substantial changes or additions, are given in the next section (The Eight Octavo Notebooks). The numbering of the aphorisms is precisely that provided by Kafka himself. Where two aphorisms appear under one number, the author had written them both on one slip of paper, although in general he used a separate slip and a separate number for each aphorism. Sometimes one aphorism has two numbers; then Kafka himself had combined into one what was originally two aphorisms. Those passages marked with an asterisk were crossed out by him in pencil, but not removed from the file containing the aphorisms. He probably intended to revise them.

[3] Among other things in Kafka's posthumous papers there were eight

little blue octavo notebooks of the kind we used to call "vocabulary notebooks" at school. Besides the aphorisms mentioned above, they contain many other reflections of which I published a selection in the sixth volume of an earlier edition—*Gesammelte Schriften* (Schocken)—under the title (not originating with Kafka) *Meditationen*, and others in the section of the same volume entitled *Tagebuchnotizen aus anderen Heften* (Diary Notes from other Notebooks). These two groupings are now obsolete, and Kafka's entries now appear in the original sequence in which they were written down. The octavo notebooks also contain numerous fragments, as well as finished stories. Concerning the contents of each individual octavo notebook, as also the dating, see the following Notes. The octavo notebooks begin by running parallel with parts of the twelfth quarto notebook and then fill the lacuna arising in this quarto notebook as a result of the fact that from November 1917 to the middle of 1919 Kafka made no entries in it. On this point, as also on the difference in style between the quarto copybooks and the octavo notebooks, see my Postscript to Vol. II of *The Diaries of Franz Kafka* (1949).

[4] The first octavo notebook contains a single dated note, that of February 19, 1917. The contents have remained for the most part unpublished until their appearance in this volume. Some entries—for instance "Jackals and Arabs"—were published by Kafka himself in *Ein Landarzt* (Munich, 1919)[1], and others in *Band V* of the Schocken edition, for instance *Die Brücke* and *Der Jäger Gracchus*.[2] This notebook also contains *Der Kübereiter*,[3] which proves this piece to have been written during the winter of 1916-17; though published in a newspaper during his lifetime, Kafka did not include it in any of his books. On the basis of the one dated note, I assume that this is the earliest of the octavo notebooks. These notebooks, unlike the quarto notebooks, were not numbered by Kafka. My arrangement of them is therefore necessarily based on conjecture.

[5] Unprinted epilogue to *The Bucket Rider*.

---

[1] "A Country Doctor," later included in *The Penal Colony*, New York 1948. (Publisher's note.)

[2] These two pieces appeared in *The Great Wall of China*, New York 1946, under the titles "The Bridge" and "The Hunter Gracchus." (Publisher's note.)

[3] The Bucket Rider," in *The Great Wall of China*. (Publisher's note.)

[6] Draft of a letter to Paul Wiegler, who during the war edited, among other things, a volume of selections from Beethoven's letters (with an introduction) and a similar little volume of Schopenhauer's letters. The initials at the beginning stand for *Verehrter Wiegler* (My dear Wiegler).

[7] Ludwig Richter's *Lebenserinnerungen eines deutschen Malers* (A German Painter's Memoirs).

[8] In the first octavo notebook there here follows a page containing the first arrangement of the stories intended for *The Country Doctor* volume, and also the draft of a letter. The titles of the stories, which may reasonably be assumed to have been finished at that time, are: *Auf der Galerie* (Up in the Gallery); *Kastengeist* (Caste Spirit); *Kübelreiter* (Bucket Rider); *Ein Reiter* (A Horseman); *Ein Kaufmann* (A Tradesman); *Ein Landarzt* (A Country Doctor); *Traum* (A Dream); *Vor dem Gesetz* (Before the Law); *Ein Brudermord* (A Fratricide); *Schakale und Araber* (Jackals and Arabs); *Der neue Advokat* (The New Advocate). The sketch *Ein Reiter* might be identical with the piece entitled *Das nächste Dorf* (The Next Village) in the *Country Doctor* volume. *Kastengeist* might perhaps be identified as *Ein Besuch im Bergwerk* (A Visit to a Mine). *Ein Kaufmann* is perhaps the piece published in *Band V* of the Schocken edition under the title *Der Nachbar* (My Neighbor).

The letter is addressed to an unidentified person (perhaps the nature-cure practitioner, Schnitzer, in Warnsdorf) and clearly relates to Kafka's sister Ottla, in whose agricultural experiments (first in Zürau, later in Planá) Kafka took a keen interest, even if it was only as a guest and a patient. This draft, which is difficult to decipher, is as follows: "I have a sister, twenty-seven years of age, healthy, [one word illegible], cheerful, considerate, and yet fairly self-confident, incidentally a strict vegetarian, which she has been for some years while living with a meat-eating family. She has hitherto worked in our parents' business; now for practical and personal reasons she is trying to fulfill an old wish of hers, which is to try her luck at agriculture. She wants to take some sort of agricultural course and then endeavor to get some appropriate job. I am sure that you, with your great experience and your wide general view of these things, can give her good and decisive advice. I should be extremely grateful if you would be so kind as to do this."

[9] For the dating of this notebook (as the second in the sequence) I let myself be guided by the fact that *Ein Bericht für eine Aka-*

demie (A Report to an Academy) was already in print in November 1917 (see Note 11). The contents of this octavo notebook are arranged in the following order: *Der Nachbar*[4] (as such, printed in Band V, but untitled by Kafka); *Eine Kreuzung* (as such, printed in Band V, but Kafka's title); unprinted material (published here for the first time); a Fragment of *Der Jäger Gracchus* (Band V); unprinted material; *Ein Bericht für eine Akademie*[5] (volume I of the Schocken edition), as well as other fragments already published in Band V.

10 The third and fourth octavo notebooks contain several dates. Yet they never assume the character of diaries, as do, for instance, the quarto copybooks, the author's private life and day-to-day happenings being indicated only briefly and in a very few words. These words are, furthermore, written in smaller handwriting, as though to express their unimportance. By far the greater space in both these notebooks is taken up by fantasies and philosophic reflections. These were written in Zürau, where Kafka went in the hope of recovering from the tuberculosis that had just been diagnosed for the first time and where he reached the decision to break off his engagement. Departure for Zürau, September 12, 1917. The editor was faced with the problem of deciding whether to publish the aphorisms, *Reflections on Sin, Suffering, Hope, and the True Way* in the form intended by Kafka and clearly established by him in his own fair copy, or in the context of the octavo notebooks, interspersed with other notes of Kafka's. He decided for the first method but indicated the place of each aphorism in the context of the octavo notebooks. An exception has been made in a single case. Aphorism number 9 has been omitted from the place intended for it by Kafka, and, instead, is given in the context with the title (later deleted by Kafka) of *Ein Leben* (A Life), because only in this way does the connection with the previous and the following notes (on the problem of Evil) become clear in its meaning.

11 Kafka's story "Jackals and Arabs" was published in October 1917, in the Zionist monthly *Der Jude*, edited by Martin Buber, and in November 1917 *Ein Bericht für eine Akademie* was published there. Both stories had, besides their particular titles, one general title: *Zwei Tiergeschichten* (Two Animal Stories).

11 Hans Blüher is the author of a number of anti-Semitic works. Tagger later wrote under the name Ferdinand Bruckner. Notes on both these writers appear in Kafka's *Diaries*.

---

4 "My Neighbor," in *The Great Wall of China*. (Publisher's note.)
5 "A Report to an Academy," in *The Penal Colony*. (Publisher's note.)

[13] Kafka was reading the memoirs of the Russian revolutionary Alexander Herzen (1812-1870); cf. *The Diaries. Die schöne Rarität* was, if I am not mistaken, a periodical published at that time.

[14] The writer Ernst Weiss.

[15] Josef Körner, who (later) edited Friedrich Schlegel's philosophic writings, a respected literary historian whose field was German Romanticism. V. Mehl was probably an office colleague of Kafka's. In the following note Pfohl is the name of a superior, Přibram the name of a former schoolmate.

[16] Kafka was at that time still engaged to F.B.

[17] The writer Oskar Baum, our common friend.

[18] Here begin the notes from the year 1918. Kafka continued to live in Zürau, but frequently came to Prague for some time in the course of this year, above all in order to get an official extension of his leave of absence. Here he also tried doing some light gardening (at the Pomological Institute in the little village of Troja, near Prague).

[19] Kafka's publisher, Kurt Wolff. The correspondence related to the volume *Ein Landarzt* (A Country Doctor).

[20] A reference to Kierkegaard's pamphlets *Ojeblikket*.

[21] Here, in my view, is a slip of the pen on Kafka's part. If so, the note would refer to the pair of opposites, "intention" and "experience," as described by Felix Weltsch in the second volume of the yearbook *Tätiger Geist* (edited by Kurt Hiller) in 1918, in his essay *Erlebnis und Intention*, and later in his book *Gnade und Freiheit* (1920). Kafka's critical comment is, after all, based on the assumption that there is an antithesis. If one reads "intuition" (in Bergson's meaning of the word), it would be difficult to perceive any antithesis; apart from this, intuition has nothing to do with "splitting up," but "splitting up" certainly does apply to "intention."

[22] This refers, as do the next five aphorisms, to Kierkegaard's *Fear and Trembling*. The two following aphorisms are a criticism of Kierkegaard. Two pages earlier the noting down of Kierkegaard's terms "Knight of Infinity" and "Knight of Faith" indicate that Kafka was reading the above-mentioned work. There follow the

words: "Abraham's mental reservation—meaning—the same voice sends him there and back."

²³ In the original manuscript it can be clearly deciphered that this aphorism was originally formulated in the first person. It began: "My spiritual poverty" and so on.

²⁴ Attached to the fourth octavo notebook is a slip on which Kafka had made notes, which, it appears, were to serve as the basis for drawing up an application to the military authorities on behalf of a poor old feeble-minded man, abandoned by one and all, which might perhaps have helped to get this man released from military service. First come notes on the relatives, a butcher in Saaz, another uncle in Oberklee, a sister who "does not come into question." "No parents." Then follows: "Not normal, just capable of digging clay, was therefore declared unfit for military service, and besides, as an old man he would not have been called up. Without quite knowing what it was all about, he pushed his way in. He cannot write or reckon, there is no question of his doing business on his own with cattle or vegetables, and for this reason too the parish cannot take on such a responsibility. What is possible, however, is that he might help his relatives with their buying of cattle by fetching the cattle that has been bought, herding it, and so on. In this way the vegetable trade would also be possible, in that he could push the barrow, fetch the vegetables, and so on. But there is no possibility at all of his working on his own, and doubtless the relatives must have been thinking the same, but then they themselves must take over the responsibility." The whole of this draft application contains something of *The Castle* atmosphere, for which reason I have given it here. Kafka first read the beginning of *The Castle* to me in 1922.

²⁵ At the end of the fifth octavo notebook Kafka notes the titles of books he intends to read (or has, perhaps, just read). The list is as follows: *Death in Venice; Confessions of St. Augustine; Summa;* Storm, Keller; *Cardinal Retz;* van Gogh's *Letters; Forty Years of a Dead Man's Life;* Baker, *Travels in Abyssinia;* Emin Pasha, Livingstone; Bernard, *Memories of Cézanne.* Then follows the address of my brother, who was at that time at the front. (*Summa* refers to Franz Blei's periodical.)

²⁶ Like the first octavo notebook, the sixth also contains (at the end) a list of titles of the stories to be published in the volume *Ein Landarzt* (A Country Doctor). It approximates more closely to the form in which the volume did in fact appear than the first plan.

The titles are as follows: *Ein Traum* (A Dream); *Vor dem Gesetz* (Before the Law); *Eine kaiserliche Botschaft* (An Imperial Message); *Die kurze Zeit* (A Short Time); *Ein altes Blatt* (An Old Manuscript); *Schakale und Araber* (Jackals and Arabs); *Auf der Galerie* (Up in the Gallery); *Der Kübelreiter* (The Bucket Rider); *Ein Landarzt* (A Country Doctor); *Der neue Advokat* (The New Advocate); *Ein Brudermord* (A Fratricide); *Elf Söhne* (Eleven Sons).

The sixth octavo notebook also contains the draft of a letter, written in a quite impossible, almost indecipherable private shorthand of Kafka's, evidently the answer to one of those patriotic Austrian projects of which so many shot up during the war, some of them perhaps quite honestly meant, but most of them tiresome schemes designed by careerists. I reconstruct the draft more or less as follows: "Your letter arrived after going somewhat astray, my address is Poříč 7. Let me first of all thank you for the interest expressed in your letter, which has given me sincere pleasure. I am sure that what you intend is a useful, or even necessary, matter. The good names on your list are a pledge of this, as they are also for the future of the whole thing. Nevertheless I must hold aloof. The fact is, I am not capable of forming any clear idea of any kind of unified Greater Austria, and still less of associating myself with any such idea. I cannot face such a decision. Now fortunately this does not do any harm to your association; on the contrary, I am physically quite unfit, my circle of acquaintances is small, and I am not at all influential. And so you would soon be sorry if I did join in. Should the Art Gallery [?] become—as I am sure it inevitably will—an association, with membership subscriptions and so on, I shall gladly join. Please do not take my refusal amiss, it is a necessity for me."

The sixth quarto notebook contains the original draft of Kafka's story *Beim Bau der chinesischen Mauer* (The Great Wall of China), so entitled by him. From this (unfinished) work he himself published only two little, self-contained fragments in *The Country Doctor* volume: "An Old Manuscript" and "An Imperial Message."

[27] By far the greatest amount of space in the seventh octavo notebook is taken up by the dramatic fragment *Der Gruftwächter* (The Watcher in the Vault, in Band V).

[28] At this place in the octavo notebook the autobiography of the Yiddish actor Isak Löwy begins. This man, concerning whom information can be found in the quarto notebooks and in my Kafka biography, yarned for many evenings, often in a fairly confused

fashion, and Kafka made notes and then wrote down the connected story, trying to preserve Löwy's style as faithfully as possible. In this work—apart from his interest in the storyteller and in the man's subject matter—Kafka was guided by the wish to help the poor actor, who was not clear about himself or his course, and to guide him toward understanding and the surmounting of a grave spiritual crisis. Besides the beginning of this record in the eighth octavo notebook, there exists a much longer but likewise unfinished fair copy: this is what is reproduced here. For the rest this last octavo notebook contains only a few notes. What follows is some Hebrew vocabulary. Of the seventy pages of this notebook, fifty-eight are devoted to this study of Hebrew.

[29] *Trefe:* torn; meat the eating of which is ritually forbidden; in general usage: something impure, forbidden. *Chazer:* pig. *Cheder:* elementary Hebrew school. *Rebbe:* teacher. *Purim:* a festival of rejoicing, cf. the Book of Esther. *Yom Kippur:* the Day of Atonement, a day of fasting. *Klaus:* a place of worship and study. *Lecho Dodi:* a hymn sung at the beginning of the Sabbath. *Baal-Teshuvah:* a sinner who repents and "returns." *Kashe:* a difficult question, a problem.

[30] This letter was written by Franz Kafka in November 1919, in Schelesen near Liboch, Bohemia. Since it was never delivered to the person to whom it was addressed, and hence never fulfilled the function of a letter, although it was undoubtedly intended to have that function (the details of this matter can be found in the first chapter of my Kafka biography), I have included this work not in the volumes containing Kafka's correspondence, but among his literary works, in which it represents the most comprehensive attempt at an autobiography that he ever made. The original is type-written by Kafka himself and corrected by him by hand. It covers forty-four-and-a-quarter large sheets of typing-paper, with an average of thirty-four lines. The forty-fifth page is for the most part blank. The manuscript breaks off in the middle of a sentence, at the words "You are unfit for life; but in order—" (*Lebensuntüchtig bist Du; um es Dir aber—*). Nevertheless the two-and-a-half final pages on smaller paper are attached and written by hand, so that there is no lacuna in the text.

[31] The youngest of Franz Kafka's three sisters. The two elder sisters, who are also mentioned in this letter, were called Elli and Valli. Since all three sisters were killed by the Nazis (together with many other members of the family), I no longer have the qualms that in 1937 (when I published my Kafka biography) compelled me to

quote only extracts from the letter. The letter as now published is reproduced without any abbreviation or change whatsoever. Only the punctuation has been slightly supplemented in places.

[82] Kafka's mother was a member of the Löwy family, a family whose peculiar spiritual and almost eccentric character is described in my Kafka biography.

[83] Franz Kafka's nephew. He too was killed.

[84] This word, Czech in origin, signifies a long balcony of the kind that ran round the inner courtyard of many of the more ancient houses in Prague. It was generally shared by several apartments.

[85] A relative of Franz Kafka's.

[86] *Wer sich mit Hunden niederlegt, steht mit Flöhen auf:* He who lies down with dogs gets up with fleas.

[87] Kafka's sister took on the management of a farm in the little German-Bohemian town of Zürau. The writer stayed with her there for sometime during his illness (1917-1918).

[88] In explanation of the relationships in the family it should be noted that Karl was Elli's husband and Felix and Gerti were their children.

[89] The word *senait*, Hebrew for "squirrel," is written in Hebrew letters.

[40] Draft of a letter to Franz Werfel, concerning his play *Schweiger*.

[41] Rashi (Rabbi Shlomo Yizhaki), the classical commentator of the Bible and the Talmud, eleventh century. His exegesis is usually printed together with the texts.

[42] The main piazza in Milan.

[43] Here it can be seen from Kafka's handwriting that he had discarded a nib that had worn flat and was making excessively thick strokes and had put a new, pointed nib into his penholder.

[44] A preliminary study for *The Castle*. A page attached to the notebook bears the date 1920.

[45] By taking some slight liberty one might read this fragment as a sceptical, coarse travesty on the theme "Israel and Israel's Mission as Peacemaker among the Nations." In the previous sketch there is a clearer visionary sketch of the Zionist work of construction in Israel. Both fragments, in any case, belong together as regards subject matter.

[46] In the manuscript this is preceded by the stories *Zur Frage der Gesetze* (The Problem of our Laws) and *Die Truppenaushebung* (Raising Troops, both in Band V). These pieces and the following notes belong thematically to the cycle of *The Great Wall of China*.

[47] Seems to refer to the stained glass window in a certain synagogue in Prague.

[48] A remarkable resemblance to the ideas of C. G. Jung, of which Kafka had no knowledge.

[49] A variant of the legend *Vor dem Gesetz* (Before the Law) in *The Penal Colony*.

[50] On December 31, 1914 Kafka made an entry (*Diaries*, Vol. II): "Worked on, but did not finish: *The Trial*, 'Memoirs of the Kalda Railroad,' 'The Village Schoolmaster,' 'The Assistant Public Prosecutor,' and the beginnings of various little things. Finished only: *In the Penal Colony* and a chapter of *Der Verschollene* (The Man Who Disappeared, afterwards known as *America*)." From this note it appears that all these works came into existence during the months August to December. From among very many unordered, loose sheets of paper it was possible to put together and reconstruct the fragment, which here follows, of the story of the "Assistant Public Prosecutor," which was doubtless unfinished, but which certainly did contain more than what has been preserved. The beginning is missing.

[51] Here follows the story *Ein Hungerkünstler* (A Hunger Artist). Taking this fact together with the small handwriting, it can be deduced that the whole notebook contains entries made in the year 1923 (Steglitz).

[52] Just as in several pieces written before the outbreak of war in 1914, Kafka describes scenes that we experienced only during the war, so too this fragment affects one as being a visionary prophecy of the deportation of Jews under Hitler.

[53] Here follows the story (without a title) *Forschungen eines Hundes* (Investigations of a Dog), later included in *The Great Wall of China*.

[54] The translation of the series "He" appears in *The Great Wall of China*.

[55] The speech (mentioned in the fourth chapter of my Kafka biography) which Kafka delivered at the beginning of an evening's recitations by the East European Jewish actor Isak Löwy in the Main Hall of the Jewish Town Hall in Prague on February 18, 1912. The original manuscript has been lost; what is extant is a careful and complete copy made by Frau Elsa Brod.

[56] This official speech, which Kafka delivered, in the name of the whole staff, in honor of the promotion of his former departmental chief to the rank of Director of the Workmen's Accident Assurance Association, is extant in a fair copy in Kafka's own hand. He had a great admiration for his chief, especially for his untiring energy, although, on the other hand, he did not entirely refrain from making satirical remarks. In some episodes in *The Trial* echoes of this strange relationship occur.

[57] Cf. Volume I of the Schocken edition and my Kafka biography.[e] Stresa on Lago Maggiore, a place to which we made a real journey. Here, according to the draft of the novel, the difficult and complex relation between the friends in the story, a relationship that borrowed some, but by no means all, essential features from reality, was to undergo a severe crisis.

[58] This document I also found among my papers. It is the draft of an answer to the Revenue Department in Žižkov, Prague, and is written on the back of the official letter of November 3, 1922, which begins (in Czech) with the words: "To Herr Dr. Frant. Kafka, clerk in Prague V, Mikulášská tř. 36. You are required to answer the communication from this office, dated September 25, 1922, Rp 38/21, within eight days. In the event of your failure to do so the matter will be referred to District Finance Headquarters, Prague, and you will become liable to payment of a fine." Kafka's answer has something of the atmosphere of *The Castle*.

[59] As a result of its strange fate this aphorism cannot be dated. According to information provided by the proprietor of the second-hand bookshop J. Halle (Hamburg), now living in Israel, the original was confiscated by the Gestapo. By chance, however, a copy

in his possession was preserved. The Gestapo confiscated a great many manuscripts that Kafka had left in Berlin, and in spite of vigorous endeavors made by the Press Attache of the Czechoslovak Legation in Berlin, the writer Camill Hoffmann, no trace of them was ever found. Hoffmann himself, a boyhood friend of Stefan Zweig's, died in a concentration camp.

MAX BROD

[6] A part of "Richard and Samuel" is printed in the Appendix of *The Penal Colony* under the title "The First Long Train Journey" by Max Brod and Franz Kafka. (Publisher's note.)

DATE DUE